Supernatural Wonders from around the World

SUPERNATURAL WONDERS from around the WORLD

BERNHARDT J. HURWOOD

BARNES
&NOBLE
BOOKS
NEW YORK

To my wife, Laura,
whose seemingly limitless expenditures of energy
and unending display of patience on behalf of
this book contributed immeasurably to it

Contents

Preface

Over the centuries much has been written by scholars, philosophers, theologians, and scientists, all seeking to explain the supernatural. Each in his own way sought answers to questions that had perplexed man since the dawn of time. Yet whenever any of these thinkers came to the ultimate enigma, not one of them could offer more than an educated guess, for no one as yet has satisfactorily proved what lies beyond the grave.

Although there is not sufficient space to offer examples of all the writings on the subject which deserve our attention, the temptation is too strong to allow me to continue without at least giving a few that are exceptionally worthy of repetition. In the preface to his *Dissertations sur les apparitions des esprits, et sur les vampires* (etc.), first published in 1746, Dom Augustine Calmet wrote:

> The great number of authors who have written upon apparitions of angels, demons, and disembodied souls is not unknown to me; and I do not presume sufficiently on my own capacity to believe that I shall succeed better in it than they have done, and that I shall enhance their knowledge and their discoveries. . . . I declare that I consider as true all the apparitions related in the sacred books of the Old and New Testament; without pretending, however, that it is not allowable to explain them, and reduce them to a natural and likely sense, by retrenching what is too marvelous about them, which might rebut enlightened persons . . . As to the other apparitions and visions related in Christian, Jewish, or heathen authors, I do my best to discern among them, and I exhort my readers to do the same . . .

Dom Calmet then went on to produce a book filled with incredible accounts of magic, witchcraft, demons, ghosts, vampires, *et al.* If only for the sheer entertainment value of the narratives, the book is still worth reading today. Though the good father was inclined to accept as true most of the stories about which he wrote, he remained a thoroughly honest man. The most significant thing to emerge from his work is the realization that without the element of religion, belief in the supernatural could not exist. If Calmet seems overly naïve and credulous to modern readers, it must be remembered that he was, for all his scholarship and personal integrity, an unworldly cleric whose opinions were founded chiefly on the teachings of his church.

Not all the thinkers of the time were quite so ready to accept supernatural phenomena as unhesitatingly. Indeed, about a century earlier, the English philosopher Thomas Hobbes wrote in *The Leviathan:*

> From this ignorance of how to distinguish Dreams and other strong fancies from Vision and Sense did arise the greater part of the religion of the Gentiles in times past that worshipped Satyres, Faunes, Nymphs, and the like; and nowadays the opinion that rude people have of Fayries, Ghosts, and Goblins, and of the power of Witches.

Certainly one of the most elegant speculations on the matter was written by Sir Walter Scott in 1830, in his absorbing book *Letters on Demonology and Witchcraft.* He said:

> The general, or, it may be termed, the universal belief of the inhabitants of the earth, in the existence of spirits separated from the encumbrance and incapacities of the body, is grounded on the consciousness of the divinity that speaks in our bosoms, and demonstrates to all men, except the few who are hardened to the celestial voice, that there is within us a portion of the divine substance, which is not subject to the law of death and dissolution, but which, when the body is no longer fit for its abode, shall seek its own place, as a sentinel dismissed from his post. Unaided by revelation, it cannot be hoped that mere earthly reason should be able to form any rational or precise conjecture concerning the destination of the soul when parted from the body; but the conviction that such an

indestructible essence exists, the belief expressed by the poet in a different sense, *Non Omnis moriar*, must infer the existence of many millions of spirits, who have not been annihilated, though they have become invisible to mortals who still see, hear, and perceive, only by means of the imperfect organs of humanity.

Some twenty-four years after the publication of Scott's *Letters on Demonology and Witchcraft*, an obscure little book called *Fiends, Ghosts, and Sprites* appeared. In its opening lines, author John Netten Radcliffe stated the case for all books that had ever been written before on the subject, and, if not for all that were to come, certainly for most of them.

A belief in the supernatural [he wrote] has existed in all ages and among all nations. To trace the origin of this belief, the causes of the various modifications it has undergone, and the phases it has assumed, is, perhaps, one of the most interesting researches to which the mind can be given, interesting, inasmuch as we find pervading every part of it the effects of those passions and affections which are most powerful and permanent in our nature.

Perhaps one of the more penetrating statements on the supernatural, one well worth remembering, was made by Sir James George Frazer, whose *The Golden Bough* earned him an immortality of his own. Writing in *Fear of the Dead in Primitive Religion*, he said of Buddha, Christ, and Mohammed:

Indeed, it is safe to conjecture that these great religious revolutionaries were not in this respect innovators, but that they owed in some measure the rapid success which attended their teaching to the circumstance that they accepted the current and popular belief in immortality and built on it, as on a sure foundation, their towering structures of theology which would topple over and crash to the ground if the belief in immortality were to be proved baseless. No doubt the founders of the historic faiths modified the existing belief in many respects, particularly by giving it an ethical character as the ultimate and supreme sanction of morality. This was a very important innovation; for in the lower religions, as a rule, the belief in immortality is entirely divested of any ethical significance; in them the virtuous are not rewarded and the bad are not punished in the life after death; all goes on in the other world much as in this; there is no awful judgment to be anticipated by all, no blissful eternity to be hoped for by the good, no eternity of torture to be dreaded by the wicked.

In a nutshell, then, the great anthropologist provided us with a lens through which to peer at the world of the supernatural, as well as a set of boundaries with which to define it. Somehow, though, the scholars, scientists, and theologians, for all the insights and knowledge they contribute, fall short of the mark when it comes to the matter of probing the supernatural for the sheer enjoyment of it. Certainly those who have delved into it from a literary standpoint have possessed an equal share of scholarly talents. But most of them appear to have plunged into the subject with much greater gusto.

Professor Edith Birkhead, for example, in her book *The Tale of Terror*, wrote essentially what the others did, but her words were loaded with imagery calculated to chill.

> The history of the tale of terror [she said] is as old as man. Myths were created in the early days of the race to account for sunrise and sunset, storm winds and thunder, the origin of the earth and of mankind. The tales men told in the face of these mysteries were naturally inspired by awe and fear.

Stating the case somewhat more emphatically, Dr. Dorothy Scarborough, writing in the introduction to her book *The Supernatural in Modern English Fiction*, said:

> The night side of the soul attracts us all. The spirit feeds on mystery. It lives not by fact alone, but by the unknowable, and there is no highest mystery without the supernatural. Man loves the frozen touch of fear, and realizes pure terror only when touched by the immortal. The hint of spectral sounds quickens the imagination as no other suggestion can do, and no human shapes of fear can awe the soul as those from beyond the grave. Man's varying moods create heaven, hell, and faery wonderlands for him, and people them with strange beings.

One of the great practitioners of supernatural horror fiction, Montague Rhodes James, had some interesting ideas on the subject. A purist to the core, James had no patience with any but the most spine-tingling tales. It was essential, he said, that readers of such material say to themselves, "If I'm not very careful, something of this kind may happen to me." He also said, "Another requisite, in my opinion, is that the ghost should be malevolent or odious: amiable and helpful apparitions are all very well in fairy tales or in local legends, but I have no use for them in a fictitious ghost story."

A rather essential ingredient was added to the caldron by that enigmatic demonologist Montague Summers, who went to his grave after the Second World War urging that the death penalty for witchcraft be reinstated in Great Britain. For all his eccentricity, however, Summers probably was better informed on the subject of the supernatural than any of his contemporaries, and it has been suggested that his vociferous expression of medieval attitudes was nothing more than a gigantic put-on. Whatever the case, he made a good point and struck a blow for believers at the same time when he wrote:

> I conceive that in the ghost stories told by one who believes in and is assured of the reality of apparitions and hauntings, such incidents as do and may occur—all other things, by which I imply literary quality and skill, being equal—will be found to have a sap and savour that the narrative of the writer who is using the supernatural as a mere circumstance to garnish his fiction must inevitably lack and cannot attain. . . .

But whether we believe in ghosts or not, it is difficult not to give serious consideration to something else that Dr. Dorothy Scarborough wrote, this time in the introduction to her book *Famous Modern Ghost Stories*. "Ghosts," she declared, "are the true immortals, and the dead grow more alive all the time."

Ghosts have always haunted literature, and doubtless always will. Specters seem never to wear out or to die, but renew their tissue both of person and raiment, in marvellous fashion, so that their number increases with a Malthusian restlessness. We of today have the ghosts that haunted our ancestors, as well as our own modern revenants, and there's no earthly use trying to banish or exorcise them by such a simple thing as disbelief in them. Schopenhauer asserts that a belief in ghosts is born with man, that it is found in all ages and in all lands, and that no one is free from it. . . . A study of animism in primitive culture shows many interesting links between the past and the present in this matter. And anyhow since man knows that whether or not he has seen a ghost, presently he'll be one, he's fascinated with the subject. And he creates ghosts, not merely in his own image, but according to his dreams of power.

There is another point that has not been mentioned. Man, recognizing his own mortality, and hoping deep down to find a cure for the condition, has always grasped for straws. This understandable longing for immortality has led to many complex and fascinating beliefs, which, though they have varied sharply throughout the ages and around the world, have been strikingly similar from time to time and from place to place.

Which finally brings us to the contents of the present volume. In all probability you will find it quite different from most of the other books dealing with the supernatural. It is not simply a collection of ghost stories, for it contains tales of many other things as well, some infinitely more terrifying than ghosts; others, not at all frightening, appear with all due apologies to the late Montague Rhodes James. More important is the fact that this is not a mere anthology of fictional yarns, because many of the narratives included here were originally written or related as accounts of true events. Since this is not an attempt to prove or disprove anything, it is up to the reader to determine for himself what is to be accepted and what is to be taken "with a grain of salt" (which, incidentally, is the title of a first-rate chiller by no less a storyteller than Charles Dickens).

Much of what you are about to read will be unfamiliar, for I have tried to select material that is relatively obscure. This does not mean that everything will be entirely new. Many of the older stories have survived over the centuries, undergoing substantial alterations in the process. You will be fascinated, I am sure, by the intriguing similarities between certain ancient Greek ghosts, for example, and their nineteenth-century English counterparts —or by the striking resemblances between Chinese and assorted European vampires.

I hope, as you travel along with me on this informal guided tour of the unknown, through the world of the past and present, you will be entertained by everything from the story of the original, real-life Dracula, to a new awareness of hope for the lovelorn ghost. Perhaps you may even acquire a few bits and pieces of miscellany that will bring unexpected insights into the everyday world of mundane reality.

I

Spirits and Demons of
Biblical Antiquity

No one can say for certain when the first ghost was born or when the first demon or evil spirit emerged from the darkness to plague and terrify human victims. Similarly, it is impossible to assign a date to the debut of witchcraft, sorcery, necromancy, or any of the other occult arts into the world. It makes no difference, really, because, from all indications, the emergence and expansion of concepts of the supernatural took centuries.

While *Homo sapiens* was in the process of imposing his supremacy over the other creatures of the earth, he was too busy coping with his environment to bother about things he could neither see, hear, nor touch. But once he managed to get matters reasonably under control and began to establish social order and civilization, he found time to concern himself with metaphysical problems. He was soon pondering the sun and the moon, the stars and the planets, the winds and the tides, the cycle of life—in short, the mysteries of nature itself. Since he was more intelligent than all the other animals, and was able to think and remember as no other living thing had ever done before, he next sought to solve the problems of everyday unreality as well as those of everyday reality. But because there was still much he had to learn, despite his superior intelligence, he was not always able to distinguish the difference between the two. Being man, however, he pushed onward into the unknown, regardless of his mental abilities.

Thus, very early in the game, a distinct pattern emerged. When confronted with obstacles, man had three choices. He could take direct physical action, work magic, or, failing both, call upon supernatural powers for assistance. Naturally, it was a hit-and-miss affair at best when it came to working magic and summoning supernatural help, but as a result of the laws of chance and his still monumental ignorance, man concluded that magic and the supernatural worked as often as not. It was an easy enough matter to find reasons that explained failure—no more difficult than it is today. Maybe an incantation wasn't recited properly. Perhaps a wrong word or phrase was used. On the other hand, maybe external conditions weren't propitious—the rite had been performed in the light of a quarter-moon instead of a full one. And then there was always the matter of being out of favor with whatever powers happened to be in control at the moment.

As time passed, the more man probed the supernatural, the more he learned and the more involved he became. In the ancient world, one did not have to be a professional to participate actively. To be sure, there were professionals: priests, astrologers, sorcerers, and necromancers. But virtually every man, woman, and child had an active role in the overall scheme of things, as H. W. F. Saggs points out in the *The Greatness That Was Babylon*.

> The ordinary man saw himself surrounded by forces which to him were gods and devils. There was a raging demon who manifested himself in the sand-storm sweeping in from the desert, and the man who opposed this demon was likely to be smitten with a painful sinusitus. . . . A host of demons stood always ready to seize a man or a woman in particular circumstances, as, in lonely places, when eating or drinking, in sleep, and particularly in childbirth.

Under the circumstances there were elaborate rules, not only to protect oneself against demons and evil spirits, but to influence those who appeared to be friendly.

The earliest written accounts indicate the existence of a full pantheon of gods, devils, demons, and spirits predating even the civilizations of biblical times. All that we do know today of these fearsome supernatural beings comes from the literature of Assyria and Babylonia, which for all practical purposes comprised a single culture.

These ancient Semitic people, dwelling in the valley of the Tigris and Euphrates Rivers, the so-called Cradle of Civilization, had three distinct varieties of ghostly presence among them. The first, and least complicated, was the disembodied dead soul. Such apparitions were wanderers, perpetually roaming the face of the earth, sometimes with malicious intent, sometimes not. The second category was more devilish in nature, consisting of entities that were half human and half demon, offspring of unions between humans and evil spirits. This concept, incidentally, survived the fall of Babylon by millennia. Thousands of years later, and a world away, long after Christianity had taken root and spread, eminent theologians including Saint Augustine and Saint Thomas Aquinas engaged in lengthy discourses on the subject of sexual relations between demons and humans, and the consequences therefrom. This idea led naturally to fascinating legends and stories. Merlin the Magician of Arthurian lore was said to be the son of a human mother (a witch, by the way) and an incubus father. Similar tales can be found among the supernatural lore of East European Hasidic Jews. The third class of Babylonian spirit was, to quote Montague Summers, "the devils, pure spirits of the same nature as the gods, fiends, who bestrode the whirlwind and the sandstorm, who afflicted mankind with plagues and pestilence."

Within these three major divisions were innumerable subdivisions comprising a pantheon of evil that would easily fill an entire catalogue. An example of such demons were those known as "the children of Anu." Lamashtu was a dreadful female spirit who menaced women in childbirth and snatched nursing infants from their mothers' breasts. Namtaru was similarly regarded with dread. He was the plague-demon, the messenger of Nergal, god-ruler of the underworld, abode of the dead. Rabisu, the Croucher, lurked in dark corners and doorways, waiting to pounce on the unwary. Then there was Lilîtu, the lewd female demon who came to sleeping men in the night, sometimes to send them lascivious dreams, sometimes to cohabit with them in order that she might spawn alu and gallu, faceless horrors, mentioned before as the offspring of man and demon. These were particularly frightful, for, among other things, they loitered about the beds of dying persons and waited for victims that they might tear to pieces in their rage.

To cope with such terrifying threats to life and limb, it was necessary for those wishing to protect themselves to be armed with a fantastic array of knowledge. One had to know incantations, exorcism rites, the preparation of amulets and charms, etc. But if ordinary people were busy with such matters, it staggers the imagination to consider what the daily routine of a priest or magician must have been in those dim, distant days.

Fortunately, not all supernatural beings were evil. There were a few regarded as benevolent. The utukku, for example, was strictly a ghost, a departed spirit of one who had lived. Some were evil, but on many occasions they were regarded as friendly. An example of a friendly encounter between man and utukku is found in the celebrated Epic of Gilgamesh. At one point the hero, Gilgamesh, begs the god Nergal to return his friend Ea-Bani from the dead. The request is granted, the earth bursts asunder, and Ea-Bani's ghost, or utukku, rises forth "like the wind." The apparition is transparent, but in the shape and general appearance of Gilgamesh's old friend, and it describes the lot of those unfortunate spirits denied entrance to the underworld.

> The man whose corpse lieth in the desert—
>   Thou and I have often seen such an one—
> His spirit resteth not in the earth;
>   The man whose spirit hath none to care for it—
> Thou and I have often seen such an one,
>   The dregs of the vessel—the leavings of the feast,
> And that which is cast out into the street are his food.

In all probability, though authorities have a tendency to be vague on this point, the ghost that Ea-Bani was describing was the ekimmu, which literally translates as "that which is snatched away." The ekimmu was a particularly dangerous kind of spirit because in certain conditions its merest presence in a house could guarantee the deaths of all who dwelt there. In some respects an ekimmu was like a vampire, in others, it was just a plain nuisance. Regardless of how it chose to behave, it was persistent, unpredictable, and difficult to get rid of once it had made up its mind to haunt a particular victim. There were two principal ways in which the less fortunate deceased were liable to be denied entrance to the underworld and thus be doomed to becoming ekimmu. The first was by dying in conditions in which their corpses were forced to lie unburied, as mentioned by the shade of Ea-Bani. These conditions could include numerous calamities such as drowning, being killed in battle, being murdered in some lonely place, or perishing of exposure in the desert. The danger also threatened those whose bodies were probably buried, but over whose graves no one observed the proper rites. This particular condition was specifically described in a tablet containing exorcism rites addressed to these spirits. Archaeologists translated part of it as:

> Whether thou art a ghost unburied,
> Or a ghost that none careth for,
> Or a ghost that hath none to make offerings to it,
> Or a ghost that hath none to pour libations to it
> Or a ghost that hath no posterity.

The dangers of being haunted by an ekimmu were ever present because it tended to attach itself to anyone with whom it might have been in contact during its lifetime, regardless of how fleeting or trivial that contact might have been. To put it in another way, the merest social contact with another person was enough to ensure a survivor's being haunted by that person's ghost at some later date. One didn't even have to deal with an individual during his lifetime. The merest glance at a corpse was sufficient cause to be attacked by its ghost.

Female ghosts were quite troublesome, and they too achieved that state via a multitude of paths. At one extreme was the woman who died a virgin, and at the other was the prostitute who had sickened and died. A woman who had died in childbirth or while nursing a baby was sure to return to regain her infant. In *Devils and Evil Spirits of Babylonia*, Reginald Campbell Thompson wrote:

> This is a common form of ghost in Oriental countries. Doughty relates how in Arabia he "heard scritching [*sic*] owls sometimes in the night; then the nomad wives and children answered them with mocking again, *Ymgebâs! Ymgebâs!* The hareem said, It is a wailful woman, seeking her lost child through the wilderness, which was turned into this forlorn bird." Among the Malays, if a woman dies in childbirth, she is supposed to become a *Langsuyar* or flying demon, a female familiar. To prevent this glass beads are put under the armpits, and needles in the palms of the hands. This stops the dead woman shrieking, waving her arms, or opening her hands. The original *Langsuyar* was supposed to be a kind of night owl, like the Lilith of Rabbinic tradition, and is similar therefore to the ghost of which Doughty speaks. In India the ghost of a woman who dies in childbed is a very terrible demon indeed.

Lilith, mentioned above, is a demon especially worthy of some attention here because in a sense she serves as a link not only between the ancient Babylonian and the subsequent Jewish demonology, but between the Jewish and the Christian as well. Her story is a curious blend of cultural crossing, superstition, and tradition. To begin with, the name Lilith is Hebrew and translates also as "screech owl." In form the word is unquestionably borrowed from the Babylonian name Lilîtu. Both words probably derive from the still earlier Sumerian words *lalû*, meaning both "to be abundant" and "luxuriousness," and *lulû*, meaning "lasciviousness" and "wantonness."

According to the rabbinic tradition that Thompson referred to, Lilith was Adam's first wife. She had a severe quarrel with him and left him in a fit of anger. Despite the fact that God sent three angels to bring her back, she refused to obey and in consequence was doomed to become a flying, bloodsucking demon of the night. Also, one hundred of her children were condemned to die daily, which leaves us to wonder how many she had. In any event, as a result of her becoming a demon she, like her Babylonian counterpart Lilîtu, sent men erotic dreams and preyed upon women in childbirth. Despite the fact that this legend was hotly disputed by many rabbis, superstitious Jews of Eastern Europe feared her for centuries. From medieval Jewish lore she slipped easily into Christian demonology, and in the sixteenth century Johann Weyer, the Protestant scholar and strong opponent of witch-hunting, asserted that Lilith was queen of the succubi (of whom more will be said later).

In concept, Lilith was also related to the ancient Greek lamia and Roman strix, both of which were female bloodsucking demons.

But we cannot leave Assyria and Babylonia without at least a passing reference to the so-called Seven. These were a collection of especially vicious evil spirits mentioned in numerous incantations, spells, and invocations. The best-known of these is an invocation against them which goes:

> Seven are they! Seven are they!
> In the Ocean Deep seven are they!
> Battening in Heaven seven are they.
> Bred in the depths of Ocean.
> Nor male nor female are they,
> But are as the roaming windblast,
> No wife have they, no son can they beget;
> Knowing neither mercy nor pity,
> They hearken not to prayer or supplication.
> They are as horses reared among the hills. . . .

Of these seven [the first] is the South Wind . . .
The second is a dragon with mouth agape
That none can [withstand];
The third is a grim leopard
That carrieth off children . . .
The fourth is a terrible serpent . . .
The fifth is a furious beast (?)
After which no restraint . . .
The sixth is a rampant . . .
Which against god and king . . .
The seventh is an evil windstorm . . .

Still another incantation about them says:

Destructive storms and evil winds are they,
An evil blast that heraldeth the baneful storm,
An evil blast, forerunner of the baleful storm.
They are mighty children, mighty sons,
Heralds of the Pestilence.
Throne bearers of Ereskigal,
They are the flood which rusheth through the land.
Seven gods of the broad earth,
Seven robber (?)-gods are they,
Seven gods of might,
Seven evil demons,
Seven evil demons of oppression,
Seven in heaven and seven on earth.

Spirits that minish heaven and earth,
That minish the land,
Spirits that minish the land,
Of giant strength,
Of giant strength and giant tread,
Demons [like] raging bulls, great ghosts,
Ghosts that break through all houses,
Demons that have no shame,
Seven are they!
Knowing no care they grind the land like corn;
Knowing no mercy they rage against mankind.
They spill their blood like rain,
Devouring their flesh [and] sucking their veins.

. . . .
They are demons full of violence, ceaselessly devouring blood.

So persistent and far-reaching was the concept of seven evil spirits that references to them both predated and followed the Babylonian period. They were found not only in the fragmentary remains of the early Sumerians, but in early Christianity as well. A Syriac charm against them is self-explanatory.

> Seven accursed brothers, accursed sons! Destructive ones, sons of men of destruction! Why do you creep along on your knees and move upon your hands? And they replied, "We go on our hands that we may eat flesh, and we crawl along upon our hands, so that we may drink blood." As soon as I saw it, I prevented them from devouring, and I cursed and bound them in the name of the Father, the Son, and the Holy Ghost, saying, "May you not proceed on your way, nor finish your journey, and may God break your teeth, and cut the veins of your neck, and the sinews thereof, that you approach not the sheep nor the oxen of the person who carries [these writs] ! I bind you in the name of Gabriel and Michael. I bind you by that angel who judged the woman that combed [the hair of] her head on the eve of Holy Sunday. May they vanish as smoke from before the wind for ever and ever, Amen."

As the fortunes of Babylonia, then Assyria, began to decline, Egypt's star was on the rise. So grand and so towering were the glories of Egypt under the pharaohs that even today we are unable to escape from the thralldom of that once mighty civilization. It is a fairly well-accepted fact now that much of what the Egyptian priests and sorcerers would have had their contemporaries believe was supernatural was in reality the practical application of jealously guarded scientific knowledge.

So much has been written on a popular level about the supernatural in ancient Egypt that more than a brief mention of it here would be superfluous. We should never forget, however, that, since most of our knowledge about these people derives from tomb excavations, there is a tendency to assume that they were overly preoccupied with death and the afterlife. This is not true. We tend to retain this misconception simply because we are distorting our backward vision by peering, as it were, through a window in the house of the dead. What am I leading up to? A fascinating little-known anecdote of Egyptian sorcery that may shatter a few illusions woven for us by our Sunday-school teachers.

According to this story, the reigning pharaoh was especially fond of spending his time cruising about in a luxurious royal galley (probably on Lake Moeris). Part of his royal pleasure was no doubt derived from the fact that the rowers were not burly oarsmen but beautiful slave girls, who delighted the eye while they provided propulsion. When she was not serving as coxswain, his majesty's favorite mistress, presumably the most beautiful member of the female entourage, saw to it that he was properly entertained.

Her most treasured possession was a silver fish that she wore on a slender chain about her neck. It was a gift of the pharaoh, and she was never without it. One day, unfortunately, while they were taking their customary jaunt around the lake the chain broke, causing the fish to slip from its place, splash into the water, and disappear from sight. Now, from the way she carried on about her loss, you would think that the end of the world had come. She wept and screamed hysterically, insisting that she had to have her fish back. Thoroughly nonplused by this outburst of emotion, the pharaoh tried to console his distraught mistress by assuring her that he would order the royal jewelers to fashion a duplicate bauble the moment they returned to the capital. But his words had about as much effect as if he had been addressing her in a foreign tongue.

Whether she shared the prevalent belief that her lord and master was indeed a living god and could work miracles, or she was simply a willful female, is impossible to say. Whichever was the case, she carried on so that the king finally summoned his attending priests and ordered them to whip up an instant miracle, if only to obtain temporary peace and quiet.

Not only did they produce a miracle, they produced one of outstanding quality. Although the legend does not tell us exactly how they went about it, they succeeded in parting the waters of the lake, enabling the king's mistress to grub about in the mud until she recovered her precious silver fish. What makes this story so intriguing is that it predates the biblical parting of the Red Sea by many years. What renders both stories perfectly understandable is the fact that Moses was educated as a high-ranking Egyptian noble, which possibly indicates that he was being groomed eventually to step into the ranks of the Egyptian priesthood. Whether or not one chooses to accept as gospel the fact that Moses did indeed perform such a miracle while leading the Children of Israel out of Egypt, it is impossible not to recognize in this ancient story another of the many links in the chain of supernatural beliefs.

II

The Other Worlds of Greece and Rome

As we all know from the vast cultural legacy they left us, the ancient Greeks and Romans were primarily concerned with the everyday world in which they lived. Nevertheless, like the peoples of those civilizations that had preceded them, they maintained an active relationship with other worlds inhabited by gods, demigods, a host of mythical supernatural creatures, and, of course, their own dead.

Although it would be extremely rash to state unequivocally that there were no ghost stories in the modern sense before the Golden Age of Greece, it would be relatively safe to say that the Greeks did give us the earliest such stories. So, for a change of pace, here are some actual examples. The first of these, "The Philosopher and the Ghost," is adapted from a letter by Pliny the Younger to Sura, in which he describes a situation that may well be taken as the prototype of subsequent haunted-house stories.

There was once in Athens a large and stately house, which had unfortunately acquired the reputation of being haunted. It was well known as a place where, in the dead of night, dreadful sounds were heard: piteous howls, clanking of chains, heavy footfalls, shrieks, and moans. Furthermore, it was whispered that the sounds were accompanied by the appearance of a ghostly old man who was the personification of misery and filth. His hair was wild, his beard was long and tangled, his robes were tattered and mangy. He was shackled with heavy fetters which rattled and clanked as he wearily dragged them about, moaning hollowly with every step.

Sometimes when he was seen he would glare balefully at the spectators and shake his arms with furious impotence. On more than one occasion skeptics offered to spend a night in the house, and invariably they were terrified to the brink of madness. Worse yet, it was the fate of nearly everyone who ventured to the

33

dreadful spot after dark to be fatally stricken soon after the frightful vigil.

In time the house was avoided by all persons. Efforts to rent it proved utterly useless, and as the years passed the place deteriorated into a crumbling ruin overgrown with vines and weeds.

Now it happened that the Stoic philosopher Athenodorus, while visiting Athens, passed this lonely spot one day and looked upon it as an ideal place to live, study, and work in solitude. Upon inquiring about the place and hearing that it was for rent at an exceedingly low price, he offered to move in at once. The owners were honest men, and they told him about the dismal reputation of the house. It did not bother the philosopher in the least. He signed a lease and asked that a single room be furnished for him. He required only the barest essentials: several chairs, a bed, a table, and a lamp.

Since his needs were so meager, he established himself before the end of the first day. He had all that he needed to pursue his contemplations, his studies, and his writing. On the first night, however, he decided to do nothing but observe and see whether the story of the dreadful phantom were indeed true. For hours nothing happened, and eventually Athenodorus became so absorbed in his philosophical reveries that he completely forgot the fact that he was in a haunted house. He took out his writing instruments and began to work. Suddenly he began to hear the sound of a rattling chain in the distance. It came closer and closer, growing louder with every passing minute. Soon the disturbance became worse. The clankings of the chains became interspersed with dreadful moans and piteous cries. It was more than he could bear; he looked up from his writing and saw before his eyes the very figure of the apparition which had been described to him.

The phantom fixed its blazing eyes on him and beckoned with a long, bony finger. To what must have been the ghost's utter consternation, the philosopher signaled with his hand that he was too busy and returned to his writing. Obviously determined not to be put off so easily, the ghost began shaking its chains and moaning so continuously that it was impossible for Athenodorus to concentrate. Realizing that there was nothing for him to do but give the apparition his undivided attention, he gazed at it intently. He realized at once that it was trying to lead him out of the room. With a sigh of resignation, he rose from his chair, took his lamp, and indicated to the spirit that he would follow it. With that the thing turned and proceeded to lead the philosopher through decaying, dust-filled chambers, creaking, cobweb-filled corridors, and finally through a door leading out into the garden. Moaning all the while, it led the way to a dense clump of shrubs; then, sighing, with a shuddering final groan it vanished into the blackness.

Athenodorus, seeing that he was now quite alone, made a little cairn of stones to mark the spot; then he returned to the house, where he went to bed and slept without interruption until sun-up.

The moment he had dressed, he went to the authorities and told them in detail what had happened the night before. An investigation was decided upon at once. Magistrates, workmen, and witnesses were dispatched to the garden, and Athenodorus led them to the spot he had marked the night before. The workmen began to dig. Several feet beneath the surface they struck something hard. Eagerly they cleared away the earth and gasped when they found the moldering remains of what had once been a man. The skeleton was chained and shackled in fetters so ancient that on exposure to air they crumbled to dust. The bones were carefully taken away and placed in a proper grave, and the house was never again troubled by a nightwalking phantom of any kind.

« »   « »   « »

Certainly, from the standpoint of genre, the story of the philosopher and the restless spirit he encountered is familiar to anyone who has ever read a ghost story. No matter what country it is set in, the pattern essentially consists of a situation in which the ghost returns with a specific purpose in mind. The next story, although written in the second century A.D., during the reign of the

Roman Emperor Hadrian, is set in the Macedonian city of Amphipolis during the reign of Philip II, father of Alexander the Great. Chronologically, then, the time would be somewhere between 300 and 400 B.C.

The author of the story was a minor writer, a freed Greek slave, Phlegon of Tralles, and it appeared in a book titled *De Rebus Mirabilis*—in English, *Of Miraculous Things*. The beginning of the story is missing, but by piecing together bits of information from other sources we know that it was taken from a letter written by Hipparchus to Arrhidaeus, half-brother of Alexander the Great.

The principal characters in the story are Philinnion, daughter of a couple named Demonstratus and Charito, and a foreign friend of theirs, Machates. What apparently happened before the story took place was that Philinnion had been married to Craterus, a celebrated general in the army of Alexander. He died six months after they were married, and the young widow herself died not long after that. Although it is not entirely clear how it came about, she obviously fell desperately in love with Machates at some point before she died, but, as the story reveals, it must have been a one-sided love from afar, for Machates did not know her name.

Six months after Philinnion died, however, she returned from the grave in order to spend the nights with Machates, who was at the time visiting *her* parents. On one of these occasions an old family nurse went up to the guest room to investigate why a light was burning so late at night. She was shocked at observing a young woman sitting on the bed with Machates, but when she recognized the girl's identity, she ran screaming to Demonstratus and Charito to apprise them of the fact that their daughter had miraculously come back from the dead. At this point let us go directly to the narrative of Phlegon.

On hearing this extraordinary story, Charito was at first overcome by it and by the nurse's excitement; but she soon recovered herself and burst into tears at the mention of her daughter, telling the old woman that she was out of her senses and ordering her out of the room. The nurse was indignant at this treatment and boldly declared that she was not out of her senses, but that Charito was unwilling to see her daughter because she was afraid. At last Charito consented to go to the door of the guest chamber, but as it was now quite two hours since she had heard the news, she arrived too late and found them both asleep. The mother bent over the woman's figure and thought she recognized her daughter's features and clothes. Not feeling sure, as it was dark, she decided to keep quiet for the present, meaning to get up early and catch the woman. If she failed, she would ask Machates for a full explanation, as he would never tell her a lie in a case so important. So she left the room without saying anything.

But early on the following morning, either because the gods so willed it or because she was moved by some divine impulse, the woman went away without being observed. When she came to him, Charito was angry with the young man in consequence, and clung to his knees and conjured him to speak the truth and hide nothing from her. At first he was greatly distressed and could hardly be brought to admit the girl's name was Philinnion. Then he described her first coming and the violence of her passion, and told how she had said she was there without her parents' knowledge. The better to establish the truth of his story, he opened a coffer and took out the things she had left behind her—a ring of gold which she had given him, and a belt which she had left on the previous night. When Charito beheld these convincing proofs, she uttered a piercing cry and rent her clothes and her cloak and tore her coif from her head and began to mourn for her daughter afresh in the midst of her friends. Machates was deeply distressed on seeing what had happened and how they were all mourning, as if for Philinnion's second funeral. He begged them to be comforted and promised them that they should see her if she appeared. Charito yielded, but bade him be careful how he fulfilled his promise.

When night fell and the hour drew near at which Philinnion usually appeared, they were on the watch for her. She came, as was her custom, and sat down upon the bed. Machates made no pretense, for he was genuinely anxious to sift the matter to the bottom, and secretly sent some slaves to call her parents. He himself could hardly believe that the woman who came to him so regularly at the same hour was really dead, and when she ate and drank with him he began to suspect what had been suggested to him—namely, that some grave-robbers had violated the tomb and sold the clothes and the gold ornaments to her father.

Demonstratus and Charito hastened to come at once, and when they saw her they were at first speechless with amazement. Then, with cries of joy, they threw themselves upon their daughter. But Philinnion remained cold. "Father and Mother," she said, "cruel indeed have ye been in that ye grudged my living with the stranger for three days in my father's house, for it brought harm to no one. But ye shall pay for your meddling with sorrow. I must return to the place appointed for me, though I came not hither without the will of Heaven." With these words she fell down dead, and her body lay stretched upon the bed. Her parents threw themselves upon her, and the house was filled with confusion and sorrow, for the blow was heavy indeed; but the event was strange and soon became known throughout the town, and finally reached my ears.

During that night I kept back the crowds that gathered round the house, taking care that there should be no disturbance as the news spread. At early dawn the theater was full. After a long discussion it was decided that we should go and open the tomb, to see whether the body was still on the bier, or whether we should find the place empty, for the woman had hardly been dead six months. When we opened the vault where all her family was buried, the bodies were seen lying on the other biers; but on the one where Philinnion had been placed, we found only one iron ring which had belonged to her lover, and the gilt-edged drinking-cup Machates had given her on the first day. In utter amazement, we went straight to Demonstratus's house to see whether the body was still there. We beheld it lying on the ground, and then went in a large crowd to the place of assembly, for the whole event was of great importance and absolutely past belief. Great was the confusion, and no one could tell what to do, when Hyllus, who is not only considered the best diviner among us but is also a great authority on the interpretation of the flight of birds, and is generally well versed in his art, got up and said that the woman must be buried outside the boundaries of the city, for it was unlawful that she should be laid to rest within them; and that Hermes Chthonios and the Eumenides should be propitiated, and that all pollution would thus be removed. He ordered the temples to be reconsecrated and the usual rites to be performed in honor of the gods below. As for the King, in this affair, he privately told me to sacrifice to Hermes, and to Zeus Xenios, and to Ares, and to perform these duties with the utmost care. We have done as he suggested.

The stranger Machates, who was visited by the ghost, has commited suicide in despair.

Now, if you think it is right that I should give the King an account of all this, let me know, and I will send some of those who gave me the various details.

« »   « »   « »

An especially fascinating aspect of Phlegon's tale of love and death in ancient Greece is that in style it closely resembles certain ghost stories of China and Japan, in which ghosts and other supernatural beings become involved in all sorts of complicated love affairs with human beings, sometimes with the most baneful of results. A second point worth noting about this tale is that it was the inspiration of Goethe's poem "The Bride of Corinth." In the Goethe work, the girl is a Christian who falls in love with a pagan. The parents of both are friends, and the children are betrothed in their childhood. He comes for an extended visit with her parents after she has died, but knowing nothing of her death, when she comes to him in the night. As in Phlegon's story, the girl's body is cold and deathlike, though animated. They are surprised by her mother while they are passionately making love. The daughter then reproaches the mother for her cruelty and pleads that she and her lover may be buried together, for by breathing life into her with his kisses, he is doomed to forfeit his own.

A Roman supernatural story of quite another stripe is the fairly well-known werewolf episode from the *Satyricon* of Petronius Arbiter. It is certainly one of the earliest tales, if not the very earliest, of lycanthropy. It occurs in the book as a story within a story, being related at the celebrated banquet of Trimalchio by the host's old friend, the freedman Niceros. There are many versions, depending upon which translation you happen to read. This one is adapted from a nineteenth-century text, and the only liberties taken with it are those involving obsolete slang. It is told in the first person as follows:

Some time ago, when I was still a slave, we used to live in Small Street, in the house which now belongs to Gavilla. And there, as luck would have it, I fell head over heels in love with the wife of Terentius the innkeeper. You all knew Melissa, she came from Tarentum originally; a fine piece of stuff she was too! Not that I cared for her just for the sake of a meal and a roll in the hay! No, no! I liked her because she was a good honest wench, frank and open. If one ever asked her for anything one never got "No" for an answer. If she made a little coin, half of it was mine, and as far as I was concerned, every penny that came my way was safe with her, and not once did she ever cheat me out of a cent.

Well, her husband, good man, died at a little country house they had, and there I was scheming to find a way to be with her by hook or by crook, for I don't have to tell you that you learn who your real friends are when you're in a fix like that. It so happened that just then my master had gone off to Capua to take care of some business he had there, and so naturally I took advantage of such a fine opportunity. I had no difficulty in convincing a young man who was staying in the house to keep me company for a good part of the way. He was a soldier, and as husky as a devil. We set off at about sunset, and before long the moon was shining bright as midday. We were on the main road with the gravestones * on either side of it, when my companion went off to one side (I assumed) to relieve himself among the tombstones, so I sat down, humming to myself and counting the stars above. After a while I looked around to see what the fellow was up to, and by the gods! my heart leaped into my very mouth. He had taken off all his clothes and piled them in a heap at the edge of the road. I tell you, you could have flattened me with a breath! Because then I saw him piss in a circle all around his clothes, and just like that—pop! he turned into a wolf. Please don't think I'm joking. I wouldn't lie, not even for a mint full of money. But as I was saying, in an instant he turned into a wolf; then he began to howl horribly, and with that ran off full tilt into the woods. I didn't know whether I was coming or going, and when I went to gather up his clothes, why, they had all been changed into stone! Frightened! By the gods! I was half dead with fear. So I drew my sword, and as I made my way along the road I kept thrusting at the haunted shadows until I finally reached my pretty mistress's house. There I staggered in, looking like a ghost. Every second I thought I was going to breathe my last. My eyes were set and staring, the sweat was pouring down my head in streams, and it was all I could do to gather my wits. Nobody could be more astonished than Melissa to see me out on so late a night jaunt, and "If you had only been here a little earlier," she said, "your help would have come in mighty handy. A huge wolf had just broken into the place and made sad havoc among the cattle and sheep. You might think a butcher had been at work with his knife from all the blood. But Master Wolf didn't get off scot-free, though, because our servant gave him a good jab in the neck with a pike." When I heard all this I couldn't so much as

* According to Roman custom, the dead were buried alongside the roads leading out of the cities and towns; the grave-markers, as well as the tombs varied in size and shape.

close an eye, but as soon as it was daylight I made tracks back to the house of my master, Gaius, and I hurried, I can tell you, as fast as our host goes after a thief. When I got to the place where the fellow's clothes had been turned to stone, I could see nothing but a ghastly pool of blood! Finally I reached home, and there I found the soldier in bed, bleeding like an ox in the slaughter-house, while a physician was busy dressing a deep gash in his neck. It was then that I knew he was a werewolf, and after that I could neither eat nor drink with him, not if you had killed me for it. Yes, you can all think what you like of my tale, but may the gods abandon me if I've told you a lying word.

« »   « »   « »

The mention in Niceros's narrative of the tombs alongside the road illustrates a rather touching Roman attitude toward the departed. Like their present-day Italian descendants, the Romans regarded family and perpetuation of family name as extremely important. It was considered by the Romans to be a curse for a man to die the last of his line. Consequently, so that the dead would not be too lonely, they were buried by the roadside so that their spirits could be cheered by the greetings of those who passed.

Despite the tendency of spirits to haunt the locale of their burial places, they were generally believed by the Romans to inhabit a specific underworld beneath the earth. Cicero wrote of how in every Roman town a deep trench was dug and regarded as the entrance to the underworld for the dead of that particular community. It was vaulted over in a manner to correspond roughly to the sky, and a gap was left, over which a stone, called the *lapis manalis* was placed. Grain was thrown into the trench; then it was filled in and an altar erected above. Then, on three days every year, the trench was opened and the *lapis manalis* removed so that the dead would have access to the world above, should they desire to visit.

As for the spirits of the dead themselves, those who had been properly buried had little to worry about in the afterlife and, conversely, were no threat to the living. However, being buried in itself was no guarantee that the dead person would behave. Those who had died before their allotted life span were doomed to wander the earth until their appointed time to leave it came. Similarly, those who died violent deaths, including murder victims, executed criminals, and the drowned, were likely candidates for troublesome ghosthood. In his dialogue on the immortality of the soul, the *Phaedo*, Plato discusses such spirits, ". . . prowling about tombs and sepulchers, near which, as they tell us, are seen certain ghostly apparitions of souls which have not departed pure. . . . These must be the souls, not of the good, but of the evil, which are compelled to wander about such places in payment of the penalty of their former way of life."

Known formally as lemures, evil spirits or ghosts were regarded, both in Greece and in Rome, as sufficiently dangerous to be dealt with by definite ceremonial methods. In the very early times they were dealt with by spilling blood. The first gladiatorial games were held in connection with important funerals. The three-day festival for propitiating these spirits was held during a period falling in February–March in Athens. The days were considered unlucky. As was the case later in Rome, temples were shut down, business was not conducted, and everyone was cautious to avoid the walking dead. In the mornings the doors of houses were smeared with pitch, and the inhabitants chewed whitethorn to keep the evil spirits away. On the final day offerings were made to Hermes, and the dead were formally enjoined to depart. The attitude toward whitethorn is interesting, because even in relatively modern times, among the superstitious peasants of Greece and neighboring regions, whitethorn is hung about to ward off vampires.

In Rome the festival was known as Lemuria or Lemuralia. It took place during the month of May, and, in addition to precautions such as those taken in Greece, marriages were avoided. Furthermore, heads of households performed a vital ritual regarded by most as essential to the maintenance of a secure home. In the dead of night the individual on whose shoulders this responsibility fell would walk barefoot through the house, making the mystic sign of the horns with the thumb crossed over the two middle fingers and the forefinger and little finger extended. This sign would protect him if he inadvertently ran into a noncorporeal spirit. Before he proceeded, however, he washed his hands solemnly and placed black beans in his mouth. Then as he marched through the house he threw others over his shoulders, calling out, "With these beans do I redeem me and mine." It was necessary to repeat this incantation nine times without looking around. The general idea was that the spirits would follow and pick up the beans. After the ninth time he would wash again, clash brass cymbals together, and order all uninvited spirits to leave the house. Then he looked around, and the rite was over for another year.

Despite the prevalent belief in ghosts, there were ever-present skeptics even in those remote days. It should be pointed out here that, unlike our traditional shades attired in diaphanous white robes, departed spirits were generally thought of as dark entities, preferring somber black garb. One prominent disbeliever, the Greek philosopher Democritus, was so determined to prove his point of view that he once moved lock, stock, and barrel into a tomb. A number of neighborhood youths, equally determined to shake him from his position, gathered together one night, dressed in black, put skull-like masks over their faces, and danced about the tomb, howling, wailing, and moaning in their best impersonation of restless spirits. Unfortunately their prank had little more effect on the philosopher than to make him stick out his head, call them a pack of idiots, and tell them to stop pestering him and go home.

III

China

It stands to reason that a people with so ancient a culture as the Chinese would be bound to have a rich, extensive, and complex literary tradition. But because Westerners have heard more about it than they have actually come to know, they have tended over the years to form a number of misconceptions. For example, it is known that the Chinese traditionally displayed, and indeed felt, a profound respect for their great classics—the works of Confucius, Mencius, Lao Tsu, and others. But, like their Western counterparts, when the Chinese had completed their studies, they spent about as much time with their classics as we do with ours. Among their favorite reading for entertainment were the absorbing and fabulous ghost stories that embodied so many of the ideas deeply rooted in the Chinese psyche.

The depth and subtlety of Chinese philosophy and tradition being what they are, it would be foolhardy for any but the most qualified scholars to offer any serious discourses on the subject. Nevertheless, a few things should be said here about Chinese ghosts, demons, fox-maidens, and supernatural ideas in general, if for no other reason than to clarify in advance certain events and circumstances occurring in the stories that follow—events and circumstances that might otherwise be completely baffling. It is also worth mentioning that, in the realm of the Chinese supernatural, inanimate objects frequently "die" and leave behind ghosts. These ghosts, for obvious reasons, are not possessed of any intelligence to speak of, so, though they may be frightening, they are not terribly dangerous.

One of the most important things to understand in order to enjoy Chinese ghost stories fully is their concept of the soul. Man, they say, has not one but two souls. First there is the hun, or superior soul, which is associated with the shên, or good spirits. After death, when seen, it generally appears as its possessor did in life. The second, or inferior soul is called the p'o. It is greatly feared for its malignant powers, and it participates in the nature of the kuei, or evil spirits. One scholar described it by saying that it "remains in the decaying body, and sometimes is strong enough to prevent it from decaying, and to give it all the appearances of life."

But in addition to ghosts, good and bad, there are countless demons, devils, goblins, vampires, werewolves, were-foxes, were-tigers—the list is formidable. And of course one cannot exclude the imposing hierarchy of gods, goddesses, and magistrates who are responsible for the order of the universe in Heaven, on earth, and in the underworld.

Benign supernatural beings in Chinese lore can be the envy of any in the world. In the proper conditions, a beautiful female ghost or fox-maiden can bring her human lover all the joys of an earthly romance and more besides. Bear in mind, however, the words, "proper conditions." A lovelorn ghost can also be the death of her lover, as can a fox-maiden. It is this delicate intermingling of peril and joy, love and death, that imparts to a certain class of Chinese ghost story an exotic charm just as appealing in its fashion as the icy hand of terror found in other types of tale. The key to the appeal of pretty ghosts and fox-maidens is that, along with their supernatural talents, they display the full spectrum of human emotions.

The malignant spirits of China are as vicious, revolting, and horrifying as any in the world, and in all likelihood they are worse. Frightful to behold, they offend the eye, the ear, and often the nose as well. If they don't inflict some hideous and gruesome death on their victims, they will at least leave the unfortunate wretches in a state of babbling insanity. Sometimes they do nothing physical, but instead perform some ghastly trick in which the object of their assault becomes in a sense his own victim—as is the case in one of the stories that follows.

The most dreaded of all Chinese spirits are the vampires, or ch'iang shih. In behavior they resemble their Western counterparts, but they are more complicated, being demons associated with the p'o. They not only animate corpses and keep them from decaying, but can assemble an entire form from as little as an old skull or a few half-rotten bones. Their tenancy of corpses, of course, ensures the freshness of reanimated bodies for as long as they are able to remain. With blazing red eyes, they have razor-sharp talons, pale white or greenish hair all over the body, resembling mold or decay, and in addition to sucking blood from their living victims, like ghouls, they devour the flesh of the dead. So, if the vampire is fairly representative of Chinese evil spirits, imagine what the others must be like!

The nature of written Chinese being what it is, translations into English—or any other language, for that matter—tend to be highly subjective. Most of the stories that follow are adapted from different versions of the *Liao Chai* of P'u Sung-ling. Written in the late seventeenth century, they eventually came to be regarded by the Chinese much in the same way as are the *Arabian Nights* in the West. Variously translated as *Strange Stories from the Lodge of Leisures*, *Pastimes of the Study*, and *Strange Stories from a Chinese Studio*, the *Liao Chai* never achieved any great prominence beyond China. It is nonetheless one of the most intriguing collections of weird and uncanny tales ever written anywhere.

Unhappily, P'u Sung-ling considered himself to be a failure during his own lifetime, for he did not pass the examinations that would have qualified him for the second or master's degree and would have assured him of a post in the ranks of scholarly officialdom to which he aspired. Yet, had he attained the minor position he hoped for, posterity would have been denied the benefit of his literary imagination. But he accepted his destiny as having been decreed by the gods, made the best of his poor existence, and spent as much time as he could in the company of other, pre-sumably more successful scholars. It is not known precisely when he began writing the *Liao Chai*, but he ultimately completed it in the year 1679—a monumental work of sixteen volumes. Unfor-tunately, he was so poor he could not afford to have his work published. It was thus read in manuscript form for many years, not achieving the dignity of print until 1740.

The most ironic blow dealt to P'u Sung-ling by an unkind fate is that he never knew during his lifetime of the eventual honor that would be heaped upon his name. In a sparse autobiograph-ical sketch he ruefully wrote, ". . . as I thus commit my thoughts to writing, truly I am an object worthy of commiseration. Alas! I am but the bird that, dreading the winter frost, finds no shelter in the tree; the autumn insect that chirps to the moon, and hugs the door for warmth. For where are they who know me?" But it was inscribed in the Register of the Underworld (as he might have put it) that those destined to know him were to be as numberless as the stars. For even in the Communist People's Republic of China, the stories of P'u Sung-ling, "The Last of the Immortals," as he came to be known, are still read.

The story that follows is characteristic of Chinese vampire tales. It is from the *Liao Chai* and has been translated in various versions as, "The Resuscitated Corpse," "The Corpse at the Inn," and "The Corpse the Blood-Drinker." This, then, is an adaptation of these others.

Night fell slowly over the remote village of Tsai Tien, located in a narrow valley of the Yang Shin district. As the gath-ering shadows grew long and black, a small pack-train made its way along the winding path cut in the hill. The mules, about twenty in all, strained beneath their heavy loads, and the drivers cursed and shouted at them in coarse, strident tones.

Seated comfortably on four of the mules were the four traveling merchants who were masters of the caravan. They were clad
in long quilted robes, thick fur boots, and heavy red woolen
hoods to protect themselves from the bitter winds that blew
down the mountain. The thickening darkness was rendered even
more impenetrable by a heavy swirling fog, and their hearts were
gladdened when they were finally able to make out the lights of
the tiny village ahead.

Upon their arrival at the only inn of the place, the four weary
travelers, happy at the prospect of a warm meal and a night's
sleep, climbed from their saddles as the innkeeper came out to
greet them. But alas, all the rooms were taken. "I have a large
chamber across the road," he said, "but it is only a poor barn,
badly closed against the cold. You may spend the night there if
you choose."

Sorely distressed, the four merchants consulted one another
with a look and consented to follow the innkeeper. The chamber
was large enough, as he had said, and the far end was closed off
by a curtain. It was a poor place to sleep, but better than the
cold outdoors, and they called for their luggage and bedrolls,
which were accordingly spread out for them on planks and trestles.

Their meal was served in the public room of the inn, amidst
laughter, noise, and activity. Vegetables, smoking rice, and warm
wine were served. When they had done, the host gave them a
small oil lamp to light their way; they found their way back to
the barn and retired to their sleeping-pallets.

Now it happened that the innkeeper's daughter-in-law had
died, and her corpse was laid out in the very barn where the unsuspecting travelers had bedded down for the night. She was
dressed in ceremonial paper robes and lay on a makeshift wooden
bier in deep shadows behind the drawn curtain at the far end of
the chamber. Near the door were the trestles and planks upon
which the bedrolls had been placed, and near these was a plain
wooden table upon which the last of the four men to enter had
placed the flickering, smoky lamp that had lighted their way.

Of the four men, one, whose name was Wang Fu, felt a strange
premonition, and while his three companions snored peacefully,

he lay awake staring at the eerie shadows cast by the sputtering lamp. With the approach of the hour of the rat, a cold sensation of uneasiness came over Wang Fu. He turned in his bed and tried to sleep, but the snoring of his three companions echoed in his ears like the buzzing of bees and he could not sleep. Finally, seeing that he was unable to rest, he rose up, trimmed the wick of the lamp to provide more light, then took a book of ancient wisdom from his baggage, stretched out again, and began to read. But this was not to be, for as he had been unable to sleep, neither could he read. For reasons he could not understand, a growing terror froze him, and though he would have chosen to awaken his companions, the fear of being ridiculed held him back, for he did not wish to lose face.

Suddenly he heard a creaking noise, accompanied by the rustling of paper. Not daring to move anything but his eyes, he glanced above his book in the direction of the ominous sounds. By now his eyes had become accustomed to the murky darkness beyond the pale glow of the lamp, and he thought he saw a slight movement shake the curtain at the far end of the barn. Fingers of ice seemed to grip Wang Fu's heart, and he was filled with an overpowering horror, despite his efforts to remain calm.

Putting his book aside and drawing the coverlet up to his nose, he fixed his widened eyes on the shadowy curtain across the chamber. Gradually it began to lift; a pale hand held the folds, and he saw that it belonged to a corpse that was beginning to move. The dead body of the girl rose stiffly from its bier, and the dim light revealed the ghastly pallor of her face. Paralyzed with terror, the poor man beheld the animated corpse standing upright, then moving slowly from behind the curtain. Wang Fu could easily have screamed, had not his throat constricted, thus allowing no sound to escape. Motionless and speechless, he followed with his horrified eyes the path of the dreadful creature as it started to glide unmistakably toward the three who slept.

As she reached the first man she bent silently over him and appeared to give him a lingering kiss. She rose up and went to the figure of the second merchant. Wang Fu distinctly saw the pale figure for the first time and nearly died on the spot, of terror. Red flames shone from her demon eyes, and the sharp fangs that were half exposed behind her ferocious smile flashed as the hideous mouth opened and closed on the throat of the sleeper. The victim twitched beneath his thin cover, then lay motionless as the corpse drank in long drafts of blood with horrible sucking noises.

As the terrified man lay there trembling, she rose up again and repeated her action over the third merchant. Wang Fu, by now half dead with fright, had just enough strength to pull the cover over his head and hold his breath. He listened for what seemed to be an eternity. A chill came over him as she approached his bed and bent down as she had over the others. He heard grumbling sounds, and a freezing breath penetrated through his coverlet. But then, hearing the sound of receding footsteps, he stealthily peeked out from his hiding place and saw her raise the curtain and return to her bier.

For a few moments he lay still. Then, ever so cautiously, he stretched out one foot and kicked the nearest of his companions. Shuddering, for it had felt as though he was touching a dead man, Wang Fu had no thought but of flight. Moving as softly as he could, he reached for his clothing so that he could make a dash for the door. But no sooner had he reached under the bed than once more he heard the awful creaking of the bier and rustling of the paper corpse clothing. Instinctively he buried his head beneath the cover again and held his breath as he had done before. After what felt like a second eternity the corpse came to him a second time and bent down to breathe its foul breath upon his face. Finally it retreated once again to resume its place back upon the bier.

This last paroxysm of terror gave Wang Fu full possession of his strength. With a convulsive movement he seized his clothes, jumped out of his bed, and, bellowing like a wild beast, ran to the door and fled into the night. But he was not alone. The dead girl, too, leaped to her feet and followed him into the darkness. As he ran he could feel her freezing breath at his back and hear her enraged shrieks. Outdoors he plunged frantically through the blackness, shrieking at the top of his lungs. But there was no one to hear him but his ghastly pursuer, who kept close upon his heels. Raising his voice as he passed the inn door availed him nothing. His screams went unheeded. So he kept running toward the main road, which led to the edge of the village.

With the corpse keeping up its pace, the fleeing Wang Fu

looked desperately about for a place to hide. Suddenly he noticed a small roadside monastery, and, rushing up to the gate, he pounded with all his might. But alas! the priests inside knew not what to make of this unexpected tumult and would not open the door. By now the corpse was only yards away. In desperation Wang Fu ran toward a huge willow tree that stood nearby. And just in time, for the dead girl reached the tree at the precise moment Wang Fu managed to dodge to one side. It now became a deadly game. The corpse, her eyes glowing fiercely, like live coals, tried to seize her intended victim with demonic ferocity. But each time she moved to the left he would rush to the right, and so it went until both were panting hoarsely, poor Wang Fu at the brink of exhaustion. Then, unexpectedly, both he and the corpse became motionless, staring at each other—he in mortal terror, she with the cold rage of an inhuman monster.

Suddenly the corpse lunged forward with outstretched arms to seize Wang Fu once and for all. Believing that his end had finally come, he fell backward, senseless, to the ground. The dead girl crashed into the tree with the force of a charging tiger.

Now the priests, who had been hearing the shrieks and howls, rushed out to find the cause of the disturbance. They found the unconscious Wang Fu lying on the ground beside the tree, so they carried him into the monastery. By daybreak they succeeded in bringing him to his senses, at which time he told them in detail of his horrible ordeal in the dark. When the sun was shining brightly they went out to investigate the tree and there found the corpse of the girl, hanging limply to the trunk, blood streaming from her mouth, staining her white paper dress.

A shudder of horror shook the witnesses, and the local magistrate was summoned at once. The moment he arrived he ordered that the body be removed, but this was impossible at first, for her long fingernails were embedded too deeply in the trunk of the tree. Finally she was detached, and word of the night's dreadful events was sent to the inn, where by now the three other merchants had been found dead. The innkeeper confessed that the body of his daughter-in-law had lain in the barn for six months, waiting for the astrologers to fix a favorable day for her burial.

The party then returned to the barn to find what condition the three dead men were in, as well as the state of the bier upon which the dead girl had lain for so long. Her three victims appeared hollow, and their faces green, for they had been deprived of all their blood. But when the curtain that hid the bier was drawn, gasps issued from the lips of the entire company, for there lay the corpse of the dead girl, restored to its place by evil influences. The dress was still bloodstained, and fresh blood trickled down from the mouth. She appeared as fresh as the day she had died, for she had not lost her inferior soul.

Upon this Wang Fu petitioned the magistrate and said to him, "Four of us left home, but only one will return. Give me something that I may show to my fellow townsmen that I may not be held responsible for the fate of the others." The magistrate complied with his wishes, and he was accordingly sent on his way.

« »   « »   « »

One of the most popular themes recurring in Chinese ghost stories is a world apart from the dark and shadowy realm inhabited by bloodthirsty corpses and ferocious demonic horrors. In tales of this gentler variety a human being, usually a young man, has a love affair with a ghost. As a rule the hero of these fanciful tales is a poor young scholar whose future is invariably altered as a result of the encounter. "The Story of Ming Yi" is a hauntingly beautiful tale written by one of the few Westerners with an ability to convey in English the poetic fragility so distinctive of certain Oriental literature. Of the writer, Lafcadio Hearn, more will be said later, for there are more of his exotic writings to come.

◄◄◄◄◄ The Story of Ming Yi

BY LAFCADIO HEARN

Sang the poet Ching Ku: "Surely the peach flowers blossom over the tomb of Si Tao."

Do you ask me who she was,—the beautiful Si Tao? For a thousand years and more the trees have been whispering above her bed of stone. And the syllables of her name come to the listener with the lisping of the leaves; with the quivering of many fingered boughs; with the fluttering of lights and shadows; with the breath, sweet as a woman's presence, of numberless savage flowers,—Si Tao. But, saving the whispering of her name, what the trees say cannot be understood; and they alone remember the years of Si Tao. Something about her you might, nevertheless, learn from any of those *kiang-ku-jin*,—those famous Chinese story tellers, who nightly narrate to listening crowds, in consideration of a few *sien*, the legends of the past. Something concerning her you may also find in the book entitled *Kin Ku Ki Koan*, which signifies in our tongue: "The Marvelous Happenings of Ancient and Recent Times." And perhaps of all things therein written, the most marvelous is this memory of Si Tao:—

Five hundred years ago, in the reign of the Emperor Hung Wu, whose dynasty was Ming, there lived in the City of Genii, the Canton, a man celebrated for his learning and for his piety, named Tien Pei-lu. This Tien Pei-lu had one son, a beautiful boy, who for scholarship and for bodily grace and for polite accomplishments had no superior among the youths of his age. And his name was Ming Yi.

Now when the lad was in his eighteenth summer, it came to pass that Pei-lu, his father, was appointed Inspector of Public Instruction at the city of Ching-tu; and Ming Yi accompanied his parents thither. Near the city of Ching-tu lived a rich man of rank, a high commissioner of the government, whose name was Chang, and who wanted to find a worthy teacher for his children. On hearing of the arrival of the new Inspector of Public Instruction, the noble Chang visited him to obtain advice in this matter; and happening to meet and converse with Pei-lu's accomplished son, immediately engaged Ming Yi as a private tutor for his family.

Now as the house of this Lord Chang was situated several miles from town, it was deemed best that Ming Yi should abide in the house of his employer. Accordingly the youth made ready all things necessary for his new sojourn; and his parents, bidding him farewell, counselled him wisely, and cited to him the words of Lao Tsu and of the ancient sages:

"By a beautiful face the world is filled with love; but Heaven may never be deceived thereby. Shouldst thou behold a woman coming from the East, look thou to the West; shouldst thou perceive a maiden approaching from the West, turn thine eyes to the East."

If Ming Yi did not heed this counsel in after days, it was only because of his youth and the thoughtlessness of a naturally joyous heart.

And he departed to abide in the house of Lord Chang, while the autumn passed, and the winter also.

When the time of the second moon of spring was drawing near, and that happy day which the Chinese call Hoa-chao, or "The Birthday of a Hundred Flowers," a longing came upon Ming Yi to see his parents; and he opened his heart to the good Chang, who not only gave him the permission he desired, but also pressed into his hand a silver gift of two ounces, thinking that the lad might wish to bring some little memento to his father and mother. For it is the Chinese custom, on the feast of Hoachao, to make presents to friends and relations.

That day all the air was drowsy with blossom perfume, and vibrant with the droning of bees. It seemed to Ming Yi that the path he followed had not been trodden by any other for many long years; the grass was tall upon it; vast trees on either side interlocked their mighty and mossgrown arms above him, beshadowing the way; but the leafy obscurities quivered with bird song, and the deep vistas of the wood were glorified by vapors of gold, and odorous with flower breathings as a temple with incense. The dreamy joy of the day entered into the heart of Ming

Yi and he sat him down among the young blossoms, under the branches swaying against the violet sky, to drink in the perfume and the light, and to enjoy the great sweet silence. Even while thus reposing, a sound caused him to turn his eyes toward a shady place where wild peach trees were in bloom; and he beheld a young woman, beautiful as the pinkening blossoms themselves, trying to hide among them. Though he looked for a moment only, Ming Yi could not avoid discerning the loveliness of her face, the golden purity of her complexion, and the brightness of her long eyes, that sparkled under a pair of brows as daintily curved as the wings of the silkworm butterfly outspread. Ming Yi at once turned his gaze away, and, rising quickly, proceeded on his journey. But so much embarrassed did he feel at the idea of those charming eyes peeping at him through the leaves, that he suffered the money he had been carrying in his sleeve to fall, without being aware of it. A few moments later he heard the patter of light feet running behind him, and a woman's voice calling him by name. Turning his face in great surprise, he saw a comely servant maid, who said to him, "Sir, my mistress bade me pick up and return you this silver which you dropped upon the road." Ming Yi thanked the girl gracefully, and requested her to convey his compliments to her mistress. Then he proceeded on his way through the perfumed silence, athwart the shadows that dreamed along the forgotten path, dreaming himself also, and feeling his heart beating with strange quickness at the thought of the beautiful being that he had seen.

It was just such another day when Ming Yi, returning by the same path, paused once more at the spot where the gracious figure had momentarily appeared before him. But this time he was surprised to perceive, through a long vista of immense trees, a dwelling that had previously escaped his notice,—a country residence, not large, yet elegant to an unusual degree. The bright blue tiles of its curved and serrated double roof, rising above the foliage, seemed to blend their color with the luminous azure of the day; the green and gold designs of its carven porticos were exquisite artistic mockeries of leaves and flowers bathed in sunshine. And at the summit of terrace steps before it, guarded by great porcelain tortoises, Ming Yi saw standing the mistress of the mansion,—the idol of his passionate fancy,—accompanied by the same waiting maid who had borne to her his message of gratitude. While Ming Yi looked, he perceived that their eyes were upon him; they smiled and conversed together as if speaking about him; and, shy though he was, the youth found courage to salute the fair one from a distance. To his astonishment, the young servant beckoned him to approach; and opening a rustic gate half veiled by trailing plants bearing crimson flowers, Ming Yi advanced along the verdant alley leading to the terrace, with mingled feelings of surprise and timid joy. As he drew near, the beautiful lady withdrew from sight; but the maid waited at the broad steps to receive him, and said as he ascended:

"Sir, my mistress understands you wish to thank her for the trifling service she recently bade me do you, and requests that you will enter the house, as she knows you already by repute, and desires to have the pleasure of bidding you good day."

Ming Yi entered bashfully, his feet making no sound upon a matting elastically soft as forest moss, and found himself in a reception chamber vast, cool, and fragrant with scent of blossoms freshly gathered. A delicious quiet pervaded the mansion; shadows of flying birds passed over the bands of light that fell through the half blinds of bamboo; great butterflies, with pinions of fiery color, found their way in, to hover a moment about the painted vases, and pass out again into the mysterious woods. And noiselessly as they, the young mistress of the mansion entered by another door, and kindly greeted the boy, who lifted his hands to his breast and bowed low in salutation. She was taller than he had deemed her, and supplely slender as a beauteous lily; her black hair was interwoven with the creamy blossoms of the chu-sha-ki; her robes of pale silk took shifting tints when she moved, as vapors change hue with the changing of the light.

"If I be not mistaken," she said, when both had seated themselves after having exchanged the customary formalities of politeness, "my honored visitor is none other than Tien-chu, surnamed Ming Yi, educator of the children of my respected relative, the High Commissioner Chang. As the family of Lord Chang is my family also, I cannot but consider the teacher of his children as one of my own kin."

"Lady," replied Ming Yi, not a little astonished, "May I dare to inquire the name of your honored family, and to ask the relation which you hold to my noble patron?"

"The name of my poor family," responded the comely lady, "is Ping,—an ancient family of the city of Ching-tu. I am the daughter of a certain Si of Mun-hao; Si is my name, likewise; and I was married to a young man of the Ping family, whose name was Kang. By this marriage I became related to your excellent patron; but my husband died soon after our wedding, and I have chosen this solitary place to reside in during the period of my widowhood."

There was a drowsy music in her voice, as of the melody of brooks, the murmurings of spring; and such a strange grace in the manner of her speech as Ming Yi had never heard before. Yet on learning that she was a widow, the youth would not have presumed to remain long in her presence without a formal invitation; and after having sipped the cup of rich tea presented to him, he arose to depart. Si would not suffer him to go so quickly.

"Nay, friend," she said; "stay yet a little while in my house, I pray you; for, should your honored patron ever learn that you had been here, and that I had not treated you as a respected guest, and regaled you even as I would him, I know that he would be greatly angered. Remain at least to supper."

So Ming Yi remained, rejoicing secretly in his heart, for Si seemed to him the fairest and sweetest being he had ever known, and he felt that he loved her even more than his father and his mother. And while they talked the long shadows of the evening slowly blended into one violet darkness; the great citron light of the sunset faded out; and those starry beings that are called the Three Councillors, who preside over life and death and the destinies of men, opened their cold bright eyes in the northern sky. Within the mansion of Si the painted lanterns were lighted; the table was laid for the evening repast; and Ming Yi took his place at it, feeling little inclination to eat, and thinking only of the charming face before him. Observing that he scarcely tasted the dainties laid upon his plate, Si pressed her young guest to partake of wine; and they drank several cups together. It was a purple wine, so cool that the cup into which it was poured became covered with vapory dew; yet it seemed to warm the veins with strange fire. To Ming Yi, as he drank, all things became more luminous as by enchantment; the walls of the chamber appeared to recede, and the roof to heighten; the lamps glowed like stars in their chains, and the voice of Si floated to the boy's ears like some far melody heard through the spaces of a drowsy night. His heart swelled; his tongue loosened; and words flitted from his lips that he had fancied he could never dare to utter. Yet Si sought not to restrain him; her lips gave no smile; but her long bright eyes seemed to laugh with pleasure at his words of praise, and to return his gaze of passionate admiration with affectionate interest.

"I have heard," she said, "of your rare talent, and of your many elegant accomplishments. I know how to sing a little, although I cannot claim to possess any musical learning; and now that I have the honor of finding myself in the society of a musical professor, I will venture to lay modesty aside, and beg you to sing a few songs with me. I should deem it no small gratification if you would condescend to examine my musical compositions."

"The honor and the gratification, dear lady," replied Ming Yi, "will be mine; and I feel helpless to express the gratitude which the offer of so rare a favor deserves."

The serving maid, obedient to the summons of a little silver gong, brought in the music and retired. Ming Yi took the manuscripts, and began to examine them with eager delight. The paper upon which they were written had a pale yellow tint, and was light as a fabric of gossamer; but the characters were antiquely beautiful, as though they had been traced by the brush of Hei-sung Che Chu himself,—that divine Genius of Ink, who is no bigger than a fly; and the signatures attached to the compositions were the signatures of Yuen-chin, Kao-pien, and Tao-mu,—mighty poets and musicians of the dynasty of Tang! Ming Yi could not repress a scream of delight at the sight of treasures so inestimable and so unique; scarcely could he summon resolution enough to permit them to leave his hands even for a moment.

"O Lady!" he cried, "these are veritably priceless things, surpassing in worth the treasures of all kings. This indeed is the handwriting of those great masters who sang five hundred years before our birth. How marvelously it has been preserved! Is not this the wondrous ink of which it was written: Po-nien-ju-chi, i-tien-ju-ki,—'After centuries I remain firm as stone, and the letters that I make like lacquer'? And how divine the charm of this composition!—the song of Kao-pien, prince of poets, and Governor of Szechwan five hundred years ago!"

"Kao-pien! darling Kao-pien!" murmured Si, with a singular light in her eyes. "Kao-pien is also my favorite. Dear Ming Yi, let us chant his verses together, to the melody of old,—the music of those grand years when men were nobler and wiser than today."

And their voices rose through the perfumed night like the voices of the wonder birds,—Fung-hong,—blending together in liquid sweetness. Yet a moment, and Ming Yi, overcome by the witchery of his companion's voice, could only listen in speechless ecstasy, while the lights of the chamber swam dim before his sight, and tears of pleasure trickled down his cheeks.

So the ninth hour passed; and they continued to converse, and to drink the cool purple wine, and to sing the songs of the years of Tang until far into the night. More than once Ming Yi thought of departing; but each time Si would begin, in that silversweet voice of hers, so wondrous a story of the great poets of the past, and of the women whom they loved, that he became as one entranced; or she would sing for him a song so strange that all his senses seemed to die except that of hearing. And at last, as she paused to pledge him in a cup of wine, Ming Yi could not restrain himself from putting his arm about her round neck and drawing her dainty head closer to him, and kissing the lips that were so much ruddier and sweeter than the wine. Then their lips separated no more;—the night grew old, and they knew it not.

The birds awakened, the flowers opened their eyes to the rising sun, and Ming Yi found himself at last compelled to bid his lovely enchantress farewell. Si, accompanying him to the terrace, kissed him fondly and said, "Dear boy, come hither as often as you are able,—as often as your heart whispers you to come. I know that you are not of those without faith and truth, who betray secrets; yet, being so young, you might also be sometimes thoughtless; and I pray you never to forget that only the stars have been the witnesses of our love. Speak of it to no living person, dearest; and take with you this little souvenir of our happy night."

And she presented him with an exquisite and curious little thing,—a paper weight in likeness of a couchant lion, wrought from a jade stone yellow as that created by a rainbow in honor of Confucius. Tenderly the boy kissed the gift and the beautiful hand that gave it. "May the Spirits punish me," he vowed, "if ever I knowingly give you cause to reproach me, sweetheart!" And they separated with mutual vows.

That morning, on returning to the house of Lord Chang, Ming Yi told the first falsehood which had ever passed his lips. He averred that his mother had requested him thenceforward to pass his nights at home, now that the weather had become so pleasant; for, though the way was somewhat long, he was strong and active, and needed both air and healthy exercise. Chang believed all Ming Yi said, and offered no objection. Accordingly the lad found himself enabled to pass all his evenings at the house of the beautiful Si. Each night they devoted to the same pleasures which had made their first acquaintance so charming: they sang and conversed by turns; they played at chess,—the learned game invented by Wu Wang, which is an imitation of war; they composed pieces of eighty rhymes upon the flowers, the trees, the clouds, the streams, the birds, the bees. But in all accomplishments Si far excelled her young sweetheart. Whenever they played at chess, it was always Ming Yi's general, Ming Yi's tsiang, who was surrounded and vanquished; when they composed verses, Si's poems were ever superior to his in harmony of word coloring, in elegance of form, in classic loftiness of thought. And the themes they selected were always the most difficult,— those of the poets of the Tang dynasty; the songs they sang were also the songs of five hundred years before,—the songs of Yuen-chin, of Tao-mu, of Kao-pien above all, high poet and ruler of the province of Szechwan.

So the summer waxed and waned upon their love, and the luminous autumn came, with its vapors of phantom gold, its shadows of magical purple.

Then it unexpectedly happened that the father of Ming Yi, meeting his son's employer at Ching-tu, was asked by him: "Why must your boy continue to travel every evening to the city, now that the winter is approaching? The way is long, and when he returns in the morning he looks fordone with weariness. Why not permit him to slumber in my house during the season of snow?" And the father of Ming Yi, greatly astonished, responded: "Sir, my son has not visited the city, nor has he been to our house all this summer. I fear that he must have acquired wicked habits, and that he passes his nights in evil company,— perhaps in gaming, or in drinking with the women of the flower boats." But the High Commissioner returned: "Nay! that is not to be thought of. I have never found any evil in the boy, and there are no taverns nor flower boats nor any places of dissipation in our neighborhood. No doubt Ming Yi has found some amiable youth of his own age with whom to spend his evenings, and only told me an untruth for fear that I would not otherwise permit him to leave my residence. I beg that you will say nothing to him until I shall have sought to discover this mystery; and this very evening I shall send my servant to follow after him, and to watch whither he goes."

Pei-lu readily assented to this proposal, and promising to visit Chang the following morning, returned to his home. In the evening, when Ming Yi left the house of Chang, a servant followed him unobserved at a distance. But on reaching the most obscure portion of the road, the boy disappeared from sight as suddenly as though the earth had swallowed him. After having long sought after him in vain, the domestic returned in great bewilderment to the house, and related what had taken place. Chang immediately sent a messenger to Pei-lu.

In the meantime Ming Yi, entering the chamber of his beloved, was surprised and deeply pained to find her in tears. "Sweetheart," she sobbed, wreathing her arms around his neck, "we are about to be separated forever, because of reasons which I cannot tell you. From the very first I knew this must come to pass; and nevertheless it seemed to me for the moment so cruelly sudden a loss, so unexpected a misfortune, that I could not prevent myself from weeping! After this night we shall never see each other again, beloved, and I know that you will not be able to forget me while you live; but I know also that you will become a great scholar, and that honors and riches will be showered upon you, and that some beautiful and loving woman will console you for my loss. And now let us speak no more of grief; but let us pass this last evening joyously, so that your recollection of me may not be a painful one, and that you may remember my laughter rather than my tears."

She brushed the bright drops away, and brought wine and music and the melodious *kin* of seven silken strings, and would not suffer Ming Yi to speak for one moment of the coming separation. And she sang him an ancient song about the calmness of summer lakes reflecting the blue of heaven only, and the calmness of the heart also, before the clouds of care and of grief and of weariness darken its little world. Soon they forgot their sorrow in the joy of song and wine; and those last hours seemed to Ming Yi more celestial than even the hours of their first bliss.

But when the yellow beauty of morning came their sadness returned, and they wept. Once more Si accompanied her lover to the terrace steps; and as she kissed him farewell, she pressed into his hand a parting gift,—a little brushcase of agate, wonderfully chiseled, and worthy the table of a great poet. And they separated forever, shedding many tears.

Still Ming Yi could not believe it was an eternal parting. "No!" he thought, "I shall visit her tomorrow; for I cannot now live without her, and I feel assured that she cannot refuse to receive me." Such were the thoughts that filled his mind as he reached the house of Chang, to find his father and his patron standing on the porch awaiting him. Ere he could speak a word, Pei-lu demanded: "Son, in what place have you been passing your nights?"

Seeing that his falsehood had been discovered, Ming Yi dared not make any reply, and remained abashed and silent, with bowed head, in the presence of his father. Then Pei-lu striking the boy violently with his staff, commanded him to divulge the secret; and at last, partly through fear of his parent, and partly through fear of the law which ordains that "the son refusing to obey his father shall be punished with one hundred blows of the bamboo," Ming Yi faltered out the history of his love.

Chang changed color at the boy's tale. "Child," exclaimed the High Commissioner, "I have no relative of the name of Ping; I have never heard of the woman you describe; I have never heard even of the house which you speak of. But I know also that you cannot dare to lie to Pei-lu, your honored father; there is some strange delusion in all this affair."

Then Ming Yi produced the gifts that Si had given him,— the lion of yellow jade, the brushcase of carven agate, also some original compositions made by the beautiful lady herself. The astonishment of Chang was now shared by Pei-lu. Both observed that the brushcase of agate and the lion of jade bore the appearance of objects that had lain buried in the earth for centuries, and were of a workmanship beyond the power of living man to imitate; while the compositions proved to be veritable masterpieces of poetry, written in the style of the poets of the dynasty of Tang.

"Friend Pei-lu," cried the High Commissioner, "let us immediately accompany the boy to the place where he obtained these miraculous things, and apply the testimony of our senses to this mystery. The boy is no doubt telling the truth; yet his story passes my understanding." And all three proceeded toward the place of the habitation of Si.

But when they had arrived at the shadiest part of the road, where the perfumes were most sweet and the mosses were greenest, and the fruits of the wild peach flushed most pinkly, Ming Yi, gazing through the groves, uttered a cry of dismay. Where the azure tiled roof had risen against the sky, there was now only the blue emptiness of air; where the green and gold façade had been, there was visible only the flickering of leaves under the aureate autumn light; and where the broad terrace had extended, could be discerned only a ruin,—a tomb so ancient, so deeply gnawed by moss, that the name graven upon it was no longer decipherable. The home of Si had disappeared!

All suddenly the High Commissioner smote his forehead with his hand, and turning to Pei-lu, recited the well-known verse of the ancient poet Chang-ku—

" 'Surely the peach flowers blossom over the tomb of SiTao.'

"Friend Pei-lu," continued Chang. "The beauty who bewitched your son was no other than she whose tomb stands there in ruin before us! Did she not say she was wedded to Ping Kang? There is no family of that name, but Ping Kang is indeed the name of a broad alley in the city near. There was a dark riddle in all that she said. She called herself Si of Moun-hao: There is no person of that name; there is no street of that name; but the Chinese characters mun and hiao, placed together, form the character kao. Listen! The alley Ping Kang, situated in the street Kao, was the place where dwelt the great courtesans of the dynasty of Tang! Did she not sing the songs of Kao-pien? And upon the brushcase and the paper weight she gave your son, are there not characters which read, 'Pure object of art belonging to Kao, of the city of Pho-hai'? That city no longer exists; but the memory of Kao-pien remains, for he was governor of the province of Szechwan, and a mighty poet. And when he dwelt in the land of Chu, was not his favorite the beautiful wanton Si,—Si Tao, unmatched for grace among all the women of her day? It was he who made her a gift of those manuscripts of song; it was he who gave her those objects of rare art. Si Tao died not as other women die. Her limbs may have crumbled to dust; yet something of her still lives in this deep wood,—her Shadow still haunts this shadowy place."

Chang ceased to speak. A vague fear fell upon the three. The thin mists of the morning made dim the distances of green, and deepened the ghostly beauty of the woods. A faint breeze passed by, leaving a trail of blossom scent,—a last odor of dying flowers,—thin as that which clings to the silk of a forgotten robe; and, as it passed, the trees seemed to whisper across the silence, "*Si Tao*."

Fearing greatly for his son, Pei-lu sent the lad away at once to the city of Canton. And there, in after years, Ming Yi obtained high dignities and honors by reason of his talents and his learning; and he married the daughter of an illustrious house, by whom he became the father of sons and daughters famous for their virtues and their accomplishments. Never could he forget Si Tao; and yet it is said that he never spoke of her,—not even when his children begged him to tell them the story of two beautiful objects that always lay upon his writing table: a lion of yellow jade, and a brushcase of carven agate.

« » « » « »

Like so many Chinese tales of supernatural horror, this one, dealing with an encounter between man and demon, has more than one version, including one in the *Liao Chai*. An appropriate title for this composite is "The Hideous Deceivers."

Night was falling when the horseshoes of the mules in my caravan clattered on the slippery flagstones of the village. Tired from a long day's travel, I made my way toward a roadside inn, with the intention of resting while my evening meal was prepared.

In the darkened room beyond the portal the glimmer of a small opium lamp lit the pale and hollow face of an elderly man, busily occupied in melting a small ball of the black drug which would soon become sweet smoke, the source of forgetfulness and dreams.

I greeted him and he returned my salutation, inviting me to lie down on the couch opposite his own. As he handed me a pipe that had already been prepared we began to converse, and as is ordained by the rules of politeness, I remarked to him that he appeared strong and hearty for his age.

"My age?" he murmured. "How old, then, do you think I am?"

"Indeed, you must have seen at least sixty harvests, not so?"

"Sixty!" he exclaimed. "I am not yet thirty years of age. But you must be a stranger from far away not to know who I am."

And as he rolled the balls of opium dexterously in the palms of his hands, and made them puff up over the heat of the lamp, he related his story.

His name was Chu Chao. Born and raised in the capital of Shansi Province, he had been elevated six years before to the post of Subprefect of the town in which he now resides. While on the way to take his new appointment, he had stopped at the very inn where now we talked. Noticing that a long pavilion, part of the inn, was locked, he inquired of the landlord the reason, and was told that it had been shut for two years. All who had stayed there complained of frightening noises and visions in the night. It having finally been concluded that the place was haunted by a yao kuai, an especially vexatious evil spirit, the pavilion was locked and left unused.

Chu Chao, having lived in the capital all his life, placed no credence in the existence of spirits and demons. He thus concluded that this would be an auspicious occasion to establish his reputation for bravery by facing dangers he himself regarded as imaginary. "I shall rid the place of this demon," he promised, and despite his wife's protests, he ordered her to take the children and their servants and go to bed in that section of the inn regarded to be safe.

Entering the haunted pavilion with only a lighted lamp, he seated himself in a chair, holding his sword across his knees, and waited. Hours passed. The deep tones of the gong struck by the watchman successively announced the passing hours, first the hour of the pig, and then the hour of the rat. By now he had grown drowsy, but suddenly he heard a knock on the door and he seized his sword. But when the door opened, an elderly man with a white beard and a scarlet cap entered. Although he greeted Chu Chao politely, the new Subprefect angrily called him yao kuai, and demanded to know what he wanted. "I am not a demon," explained the old man. "I am the Guardian Spirit of this district. I have come to tell you that your coming has forced the yao kuai who haunted this place to leave. You have my gratitude. Of course, if he and others of his kind return, you must attack them with your sword." With that the old man bowed; Chu Chao returned his salutation and escorted him from the room.

Again, after settling down in his chair, Chu Chao grew drowsy. Suddenly he was roused from his torpor by the gnashing of teeth. He jumped and realized that the lamp had gone out. But the darkness was not so deep that he could see nothing. All his eyes could distinguish, however, were confused shadows. He was seized with anguish; his heart pounded violently, and with his eyes wide he stared fixedly at the door. Slowly it began to open, and as he watched, transfixed with horror, a round white mass oozed gradually into the room. First the deformed and monstrous head appeared, then little by little the hideous thing reached out toward him with long hands and bony, twisted fingers and claws.

Mechanically, Chu Chao raised his sword, the blood freezing to ice in his veins. Though he could barely see the dreadful creature in the gloom, he struck out and it shrieked frightfully, raising by its cry a chorus of terrifying wails and screams on all sides as though all the demons of the underworld had been turned loose in the chamber. The windows rattled, the floor trembled, the cries grew louder, and from all sides Chu Chao could feel hands clutching invisible weapons closing in on him. Brandishing his sword in the direction that seemed most likely, he slashed and struck something, slicing it through like a melon.

But still the horrors continued. More unknown creatures streamed into the room uninterrupted. Slashing first one way and then the other, the Subprefect fought for his life, his eyes now growing accustomed to the darkness. One after the other he struck their heads from their bodies, snarling with rage as he struck them with his weapon. One of the monsters lunged, showing a long black crocodile-snout, gleaming sharp fangs, and a serpent's twisted neck. Then came another, a frightful giant bird with the body and feet of a donkey. Trembling and panting for breath, he struck right and left. Cold sweat broke out over his body, and gradually he felt his strength deserting him as the cock crowed to herald the rising of the sun.

Slowly, steadily the gray dawn turned pink and the sun appeared over the horizon, sending its warming rays through the lattices of the windows. As his senses returned, Chu Chao's heart stood still, for there littering the floor in pools of blood were human bodies—bodies that he knew well. One looked like his wife; a little head that had rolled beneath a table he could have sworn belonged to his youngest son.

With a wild cry of anguish he threw his weapon aside and ran through the open door to the sunlit courtyard outside. A crowd of armed men approached him. "My family!" he cried. "Where is my family?"

"They are all with you in the pavilion," replied the innkeeper.

And as the man spoke those very words, the crowd drew in its breath as the hair of Chu Chao turned white, and the wrinkles of old age shriveled his face. Standing motionless before them as though entranced, the Subprefect then collapsed and rolled before them on the ground.

"And so," ended the unhappy man in the stillness of the dark room, where only the dim light of the little opium lamp glowed, "I remained several days knowing nothing. When I regained my senses, I had to bear the sorrow of having slain my whole family so atrociously, for I had been cruelly tricked by the yao kuai. I resigned my position, I had the finest of possible tombs built for all those who had died at my hand, and ever since I unceasingly smoke the agreeable drug in order to flee from the memory which will haunt me until my dying day."

« »   « »   « »

No sampling of Chinese supernatural tales would be complete without at least one story involving a fox-maiden. One might call her a were-fox, because she corresponds to the werewolf of the west. Her chief point of departure from the werewolf, however, is that what she lacks in ferocity she makes up in amorousness. Although Chinese foxes can be troublesome and dangerous, they are not nearly as much so as their cousins in Japan. A curious fact about were-foxes is that they occupy a special position in both Chinese and Japanese lore that is considerably different from anything Western. For example, they are not basically human beings doomed to metamorphose into animal form, nor are they sorcerers who shift shape for ulterior motives. They are honest-to-goodness foxes, the belief being that they are the intrinsic possessors of supernatural powers themselves.

It should be mentioned at this point that there are also Chinese accounts of werewolves, but they are so similar to their Western counterparts that we can leave them out with nothing more than this acknowledgment that they are to be found.

Certainly the most singular Chinese tale involving the relationship of a fox and a human is the curious story of the maiden Lien-hsiang. It is doubly fascinating, for it incorporates a considerable body of supernatural beliefs, including the concept we call transmigration of souls. Not surprisingly, this story, too, is adapted from the *Liao Chai* of P'u Sung-ling.

In the city of I-chu there once lived a poor young man named Sang Tsu-ming, who had been orphaned when he was very young. He dwelt near the Saffron market and kept mostly to himself, going out only twice each day to the house of a neighbor, where he took his meals. But the rest of his time Sang spent sitting quietly at home.

One day the neighbor came over and jokingly asked Sang if he was not afraid of fox-demons or ghosts, living alone as he did. But Sang laughed and said, "I have nothing to fear from fox-demons or ghosts. If they come in the shape of men I have a sharp sword to defend myself. If they come as women, I shall open my door and invite them in."

Not long after this, the neighbor, with the assistance of a friend, arranged for a young lady to climb over Sang's wall after dark, knock on his door, and identify herself as a ghost. Poor Sang was so terrified that his teeth chattered, and he did not learn that he had been tricked until the next day, when his neighbor came, and upon hearing what had happened the night before, clapped his hands together and asked, "Why did you not ask her in?" With that Sang returned to his previous mode of tranquil existence.

One night after some six months a girl knocked once again on Sang's door. Assuming that his friends were up to their old tricks again, he opened it and invited her in. When she entered he was astonished, for she was of such surpassing beauty that his heart began to pound, and the blood rushed through his veins. When he asked her who she was, she introduced herself as Lien-hsiang, a singing girl from one of the village "green houses." She explained that she lived nearby and had longed to meet him for some time. Barely able to contain himself, Sang bade her welcome and ere long they abandoned themselves to the toils of love. Although Lien-hsiang left at dawn, she returned to see him about every four days.

One evening as Sang sat alone studying, expecting the lovely girl to visit him, he looked up and was astonished to see that another girl had entered without knocking. She was about sixteen and appeared both lovely and elegant. She had long flowing sleeves on her gown, and her hair fell loose over her shoulders in the fashion of unmarried girls. At first Sang was greatly alarmed, for he feared that she was a fox, but she told him that her name was Li, that she belonged to a respectable family, and that she had long been anxious to meet him, having heard of his talent and virtue. At this Sang laughed and took her by the hand, which he found to be as cold as ice. When he asked her the reason for this, she explained that she had always been very delicate, and that she had been chilled by the frosty night air.

In declaring her love for him, Li announced that she intended to visit him often, adding that she hoped her presence would not inconvenience him. He assured her that it would not, for no one came to see him but a singing girl of the district, who came only occasionally. Upon hearing of this, Li said that she must avoid the other girl at all costs, for they were of different classes. With that she gave him a tiny embroidered slipper that she had worn, explaining, "When you shake this it will mean that you are thinking of me and wish to see me. I will then know and come to you. But you must never shake it before strangers." And when the cock crowed she left him.

The following evening as he sat alone in his study Sang took out the little slipper and shook it. Then as softly as a breath of air Li appeared, much to the scholar's delight. From then on, whenever he took the shoe into his hands the lovely girl came to him. He finally asked her for an explanation, but she merely laughed evasively and insisted that it was a coincidence.

One evening not long after this when Lien-hsiang came to see him, she contemplated his face with alarm and said, "You look so pallid and wan. Is there something wrong?" But when he insisted that nothing was the matter with him, she only looked strangely at him and said no more. The next day before leaving, Lien-hsiang told Sang that she would not be back for ten whole days.

During that time, however, Sang did not lack for companionship, for Li came to see him every night. On one of those evenings she asked him how she compared with Lien-hsiang. He replied, "Both of you are perfection itself, but of the two you are colder." Somewhat annoyed at this, Li frowned and cried, "To me you say we are both perfection. In that case she must be like unto the very Moon-Goddess and I am no match for her." As she brooded about this, Li reckoned that Lien-hsiang's ten days had passed and that she would return the next evening. But she persuaded the scholar to permit her also to come, and to hide in order that she might see what her rival looked like.

True to her word, Lien-hsiang arrived at her usual hour, but in the midst of their happy talking she suddenly grew alarmed and said, "Alas! You are worse than when I saw you last, and only ten days have passed. You must have encountered something of extreme evil."

"How so?" asked Sang.

"First," replied Lien-hsiang, "there is the matter of your appearance. Second, your pulse has become as weak as thread. You have the ghost disease."

The next night when Li appeared again, she admitted that Lien-hsiang possessed great beauty, but she had a startling revelation. "She is a fox," declared Li. "When she left I followed her to her burrow in the hill." Sang, however, did not believe her words, attributing them to jealousy, and so nothing more was said on the matter that night. Nevertheless, on the following evening when Lien-hsiang returned, Sang told her what he had heard. To this she replied, "What, then, is the difference between a fox and a human being?"

"Why, foxes bewitch men, and deprive them of their strength and vigor until they die. That is why they are dreaded."

"Don't you believe a word of that!" exclaimed Lien-hsiang. "A young man such as you recovers his vitality three days after playing the game of love—even with a fox. Yet, if he played it daily, even a human would cause him harm. It is fatal only when a man makes love with a ghost!"

With that Lien-hsiang began cajoling Sang, and finally got him to admit that it was Li who came to him night after night and who had made the fox accusation. "So that is the answer," said Lien-hsiang. "She is most certainly no human being, for no mortal woman could cause such changes to come about in you. Tomorrow I shall spy on her even as she spied upon me."

Shortly after Li's arrival the next evening, the sound of a cough outside of Sang's window made her flee. Immediately Lien-hsiang came in and said sadly, "You are all but lost, for she is a ghost and if you do not abandon her at once you will soon enter the other world."

Dismissing her words as those of a jealous female, Sang said nothing, and she went on. "I know, you do not wish to seem impolite. But I cannot stand by and allow you to die. Tomorrow I shall return with some medicine which will drive the poison from your system. Happily, the disease does not yet have you in its grip so strongly that it cannot be reversed. In ten days you will recover."

Returning the next evening as she had promised, Lien-hsiang administered the medicine, which made Sang feel better at once. He was very grateful, but he would not believe that he had been suffering from the ghost disease. Remaining by his side until she had nursed him back to health, Lien-hsiang finally took her leave, warning Sang that he must never see Li again.

But on the very night that Lien-hsiang left, he took out the little slipper and shook it, whereupon Li appeared at once. She was angry and jealous at not having been called sooner, but when Sang explained that he had been sick and that the other girl had nursed him back to health, Li brightened somewhat. It was another story entirely, though, when he told her he had heard that she was a ghost.

"It was that wicked fox!" she exclaimed angrily. "If you do not break with her I'll never come back here again!" Then she broke down and sobbed piteously, so that Sang had to do everything in his power to calm her down.

When Lien-hsiang learned the following night that Li had been back, she became very upset. "Now you will certainly die!" she said.

"Why must you be so jealous?" he asked laughingly, to which she answered, even more angrily than ever, "Had I not been jealous and snatched you from the arms of death, where would you be now?"

Still in his jesting mood, Sang retorted, "She told me that my sickness was due to the evil influences of a fox."

"It is certainly due to evil influences," replied Lien-hsiang. "But alas, you cannot see whose they are. If anything should happen to you I could never clear myself in your eyes, had I a hundred mouths. We will have to part, therefore, and in a hundred days I shall see you in your sickbed again."

Sang could not persuade her to remain any longer and she left. After this Li came to him regularly, and for a while all was pleasure and happiness.

After the passage of two months, however, Sang began to feel a great languor and weakness. Soon he became so pale and emaciated that he could only take in gruel. But despite his worsening condition, he could not bear to spend a night without the lovely Li. Within days he grew so weak he was unable to leave his bed. His next-door neighbor, seeing what condition he was in, sent his boy over with food and drink. By now the unfortunate scholar began to suspect that perhaps Lien-hsiang had been right about Li, and so he said to her one evening, "How sorry I am that I did not pay attention to the words of Lien-hsiang before it was too late." And with that he closed his eyes for a long time. When he finally opened them again Li was gone. Their liaison had come to an end.

Now, as he lay weak and wasted on his bed, Sang languished all day thinking about Lien-hsiang. One day, as his thoughts of her were strongest, the screen was drawn aside, and in walked Lien-hsiang herself. "Well," she said softly, "was I indeed talking madness?" Sang struggled to answer her, but he was so weak that at first he could not form the words. Finally admitting how wrong he had been, he pleaded with her to save him, but she reluctantly shook her head. "When the disease reaches such a stage," she said, "there is virtually nothing that can be done. I came only to bid you farewell, and to dispel your doubts concerning my jealousy."

Grievously distressed, Sang requested Lien-hsiang to take something from beneath his pillow and destroy it. Doing as he had asked, she took forth the slipper, which she examined carefully by the dim light of the flickering bedside lamp. As she turned it over and over in her hands Li entered, but turned to flee when she caught sight of Lien-hsiang, who leaped to the door and barred her way. Weakly Sang reproached her, and she bowed her head in shame, making no reply.

"So," said Lien-hsiang, "at last we meet. You blamed my beloved's illness on me. What have you to say about it now?" As Li hung her head in acknowledgment of her guilt, Lien-hsiang went on. "How could a beautiful young woman like you turn love into hate and destroy the object of your affection?"

Flinging herself to the floor, Li wept profusely and begged for forgiveness, but Lien-hsiang raised her up and asked of her former life.

"I was the daughter of a Subprefect named Li," she murmured. "But I died young, leaving the web of my destiny incomplete, like the silkworm who perishes in the spring. It was my most ardent wish to be the partner of Sang, but never did I intend to cause his death."

"I have heard that the advantage ghosts obtain by causing the deaths of others," said Lien-hsiang, "is that their victims remain with them forever after death. Is that so?"

"No," replied Li. "It is not so. The companionship of one ghost for another gives neither pleasure. Were it any other way, I should never have wanted for lovers in the inferior regions. Tell me, though. How is it that foxes may have human lovers and yet not kill them?"

"You refer to those foxes who suck the life force out of people. I do not belong to that class. Some foxes are harmless, but no ghosts are, because of the predominance of the yin in their natures."

At last Sang knew that the two girls were in reality a ghost and a fox, but because he had grown to know them so well he was not alarmed in the least. But as his breathing dwindled to a mere strand he uttered a weak cry of pain.

Looking around, Lien-hsiang said, "How can we cure him? If

he recovers, your jealousy will be boundless." Li drew back and blushed deeply at these words, then said softly, "If a physician capable of wiping out the wrong I have done could be found, I would gladly bury my head in the ground. How could I ever look the world in the face?"

Upon hearing this, Lien-hsiang produced a bag from which she took forth some drugs, declaring, "I have looked forward to this day. When I last departed I went away to gather herbs, and it took me three months to prepare the proper medicine, for even if a person is at death's door, it will be able to call him back. There is only one condition. It must be administered by the same hand that brought about the evil."

At first Li blushed and hesitated when Lien-hsiang instructed her in the method of administering the pills, but she did as she was told and put them into his mouth, after each of which she pressed her own cold lips to his. They burned his insides like hot coals. Then Lien-hsiang bent over and breathed life into him herself and his vitality began coming back. "He is cured!" cried Lien-hsiang triumphantly. But at that moment the cock crowed and Li vanished.

For the next three months Lien-hsiang attended Sang constantly, remaining with him night and day. She bolted the outside door so that people would think the scholar had gone away. By night the lovely Li returned and assisted in whatever way she could, looking upon Lien-hsiang as an elder sister, and being treated by her in return with kindness and consideration. By the end of the three months Sang was as healthy and strong as he ever had been. After he had regained his strength, Li no longer came every night, and when she did, stayed only for a few moments, appearing to be troubled and uneasy. One night as she left, Sang ran after her and carried her back in his arms, noticing that she was as light as a pile of straw. Unable to leave, she lay down and curled up in a state of unconsciousness. By morning she had disappeared.

Now when many days passed and they heard nothing of her, Sang became distraught. Often he took out her little slipper and shook it, but often as he did so, Li never appeared. "I am not surprised that you miss her," said Lien-hsiang, "for even I feel an emptiness in my heart for her."

"Before," said Sang, "when I took her slipper in my hand and shook it, she invariably came. Indeed, I thought it very odd, but I never suspected her of being a ghost. But now, alas! as I think about her, and hold this slipper in my hand, I am overcome with grief." And with that he burst into tears.

Now it so happened that a young girl of the wealthy Chang family died suddenly of no manifest cause. Her name was Yen-erh, and she was only fifteen years of age. But in the middle of the night she came back to life and demanded to leave the house. Naturally the family barred the door and would not permit her to depart, whereupon she said, "I am the ghost of the daughter of a Subprefect. Sang Tsu-ming was very kind to me and I left my slipper at his house. So as I am actually the ghost I claim to be, what purpose is there in keeping me here?"

As there was a certain logic in what she said, they asked her why she had come to their house, but she was only able to look about without offering them any explanation. At this someone remarked that Sang had moved out of his house, but the girl refused to accept this. Naturally the family was extremely concerned about all of this. Meanwhile, Sang's neighbor heard about it and leaped over the wall to see for himself, at which time he beheld Sang seated, conversing with a pretty girl. He entered uninvited, causing considerable commotion, and the beautiful visitor disappeared. When the neighbor asked Sang the meaning of what he had discovered, Sang laughed and reminded him that he had once said that if any girls came to his door they would be invited in. The friend then told Sang what Yen-erh had said, and, unlocking his door, the scholar resolved to go and take a peek at her, but unhappily he had no way of doing so.

Meanwhile, Mrs. Chang, upon learning that Sang had not left, was more amazed than ever and dispatched an old serving woman to recover the slipper of Li. Sang gave it to her without hesitation, and Yen-erh was overjoyed to get it; however, when she tried to put it on, it was a good inch too small. Disconcerted, she seized a mirror that she might look at herself, and upon doing so realized at once that she had returned to life in the body of another.

Now she told the entire story to the mother, who was finally convinced of its truth, but as she spoke she wept bitterly, for she felt that she was no longer as pretty as she had been previously. Even before, when she had seen Lien-hsiang, she had been disconcerted, but now she was convinced that she had been better off as a disembodied spirit than as a human being. She would sit weeping over the slipper and let no one comfort her. Then finally she lay down on her bed, drawing the covers over her, refusing to take nourishment, and remaining as still as a corpse. For seven full days she refused to eat, but would not die. Finally the swelling gradually subsided and she was overcome by an intense hunger which she could not ignore. Next she was stricken with a severe irritation which caused the entire skin of her body to peel away. But when she arose the next morning, she saw that her slippers fell off, and when she tried to put them back on once more, she saw that they no longer fitted. When she went back to a pair that had belonged to her in her former existence, she found them to be exactly the proper size. In a burst of ecstatic joy, she looked into the mirror and saw to her everlasting delight that her features had returned exactly to their former appearance.

After washing and dressing, she went to see her mother. Naturally, everyone was amazed, and when Lien-hsiang heard about all of this, she sought to convince Sang to make a marriage offer. But as the girl was rich and Sang was but a poor scholar, he could not hope to do such a thing.

At this time Mrs. Chang celebrated her sixtieth birthday, which was considered to be an especially auspicious occasion. On account of this Sang accompanied all the others who went to offer her their respects and best wishes. Learning that he was in the company, the old woman bade Yen-erh take a peek at him from behind the curtain. Sang was the last guest to arrive, and the moment she saw him Yen-erh rushed out and grabbed his sleeve, insisting that she must go back to his house with him. Her mother reprimanded her severely for this, and she ran back to her chamber in shame. Sang, however, who had looked very closely at her, began weeping profusely, and prostrated himself at the feet of Mrs. Chang, who raised him up gently without uttering an unkind word. Taking his leave, Sang had his uncle serve as a go-between and arrange for an auspicious day for a marriage to Yen-erh.

On the day of the wedding, Sang went to the Chang house to get Yen-erh. When he returned home he found that the poorly furnished abode he had left was now beautifully carpeted and appointed, among other things with countless colored lanterns arrayed in elegant style. Lien-hsiang assisted the bride and upon removing her veil found her to be the same lovely girl she had come to know previously. She also joined the couple as they drank from the bridal cup, after which she questioned Yen-erh as to the details of her unexpected transmigration. To which the girl replied, "Overcome by grief, I came to regard myself as an unclean thing. Thus when I parted from you on that last day I could not bring myself to return again to my grave. Instead I wandered about aimlessly, lurking by day among trees and shrubs, and by night wandering like the disembodied, homeless spirit that I was. One night I came to the Chang household and, seeing the girl lying dead, took possession of her body, not knowing she was to be restored once again to life."

Upon hearing this Lien-hsiang became pensive and silent. Shortly afterward she became very ill, but as she refused all medical aid, her condition became steadily worse. As Sang and Yen-erh stood by her bedside weeping, she opened her eyes weakly and said, "You wish to live but I do not. If it is ordained by fate, we shall meet again ten years from now." And as she murmured these words her spirit departed, and all that remained before them was the body of a fox. In the circumstances Sang insisted that it be buried with all the ceremony due a beloved member of the family.

Now as it happened, Yen-erh had no children. But one day one of the servants came to her and said, "There is an old woman outside who wishes to sell a little girl." Giving orders that the child be shown in, Sang's wife waited, and upon seeing her, cried out, "Why, she is the very image of Lien-hsiang!" Sang looked at her too and discovered to his amazement that this was true. He then settled on a price with the old woman, whose only wish was to ensure that she receive a proper burial when she died.

Taking the girl to a room with her husband, Yen-erh lifted the child's chin and asked gently, "Do you know me?" "No," she replied, explaining that her name was Wei, and that her father, a former pickle merchant of Hsu-cheng, had died three years earlier. Knowing Wei to be exactly fourteen years of age, Sang calculated that her birth must have coincided with the death of Lien-hsiang. "Ah, little sister," exclaimed Yen-erh. "You have been false to us. You promised to see us again after ten years, and you have not kept your word."

Suddenly starting, as though awakening from a dream, the girl uttered an exclamation of amazement and stared steadily at Sang's wife. As for Sang himself, he laughed happily and said, "You have returned just like an old familiar swallow."

Bursting into tears of joy, the girl cried, "Now I understand. I recall my mother saying that I was born with the ability to speak, and, regarding this as an omen of evil, she caused me to drink dog's blood so that all memory of my previous existence would be gone. Am I dreaming, or are you not the very same Li who was ashamed of being a ghost?"

And so they talked of their existences in a former life, now laughing, now weeping, but rejoicing at their reunion.

Some time afterward, when a day came to worship at the tombs of the departed, Yen-erh explained to Wei that she and Sang annually visited her grave and mourned there. The young girl said that she would accompany them this year. When they arrived, they found the tomb in great disarray and the wood of the coffin badly warped. Seeing this, Yen-erh said to Sang, "Lien-hsiang and I have come to love each other in two different states of existence, therefore let not our bones be separated; bury mine here with hers." Sang consented at once, and Li's tomb was opened; her bones were taken out and reburied with those of Lien-hsiang, the fox-maiden. It was done in the company of many friends and relatives garbed in ceremonial dress, for hundreds of them had heard the strange story.

I learned of these events while traveling through I-chu, where I was detained by rain at an inn and read Sang's biography, which had been written by a friend of his named Wang Tsu-chang. It was a long account, of which this is but a brief outline.

IV

Japan

Although there is a common tendency in the Western world to mention China and Japan in the same breath, to do so is not only unfair to both cultures but grossly incorrect. There is no denying that many things Japanese are derived directly from China, including a number of supernatural concepts. Foxes, for example, occupy a prominent position in Japanese mythology, but if one takes the time to look for the differences that exist, they are readily found. In Japan the fox is generally regarded to be more mischievous than amorous, although, like Chinese foxes, the Japanese variety can also be dangerous.

A good example of the lasting power of Japanese superstition regarding foxes can be found in the fact that during the Second World War the American military establishment seriously embarked on a secret project to breed phosphorescent foxes that could be turned loose at key points in Japan prior to the projected invasion. The idea behind this incredible scheme was that the sight of foxes that glowed in the dark would have a demoralizing effect on the Japanese public. The problems involved in producing such extraordinary foxes, however, proved more time-consuming than originally anticipated, and by the time a breakthrough was imminent the war had ended.

There are probably fewer Japanese today than formerly who take such precautions as looking into the water to see if the reflections of suspiciously beautiful ladies appear more vulpine than human: yet old beliefs die slowly. In the late nineteen-fifties an attractive Japanese girl studying in the United States told the following straight-faced account of what had happened before she came to America, when her uncle met a fox-maiden one night. He had been at a party some distance from home, and when he finally left it was quite late. Apparently his host had prevailed upon him to take home some food, which he wrapped up in a napkin. Because of the late hour, he took a shortcut across a field, hurrying as fast as he could because he was quite tired. Fortunately there was a bright moon to light his way, but he quickened his pace as he walked because the long, dark shadows made him a bit nervous. After he had been walking for some time he heard the distinct sound of silk rustling behind him, and half out of curiosity, half out of apprehension, he stopped and turned around. To his astonishment he saw a lovely girl in an elaborately embroidered kimono just behind him. She appeared to have materialized out of thin air, and she stared at him with a long, imploring look. As he did not believe in ghosts, the thought that she might be a disembodied spirit never occurred to him; besides, he could see her perfectly well in the moonlight, and she was quite solid. For a moment or two he just stood there gawking at her, not having the vaguest idea what to say under the circumstances. Then she walked toward him with her hands outstretched and asked him for the food he carried. This struck him as very strange: not only was she too richly dressed to be a poor girl, but there was something distinctly peculiar about her manner. Contemplating her with undisguised suspicion, he refused her request. The girl, instead of taking "no" for an answer, pressed forward and repeated her demand, a bit more sharply this time. Again he refused, but this time, instead of asking him anything, she reached out and tried to snatch the bundle from his hand. In that split second she metamorphosed from a girl to an angry, snarling fox. The uncle, now frightened out of his wits, dropped the food, turned, and fled as fast as he could run, happy to get away with nothing more than a sudden fright.

Unfortunately the young lady who related the story was not terribly proficient in English at the time and was unable to answer the inevitable barrage of questions that followed her narrative.

Happily the English of the material that follows is extremely lucid. Once again we will rely heavily on the considerable talents of Lafcadio Hearn, for though he succeeded so admirably in capturing the feeling of Chinese stories, he surpassed himself when it came to the lore of Japan. This is in no way surprising, for Hearn became so enamored of Japan and its way of life that he renounced his Western heritage and American citizenship to become a Buddhist and a Japanese subject, and died in 1904 as an honored teacher known as Koizumi Yakumo. Before going on to our Japanese supernatural tales, however, it is appropriate to reproduce *in toto* Hearn's essay "Gaki," which in itself is one of the best explanations of occult Japan both in substance and in spirit.

Gaki

> —"*Venerable Nagasena, are there such things as demons in the world?*"
> —"*Yes, O King.*"
> —"*Do they ever leave that condition of existence?*"
> —"*Yes, they do.*"
> —"*But, if so, why is it that the remains of those demons are never found? . . .*
> —"*Their remains are found, O King. . . . The remains of bad demons can be found in the form of worms and beetles and ants and snakes and scorpions and centipedes.*" . . .
> —*The Questions of King Milinda*

I

There are moments in life when truths but dimly known before —beliefs first vaguely reached through multiple processes of reasoning—suddenly assume the vivid character of emotional convictions. Such an experience came to me the other day, on the Suruga coast. While resting under the pines that fringed the beach, something in the vital warmth and luminous peace of the hour—some quivering rapture of wind and light—very strangely bestirred an old belief of mine: the belief that all being is One. One I felt myself to be with the thrilling of breeze and the racing of wave,—with every flutter of shadow and flicker of sun,—with the azure of sky and sea,—with the great green hush of the land. In some new and wonderful way I found myself assured that there never could have been a beginning,—that there never could be an end. Nevertheless, the ideas of the moment were not new: the novelty of the experience was altogether in the peculiar intensity with which they presented themselves; making me feel that the flashing dragon flies, and the long gray sand crickets, and the shrilling semi [cicadas] overhead, and the little red crabs astir under the roots of the pines, were all of them brothers and sisters. I seemed to understand, as never before, how the mystery that is called the Soul of me must have quickened in every form of past existence, and must as certainly continue to behold the sun, for other millions of summers, through eyes of other countless shapes of future being. And I tried to think the long slow thoughts of the long gray crickets,—and the thoughts of the darting, shimmering dragon flies,—and the thoughts of the basking, trilling cicadae,—and the thoughts of the wicked little crabs that lifted up their claws from between the roots of the pines.

Presently I discovered myself wondering whether the consequence of such thoughts could have anything to do with the recombination of my souldust * in future spheres of existence. For thousands of years the East has been teaching that what we think or do in this life really decides,—through some inevitable formation of atom tendencies, or polarities,—the future place of our substance, and the future state of our sentiency. And the belief is worth thinking about—though no amount of thinking can enable us either to confirm or to disprove it. Very possibly,

* "Souldust" probably comes from the Sanskrit word *skandhas*, "transitory personal elements of body, perception, conception, volition, and consciousness, whose temporary concatenation forms the individual self."

like other Buddhist doctrines, it may adumbrate some cosmic truth; but its literal assertions I doubt, because I must doubt the power ascribed to thought. By the whole infinite past I have been molded, within and without: how should the impulse of a moment reshape me against the weight of the eternities? . . . Buddhism indeed answers how, and that astounding answer is irrefutable,—but I doubt. . . .

Anyhow, acts and thoughts, according to Buddhist doctrine, are creative. Visible matter is made by acts and thoughts,— even the universe of stars, and all that has form and name, and all of the conditions of existence. What we think or do is never for the moment only, but for measureless time: it signifies some force directed to the shaping of worlds,—to the making of future bliss or pain. Remembering this, we may raise ourselves to the zones of the Gods. Ignoring it, we may deprive ourselves even to the right to be reborn among men, and may doom ourselves, though innocent of the crimes that cause rebirth in hell, to re-enter existence in the form of animals, or of insects, or of goblins,—gaki. [The word *gaki* is the Japanese Buddhist rendering of the Sanskrit term *preta*, signifying a spirit in that circle or state of torment called the World of Hungry Ghosts.]

So it depends upon ourselves whether we are to become insects or goblins hereafter; and in the Buddhist system the difference between insects and goblins is not so well defined as might be supposed. The belief in a mysterious relation between ghosts and insects, or rather between spirits and insects, is very ancient belief in the East, where it now assumes innumerable forms,—some unspeakably horrible, others full of weird beauty. "The White Moth" of Mr. Quiller-Couch would not impress a Japanese reader as novel; for the night moth or the butterfly figures in many a Japanese poem and legend as the soul of a lost wife. The night cricket's thin lament is perhaps the sorrowing of a voice once human;—the strange red marks upon the heads of cicadae are characters of spirit names;—dragon flies and grasshoppers are the horses of the dead. All these are to be pitied with the pity that is kin to love. But the noxious and dangerous insects represent the results of another quality of karma,—that which produces goblins and demons. Grisly names have been given to some of these insects,—as, for example, jigoku-mushi, or "Hell insect," to the ant lion; and kappa-mushi, to a gigantic water beetle which seizes frogs and fish, and devours them alive, thus realizing, in a microcosmic way, the hideous myth of the kappa, or river-goblin. Flies, on the other hand, are especially identified with the world of hungry ghosts. How often, in the season of flies, have I heard some persecuted toiler exclaim, *"Kyo no hai wa, gaki no yo da ne?"* (The flies today, how like gaki they are!)

II

In the old Japanese, or, more correctly speaking, Chinese Buddhist literature relating to the gaki, the Sanskrit names of the gaki are given in a majority of cases; but some classes of gaki described have only Chinese names. As the Indian belief reached Japan by way of China and Korea, it is likely to have received a peculiar coloring in the course of its journey. But, in a general way, the Japanese classification of gaki corresponds closely to the Indian classification of the pretas.

The place of gaki in the Buddhist system is but one degree removed from the region of the Hells, or Jigokudo,—the lowest of all the states of existence. Above the Jigokudo is the Gakido, or World of Hungry Spirits; above the Gakido is the Chikushodo, or World of Animals; and above this, again, is the Shurado, a region of perpetual fighting and slaughter. Higher than these is placed the Ningendo, or World of Mankind.

Now a person released from Hell, by exhaustion of the karma that sent him there, is seldom reborn at once into the zone of human existence, but must patiently work his way upward thither, through all the intermediate states of being. Many of the gaki have been in Hell.

But there are gaki also who have not been in Hell. Certain kinds or degrees of sin may cause a person to be reborn as a gaki immediately after having died in this world. Only the greatest degree of sin condemns the sinner directly to Hell. The second degree degrades him to the Gakido. The third causes him to be reborn as an animal.

Japanese Buddhism recognizes thirty-six principal classes of gaki. "Roughly counting," says the *Shobo-nen-jo-kyo*, "we find thirty-six classes of gaki; but should we attempt to distinguish all the different varieties, we should find them to be innumerable." The thirty-six classes form two great divisions, or orders. One comprises all "Gaki World dwellers" (gaki-sekai-ju);—that is to say, all Hungry Spirits who remain in the Gakido proper, and are, therefore, never seen by mankind. The other division is called nin-chu-ju, or "dwellers among men": these gaki remain always in this world, and are sometimes seen.

There is yet another classification of gaki, according to the character of their penitential torment. All gaki suffer hunger and thirst; but there are three degrees of this suffering. The muzai-gaki represent the first degree: they must hunger and thirst uninterruptedly, without obtaining any nourishment whatever. The shozai-gaki suffer only in the second degree: they are able to feed occasionally upon impure substances. The usai-gaki are more fortunate: they can eat such remains of food as are thrown away by men, and also the offerings of food set before the images of the gods, or before the tablets of the ancestors. The last two classes of gaki are especially interesting, because they are supposed to meddle with human affairs.

Before modern science introduced exact knowledge of the nature and cause of certain diseases, Buddhists explained the symptoms of such diseases by the hypothesis of gaki. Certain kinds of intermittent fever, for example, were said to be caused by a gaki entering the human body for the sake of nourishment and warmth. At first the patient would shiver with cold, because the gaki was cold. Then, as the gaki gradually became warm, the chill would pass, to be succeeded by a burning heat. At last the satiated haunter would go away, and the fever disappear; but upon another day, and usually at an hour corresponding to that of the first attack, a second fit of ague would announce the return of the gaki. Other zymotic disorders could be equally well explained as due to the action of gaki.

In the *Shobo-nen-jo-kyo* a majority of the thirty-six kinds of gaki are associated with putrescence, disease, and death. Others are plainly identified with insects. No particular kind of gaki is identified with any particular kind of insect, but the descriptions suggest conditions of insect life; and such suggestions are reinforced by a knowledge of popular superstitions. Perhaps the descriptions are vague in the case of such spirits as the jiki-ketsu-gaki, or bloodsuckers; the jiki-niku-gaki, of flesh-eaters; the jiki-da-gaki, or————eaters; the jiki-fun-gaki, [feces] eaters; the jiki-doku-gaki, or poison-eaters; the jiki-fu-gaki, or wind-eaters; the jiki-ke-gaki, or smell-eaters; the jiki-kwa-gaki, or fire-eaters (perhaps they fly into lamps?); the shikko-gaki, who devour corpses and cause pestilence; the shinen-gaki, who appear by night as wandering fires; the shin-ko-gaki, or needle-mouthed; and the kwaku-shin-gaki, or caldron bodies,—each a living furnace, filled with flame that keeps the fluids of its body humming like a boiling pot. But the suggestion of the following excerpts will not be found at all obscure [abridged from the *Shobo-nen-jo-kyo*. A full translation of the extraordinary chapter relating to the gaki would try the reader's nerves rather severely]:—

"*Jiki-man-gaki.*—These gaki can live only by eating the wigs of false hair with which the statues of certain divinities are decorated. . . . Such will be the future condition of persons who steal objects of value from Buddhist temples.

"*Fujo-ko-byaku-gaki.*—These gaki can eat only street filth and refuse. Such a condition is the consequence of having given putrid or unwholesome food to priests or nuns, or pilgrims in need of alms.

"*Cho-ken-ju-jiki-netsu-gaki.*—These are the eaters of the refuse of funeral pyres and of the clay of graves. . . . They are the spirits of men who despoiled Buddhist temples for the sake of gain.

"*Ju-chu-gaki.*—These spirits are born within the wood of trees, and are tormented by the growing of the grain. . . . Their condition is the result of having cut down shade trees for the purpose of selling the timber. Persons who cut down the trees in Buddhist cemeteries or temple grounds are especially likely to become *ju-chu-gaki*."

Moths, flies, beetles, grubs, worms, and other unpleasant creatures seem thus to be indicated. But some kinds of gaki cannot be identified with insects,—for example, the species called jiki-ho-gaki, or "doctrine-eaters." These can exist only by hearing the preaching of the Law of the Buddha in some temple. While they hear such preaching, their torment is assuaged; but at all other times they suffer agonies unspeakable. To this condition are liable after death all Buddhist priests or nuns who proclaim the law for the mere purpose of making money. . . . Also there are gaki who appear sometimes in beautiful human shapes. Such are the yoku-shiki-gaki, spirits of lewdness,—corresponding in some sort to the incubi and succubi of our own Middle Ages. They can change their sex at will, and can make their bodies as large or as small as they please. It is impossible to exclude them from any dwelling, except by the use of holy charms and spells, since they are able to pass through an orifice even smaller than the eye of a needle. To seduce young men, they assume beautiful feminine shapes,—often appearing at wine parties as waitresses or dancing girls. To seduce women they take the form of handsome lads. This state of yoku-shiki-gaki is a consequence of lust in some previous human existence; but the supernatural powers belonging to their condition are results of meritorious karma which the evil karma could not wholly counterbalance.

Even concerning the yoku-shiki-gaki, however, it is plainly stated that they may take the form of insects. Though wont to appear in human shape, they can assume the shape of any animal or other creature, and "fly freely in all directions of space,"—or keep their bodies "so small that mankind cannot see them. . . ." All insects are not necessarily gaki; but most gaki can assume the form of insects when it serves their purpose.

III

Grotesque as these beliefs now seem to us, it was not unnatural that ancient Eastern fancy should associate insects with ghosts and devils. In our visible world there are no other creatures so wonderful and so mysterious; and the true history of certain insects actually realizes the dreams of mythology. To the minds of primitive men, the mere facts of insect metamorphosis must have seemed uncanny; and what but goblinry or magic could account for the monstrous existence of beings so similar to dead leaves, or to flowers, or to joints of grass, that the keenest human sight could detect their presence only when they began to walk or to fly? Even for the entomologist of today, insects remain the most incomprehensible of creatures. We have learned from him that they must be acknowledged "the most successful of organized beings" in the battle for existence;—that the delicacy and the complexity of their structures surpass anything ever imagined as marvelous before the age of the microscope;—that their senses so far exceed our own in refinement as to prove us deaf and blind by comparison. Nevertheless the insect world remains a world of hopeless enigmas. Who can explain for us the mystery of the eyes of a myriad facets, or the secret of the ocular brains connected with them? Do those astounding eyes perceive the ultimate structure of matter? does their vision pierce opacity, after the manner of the Röntgen rays? (Or how interpret the deadly aim of that ichneumon fly which plunges its ovipositor through solid wood to reach the grub embedded in the grain?) What, again, of those marvelous ears in breasts and thighs and knees and feet,—ears that hear sounds beyond the limit of human audition? and what of the musical structures evolved to produce such fairy melody? What of the ghostly feet that walk upon flowing water? What of the chemistry that kindles the firefly's lamp,—making the cold and beautiful light that all our electric science cannot imitate? And those newly discovered, incomparably delicate organs for which we have yet no name, because our wisest cannot decide the nature of them—do they really, as some would suggest, keep the insect mind informed of things unknown to human sense,—visibilities of magnetism, odors of light, tastes of sound? . . . Even the little that we have been able to learn about insects fills us with the wonder that is akin to fear. The lips that are hands, and the horns that are eyes, and the tongues that are drills; the multiple devilish mouths that move in four ways at once; the living scissors and saws and boring pumps and brace bits; the exquisite elfish weapons which no human skill can copy, even in the finest watchspring steel—what superstition of old ever dreamed of sights like these? Indeed, all that nightmare ever conceived of faceless horror, and all that ecstasy ever imagined of phantasmal pulchritude, can appear but vapid and void by comparison with the stupefying facts of entomology. But there is something spectral, something alarming, in the very beauty of insects. . . .

Whether gaki do or do not exist, there is at least some shadowing of truth in the Eastern belief that the dead become insects. Undoubtedly our human dust must help, over and over again for millions of ages, to build up numberless weird shapes of life. But as to that question of my revery under the pine trees,— whether present acts and thoughts can have anything to do with the future distribution and requickening of that dust,—whether human conduct can of itself predetermine the shapes into which human atoms will be recast,—no reply is possible. I doubt— but I do not know. Neither does anybody else.

Supposing, however, that the order of the universe were really as Buddhists believe, and that I knew myself foredoomed, by reason of stupidities in this existence, to live hereafter the life of an insect, I am not sure that the prospect would frighten me. There are insects of which it is difficult to think with equanimity; but the state of an independent, highly organized, respectable insect would not be so very bad. I should even look forward, with some pleasurable curiosity, to any chance of viewing the world through the marvelous compound eyes of a beetle, an ephemera, or a dragon fly. As an ephemera, indeed, I might enjoy the possession of three different kinds of eyes, and the power to see colors now totally unimaginable. Estimated in degrees of human time, my life would be short,—a single summer day would include the best part of it; but to ephemeral consciousness a few minutes would appear a season; and my one day of winged existence—barring possible mishaps—would be one unwearied joy of dancing in golden air. And I could feel in my winged state neither hunger nor thirst,—having no real mouth or stomach: I should be, in very truth, a wind-eater. . . . Nor should I fear to enter upon the much less ethereal condition of a dragon fly. I should then have to bear carnivorous hunger, and to hunt a great deal; but even dragon flies, after the fierce joy of the chase, can indulge themselves in solitary meditation. Besides, what wings would then be mine!—and what eyes! . . . I could pleasurably anticipate even the certainty of becoming an amembo [a water insect, much resembling what we call a "skater"; in some parts of the country it is said that the boy who wants to become a good swimmer must eat the legs of an amembo], and so being able to run and to slide upon water—though children might catch me and bite off my long fine legs. But I think that I should better enjoy the existence of a semi,—a large and lazy cicada, basking on wind-rocked trees, sipping only dew, and singing from dawn till dusk. Of course there would be perils to encounter,—danger from hawks and crows and sparrows,—danger from insects of prey—danger from bamboos tipped with birdlime by naughty little boys. But in every condition of life there must be risks; and in spite of the risks, I imagine that Anacreon uttered little more that the truth, in his praise of the cicada: "O thou earth-born,—song-loving,—free from pain,—having flesh without blood,—thou art nearly equal to the Gods!" . . . In fact I have not been able to convince myself that it is really an inestimable privilege to be reborn a human being. And if the thinking of this thought, and the act of writing it down, must inevitably affect my next rebirth, then let me hope that the state to which I am destined will not be worse than that of a cicada or of a dragon fly;—climbing the cryptomerias to clash my tiny cymbals in the sun,—or haunting, with soundless flicker of amethyst and gold, some holy silence of lotus pools.

« »　　« »　　« »

Before going on to the stories themselves—stories in which we will encounter not only ghosts but demons, foxes, and other supernaturals, this observation by a contemporary author, Eric Maple, is well worth repetition:

> Some Oriental ghosts are particularly loathsome. Those of Siam attack the feet and ankles, leaving the remainder of the body religiously alone. The ghosts of Japan are invariably deformed beings without legs, while the more horrific among them possess unusual combinations of eyes, ranging from one to a maximum of three, and are endowed with elongated tongues and snake-like necks. They haunt old houses and cemeteries and, according to one an-

cient authority, "are especially likely to be seen by those who are out of health, feeble in mind, deficient in knowledge or impressionable."

Though some, as Mr. Maple states, are indeed unspeakably horrible, some others are lighthearted. All, however, are thoroughly Japanese.

The Vampire Cat of Nabeshima
ADAPTED FROM THE JAPANESE

It is written that long ago, one of the Nabeshima princes was plagued by the foul spell of a demoniac, vampire cat. There lived in this prince's household a ravishing beauty named Otoyo, whose charm and wit made her the favorite royal concubine. One afternoon His Highness chose to enjoy Otoyo's favors in the garden, amidst the fragrance of the blossoms. Forgetting about the passage of time, the amorous couple dallied until after the sun had set. Thus, amongst the creeping shadows of dusk, they failed to notice the silent tread of a huge cat that followed them stealthily back to the palace.

After bidding her lord a tender farewell Otoyo went to her apartment and retired for the night. But restful sleep did not come to her. After many hours of fearful dreams the girl awoke suddenly at midnight, her heart pounding heavily within her dainty breast. Struck dumb with terror, she saw two hideous red eyes gleaming like embers in the darkness. As they grew larger she could make out the dreadful shape of a monstrous cat approaching her like the figure of doom. Frozen with fear, she watched the creature helplessly as it prepared to spring. Only as it leaped did she find her voice and cry out, but it was too late. Burying its powerful fangs in her pale throat, the beast held Otoyo fast until her spirit had fled to the abode of her ancestors. After accomplishing its cruel and wicked deed, the unnatural cat dug a grave beneath Otoyo's window, into which it dragged her torn and bleeding corpse. Then, transforming itself into the identical likeness of the dead girl, it began casting its evil spell upon the prince.

The prince, of course, knew nothing about the dreadful event which had taken place. He continued, therefore, to sport daily in the scented arms of his beautiful mistress. Lost as he was in the delicious transports of passion, the prince never suspected that he was in the clutches of a fiendish vampire that desired only to suck out his blood and life.

As time passed the prince began to grow weak. His complexion became sallow and leaden, and it became apparent that he was the victim of some strange and awful malady. With growing alarm his wife and ministers sent for physicians to heal their lord. But it was in vain, for despite the medicines which were prescribed, the prince's condition became more grave. The most baffling part of the illness was his nocturnal distress. Each night after sleep had overtaken him he was plagued by ghastly nightmares. In an attempt to overcome their liege's troubled sleep, the ministers ordered a guard of one hundred men to sit with the prince and maintain a close watch over him. But no matter how hard they tried, each night at about ten, a mysterious drowsiness overcame the guards, and soon they were in a deep and dreamless slumber. It was then that the demon, in the shape of the unfortunate Otoyo, would come creeping to the prince's bedside and take its terrible toll of his life's blood.

After such a lack of success, several of the prince's ministers determined to stay with him themselves in hopes of fathoming the mystery. But unfortunately, when the hour of ten arrived, their eyes too were closed by the overpowering fingers of the mysterious sleep. Thus, on the following day, they gathered in solemn session, and Isahaya Buzen, the Prime Minister, spoke. "It is very strange indeed that a hundred guards should be overtaken by sleep each night at the same hour. Most assuredly an evil spirit is upon our prince and his servants. Since our efforts avail us nothing, let us call upon Ruiten, the chief priest of the Miyo Temple. We shall then ask him to make prayers and offerings for our lord's recovery."

Wholeheartedly approving of Isahaya Buzen's proposal, the

ministers carried it out at once, and called upon the holy offices of the priest. That night Ruiten the priest began his special prayers for the prince. After several nights had passed, the priest, after finishing his ceremonial duties, prepared to go to sleep. Just as he was about to lie down he heard an unfamiliar sound coming from the grounds outside. Looking down from his window, he observed a young soldier washing himself near the well. After finishing his ablutions he stood reverently before the image of Buddha and began praying for the prince's recovery. When he had completed his prayer the soldier rose to depart, but he was stopped by the priest, who called to him, "Wait, honored warrior, I would have some words with you."

Looking up, the soldier answered, "I am at your service, revered sir. What is your pleasure?"

"Be so kind as to come up here, that we may talk together."

"At once," said the young man, hurrying to obey the priest.

When the soldier had entered the temple, Ruiten said to him, "It is very pleasing for me to see a young man with such a loyal heart. I am the chief priest of this temple and even now I am offering prayers for the recovery of our prince. Tell me, who are you?"

The soldier answered, "My name, reverend sir, is Ito Soda, and I am a humble foot soldier in the Nabeshima army. Ever since my prince began suffering from his dread sickness, I have wished with all my heart to aid in caring for him. But alas, I am of so low a rank it would be improper for me to appear before him. Therefore I can do nothing but pray to Buddha for the recovery of my lord."

Ruiten wept upon hearing such a declaration of loyalty. With that he related to Ito Soda the story of their prince's terrible nightmares, and of the strange sleep that descended nightly upon the royal guards. After listening to the priest's tale, a knowing look came over the face of Ito Soda.

"This must be the work of an evil spirit," he said. "If only I might be permitted to watch over the prince for one night I would try to fight off the spell and learn the nature of the demon."

Ruiten paused for a moment, then said, "I am on terms of

friendship with the Prime Minister, Isahaya Buzen. Perhaps if I speak with him your desire to help the prince may be fulfilled."

With heartfelt expressions of gratitude, Ito Soda promised to await the answer of the Prime Minister, so after the proper formalities the two men parted.

The next night Ruiten took Ito Soda to the house of Isahaya Buzen and spoke on the young man's behalf. Although the soldier was of a very humble rank, it was finally decided that he might be allowed to watch over the prince in the company of the other hundred men.

The prince's bedroom was quite large. Sleeping in the very center, he was thus able to surround himself with the loyal men who sought to guard him through the night. Ito Soda observed that as the others conversed among themselves to pass away the time they began to fall asleep, one by one. As the hour of ten approached, he too began to feel an overpowering drowsiness beginning to spread through his limbs. Trying every device imaginable to keep himself awake, Ito Soda realized that he would have to take extreme steps. Fighting the somnolence that threatened to deprive him of his senses, he spread a piece of oiled paper upon the floor at the spot upon which he sat. Then he reached beneath his robe, drew out a small, sharp dagger, and plunged it into his thigh. The pain was excruciating, but it enabled him to stay the crushing hand of sleep. But since it was a sleep induced by sorcery, it nevertheless began to get the better of him. Seizing the hilt of his dagger, Ito Soda twisted it sharply. The pain became so strong that all drowsiness left him, and he watched the prince so intently that he hardly noticed his own blood stream from the wound and onto the oiled paper.

Before long Ito Soda's alertness bore him fruit. He stiffened as he heard the doors to the prince's chamber slide softly open. Looking in the direction of the doors, he observed a muffled figure that tiptoed gently into the room. It approached the sleeping figure of the prince. Ito Soda strained in the darkness to see, and when he was able to distinguish the details of the intruder's form he gasped. It was the most beautiful maiden he had ever seen. She glanced about the chamber and smiled at the sight of the sleeping men. Then, just as she was about to approach the prince, she noticed Ito Soda staring at her.

"Who are you?" she asked with surprise.

"I am Ito Soda and this is my first night here."

"How is it that you are not asleep like the others?"

"I am here to stand guard, not to sleep."

Observing the dark red stain on Ito Soda's thigh, the masquerading demon pointed and asked, "I see blood on your thigh, how were you wounded?"

"I felt so drowsy that I had to stab my thigh to keep awake."

"Such fidelity," said the demon, inwardly briming with hatred.

Ito Soda shrugged. "The soldier who is not willing to die for his lord is delinquent in his duty."

The false Otoyo then bent over the recumbent prince and asked, "How does my lord feel this night?"

But as he was weak to the point of utter debilitation he said nothing. Watching suspiciously, Ito Soda determined to kill the girl on the spot should she attempt to make any untoward movements in the prince's direction. She was unable to do anything, however, for she could feel the eyes of Ito Soda virtually burning holes in her back. In the circumstances, she left the prince alone and withdrew from his chamber.

At daybreak when the hundred others awoke and discovered that Ito Soda had stabbed himself to remain awake, they were covered with shame and departed with downcast spirits. The ministers of the prince, however, were overjoyed at the young soldier's bravery and enjoined him to stand watch again that night. Sure enough, at the usual hour all the men fell asleep except Ito Soda. As before, the demon entered and approached its sleeping victim only to be thwarted by the faithful soldier who had remained awake.

After many nights, the false Otoyo, seeing that her nocturnal attempts upon the prince were doomed to failure, came no more. The prince began to sleep again untroubled by nightly horrors, and he recovered his health quite rapidly. Honors and rank were bestowed upon Ito Soda and he was granted a fine estate.

Several weeks later Ito Soda noticed something very interesting. The hundred guards no longer fell asleep each night at the stroke of ten. It seemed odd to him that this sudden change should correspond with the cessation of Otoyo's midnight visits. It became clear to him that the beautiful concubine was actually a vampire, and he revealed his suspicion to Isahaya Buzen, the Prime Minister.

After listening to Ito Soda, Isahaya Buzen asked, "How do you propose to rid us of this monster dwelling in our midst?"

"I will go directly to her apartment and endeavor to kill her. If, however, she attempts to escape, I pray that you place eight armed men outside to destroy her lest I fail."

Accordingly, Ito Soda waited until nightfall. Then he knocked at the demon's door, pretending to have a message for her from her lord. Upon opening the door to her chamber, she asked, "What is the message you bring me?"

"Look at this," replied Ito Soda.

Then, reaching under his cloak, he drew forth not a letter but a long, gleaming dagger. He sprang, but the demon was too agile. Seizing a battle ax, she glared ferociously and shrieked in a voice like the winds, "How dare you assault me thus?" And she struck fiercely at him with the weapon. Again and again she lunged at him, but each time Ito Soda managed to parry her thrusts. Unable to match his warlike skill, she cast away the battle ax and changed before his eyes into a great shaggy cat. Then, leaping to the window, she sprang to the roof and disappeared.

Isahaya Buzen and the eight armed men were taken completely by surprise. Although they shot arrows at the creature, it eluded them and escaped to the mountains. There it wreaked much havoc among the hill folk until at last Prince Nabeshima organized a great hunt. It was thus the monster was finally tracked down and killed.

The Legend of Yurei-Daki
BY LAFCADIO HEARN

Near the village of Kurosaka, in the province of Hoki, there is a waterfall called Yurei-Daki, or the Cascade of Ghosts. Why it is so called I do not know. Near the foot of the fall there is a small Shinto shrine of the god of the locality, whom the people name

Taki-Daimyojin; and in front of the shrine is a little wooden money box—saisen-bako—to receive the offerings of believers. And there is a story about that money box.

One icy winter's evening, thirty-five years ago, the women and girls employed at a certain asa-toriba, or hemp factory, in Kuro-saka, gathered around the big brazier in the spinning room after their day's work had been done. Then they amused themselves by telling ghost stories. By the time that a dozen stories had been told, most of the gathering felt uncomfortable; and a girl cried out, just to heighten the pleasure of fear, "Only think of going this night, all by one's self, to the Yurei-Daki!" The suggestion provoked a general scream, followed by nervous bursts of laughter. . . . "I'll give all the hemp I spun today," mockingly said one of the party, "to the person who goes!" "So will I," exclaimed another. "And I," said a third. "All of us," affirmed a fourth. . . . Then from among the spinners stood up one Yasumoto O-Katsu, the wife of a carpenter;—she had her only son, a boy of two years old, snugly wrapped up and asleep upon her back, "Listen," said O-Katsu; "if you will all really agree to make over to me all the hemp spun today, I will go to the Yurei-Daki." Her proposal was received with cries of astonishment and of defiance. But after having been several times repeated, it was seriously taken. Each of the spinners in turn agreed to give up her share of the day's work to O-Katsu, providing that O-Katsu should go to the Yu-rei-Daki. "But how are we to know if she really goes there?" a sharp voice asked. "Why, let her bring back the money box of the god," answered an old woman whom the spinners called Obaa-San, the Grandmother; "that will be proof enough." "I'll bring it," cried O-Katsu. And out she darted into the street, with her sleeping boy upon her back.

The night was frosty, but clear. Down the empty street O-Katsu hurried; and she saw that all the house fronts were tightly closed, because of the piercing cold. Out of the village, and along the highroad she ran—*picha-picha*—with the great silence of frozen rice fields on either hand, and only the stars to light her. Half an hour she followed the open road; then she turned down a narrower way, winding under cliffs. Darker and rougher the path became as she proceeded; but she knew it well, and she soon heard the dull roar of the water. A few minutes more, and the way widened into a glen,—and the dull roar suddenly became a loud clamor,—and before her she saw, looming against a mass of blackness, the long glimmering of the fall. Dimly she perceived the shrine,—the money box. She rushed forward,—put out her hand. . . .

"Oi! O-Katsu-San!" (The exclamation Oi! is used to call the attention of a person: it is the Japanese equivalent for such English exclamations as "Halloa!" "Ho, there!" etc.) suddenly called a warning voice above the crash of the water.

O-Katsu stood motionless,—stupefied by terror.

"Oi! O-Katsu-San!" again pealed the voice,—this time with more of menace in its tone.

But O-Katsu was really a bold woman. At once recovering from her stupefaction, she snatched up the money box and ran. She neither heard nor saw anything more to alarm her until she reached the highroad, where she stopped a moment to take breath. Then she ran on steadily,—*picha-picha*,—till she got to Kurosaka, and thumped at the door of the asa-toriba.

How the women and the girls cried out as she entered, panting, with the money box of the god in her hand! Breathlessly they heard her story; sympathetically they screeched when she told them of the Voice that had called her name, twice, out of the haunted water. . . . What a woman! Brave O-Katsu!—well had she earned the hemp! . . . "But your boy must be cold, O-Katsu!" cried the Obaa-San, "let us have him here by the fire!"

"He ought to be hungry," exclaimed the mother; "I must give him his milk presently. . . . "Poor O-Katsu!" said the Obaa-San, helping to remove the wraps in which the boy had been carried, —"why, you are all wet behind!" Then, with a husky scream, the helper vociferated, "*Ara! it is blood!*"

And out of the wrappings unfastened there fell to the floor a blood-soaked bundle of baby clothes that left exposed two very small brown feet, and two very small brown hands—nothing more.

The child's head had been torn off! . . .

Rokuro-Kubi

BY LAFCADIO HEARN

Nearly five hundred years ago there was a Samurai, named Isogai Heidazaemon Taketsura, in the service of the Lord Kikuji, of Kyushu. This Isogai had inherited, from many warlike ancestors, a natural aptitude for military exercises, and extraordinary strength. While yet a boy he had surpassed his teachers in the art of swordsmanship, in archery, and in the use of the spear, and had displayed all the capacities of a daring and skillful soldier. Afterwards, in the time of the Eikyo war (1429–1441), he so distinguished himself that high honors were bestowed upon him. But when the house of Kikuji came to ruin, Isogai found himself without a master. He might then easily have obtained service under another daimyo; but as he had never sought distinction for his own sake alone, and as his heart remained true to his former lord, he preferred to give up the world. So he cut off his hair, and became a traveling priest—taking the Buddhist name of Kwairyo.

But always, under the koromo of the priest, Kwairyo kept warm within him the heart of the samurai. As in other years he had laughed at peril, so now also he scorned danger; and in all seasons he journeyed to preach the good Law in places where no other priest would have dared to go. For that age was an age of violence and disorder; and upon the highways there was no security for the solitary traveler, even if he happened to be a priest.

In the course of his first long journey, Kwairyo had occasion to visit the province of Kai. One evening, as he was traveling through the mountains of that province, darkness overtook him in a very lonesome district, leagues away from any village. So he resigned himself to pass the night under the stars; and having found a suitable grassy spot, by the roadside, he lay down there, and prepared to sleep. He had always welcomed discomfort; and even a bare rock was for him a good bed, when nothing better could be found, and the root of a pine tree an excellent pillow. His body was iron; and he never troubled himself about dews or rain or frost or snow.

Scarcely had he lain down when a man came along the road, carrying an ax and a great bundle of chopped wood. This wood-cutter halted on seeing Kwairyo lying down, and, after a moment of silent observation, said to him in a tone of great surprise, "What kind of a man can you be, good sir, that you dare to lie down alone in such a place as this? . . . There are haunters about here—many of them. Are you not afraid of Hairy Things?"

"My friend," cheerfully answered Kwairyo, "I am only a wandering priest—a 'cloud and water guest,' as folks call it: un-wui-no-ryokaku. And I am not in the least afraid of Hairy Things—if you mean goblin foxes, or goblin badgers, or any creatures of that kind. As for lonesome places, I like them: they are suitable for meditation. I am accustomed to sleeping in the open air: and I have learned never to be anxious about my life."

"You must be indeed a brave man, Sir Priest," the peasant responded, "to lie down here! This place has a bad name—a very bad name. But, as the proverb has it, 'Kunshi ayayuki ni chika-yorazu' (The superior man does not needlessly expose himself to peril); and I must assure you, sir, that it is very dangerous to sleep here. Therefore, although my house is only a wretched thatched hut, let me beg of you to come home with me at once. In the way of food, I have nothing to offer you; but there is a roof at least, and you can sleep under it without risk."

He spoke earnestly; and Kwairyo, liking the kindly tone of the man, accepted this modest offer. The woodcutter guided him along a narrow path, leading up from the main road through mountain forest. It was a rough and dangerous path—sometimes skirting precipices—sometimes offering nothing but a network of slippery roots for the foot to rest upon—sometimes winding over or between masses of jagged rock. But at last Kwairyo found himself upon a cleared space at the top of a hill, with a full moon shining overhead; and he saw before him a small thatched cottage, cheerfully lighted from within. The woodcutter led him to a shed at the back of the house, whither water had been conducted, through bamboo pipes, from some neighboring stream; and the two men washed their feet. Beyond the shed was a vegetable garden, and a grove of cedars and bamboos; and beyond the trees appeared the glimmer of a cascade, pouring from some loftier height, and swaying in the moonshine like a long white robe.

As Kwairyo entered the cottage with his guide, he perceived four persons—men and women—warming their hands at a little fire kindled in the ro of the principal apartment. They bowed low to the priest, and greeted him in the most respectful manner. Kwairyo wondered that persons so poor, and dwelling in such a solitude, should be aware of the polite forms of greeting. "These are good people," he thought to himself; "and they must have been taught by someone well acquainted with the rules of propriety." Then turning to his host—the aruji or house master, as the others called him—Kwairyo said, "From the kindness of your speech, and from the very polite welcome given me by your household, I imagine that you have not always been a woodcutter. Perhaps you formerly belonged to one of the upper classes?"

Smiling, the woodcutter answered, "Sir, you are not mistaken. Though now living as you find me, I was once a person of some distinction. My story is the story of a ruined life—ruined by my own fault. I used to be in the service of a daimyo; and my rank in that service was not inconsiderable. But I loved women and wine too well; and under the influence of passion I acted wickedly. My selfishness brought about the ruin of our house, and caused the death of many persons. Retribution followed me; and I long remained a fugitive in the land. Now I often pray that I may be able to make some atonement for the evil which I did, and to re-establish the ancestral home. But I fear that I shall never find any way of so doing. Nevertheless, I try to overcome the karma of my errors by sincere repentance, and by helping, as far as I can, those who are unfortunate."

Kwairyo was pleased by this announcement of good resolve; and he said to the aruji, "My friend, I have had occasion to observe that men, prone to folly in their youth, may in after years become very earnest in right living. In the holy sutras it is written that those strongest in wrong doing can become, by power of good resolve, the strongest in right doing. I do not doubt that you have a good heart; and I hope that better fortune will come to you. Tonight I shall recite the sutras for your sake, and pray that you may obtain the force to overcome the karma of any past errors."

With these assurances, Kwairyo bade the aruji good night; and his host showed him to a very small side room, where a bed had been made ready. Then all went to sleep except the priest, who began to read the sutras by the light of a paper lantern. Until a late hour he continued to read and pray: then he opened a window in his little sleeping room, to take a last look at the landscape before lying down. The night was beautiful: there was no cloud in the sky; there was no wind; and the strong moonlight threw down sharp black shadows of foliage, and glittered on the dews of the garden. Shrillings of crickets and bell insects made a musical tumult; and the sound of the neighboring cascade deepened with the night. Kwairyo felt thirsty as he listened to the noise of the water; and, remembering the bamboo aqueduct at the rear of the house, he thought that he could go there and get a drink without disturbing the sleeping household. Very gently he pushed apart the sliding screens that separated his room from the main apartment; and he saw, by the light of the lantern, five recumbent bodies—without heads!

For one instant he stood bewildered—imagining a crime. But in another moment he perceived that there was no blood, and that the headless necks did not look as if they had been cut. Then he thought to himself: "Either this is an illusion made by goblins, or I have been lured into the dwelling of a rokuro-kubi. . . . In the book *Soshinki* it is written that if one find the body of a rokuro-kubi without its head, and remove the body to another place, the head will never be able to join itself again to the neck. And the book further says that when the head comes back and finds that its body has been moved, it will strike itself upon the floor three times—bounding like a ball—and will pant as in great fear, and presently die. Now, if these be rokuro-kubi, they mean me no good;—so I shall be justified in following the instructions of the book." . . .

He seized the body of the aruji by the feet, pulled it to the window, and pushed it out. Then he went to the back door, which he found barred; and he surmised that the heads had made their exit through the smoke hole in the roof, which had been left open. Gently unbarring the door, he made his way to the garden, and proceeded with all possible caution to the grove beyond it. He heard voices talking in the grove; and he went in the direction of the voices—stealing from shadow to shadow, until he reached a good hiding place. Then, from behind a trunk, he caught sight of the heads—all five of them—flitting about, and chatting as they flitted. They were eating worms and insects which they found on the ground or among the trees. Presently the head of the aruji stopped eating and said, "Ah, that traveling priest who came tonight!—how fat all his body is! When we shall have eaten him, our bellies will be well filled. . . . I was foolish to talk to him as I did;—it only set him to reciting the sutras on behalf of my soul! To go near him while he is reciting would be difficult; and we cannot touch him so long as he is praying. But as it is now nearly morning, perhaps he has gone to sleep. . . . Some one of you go to the house and see what the fellow is doing."

Another head—the head of a young woman—immediately rose up and flitted to the house, lightly as a bat. After a few minutes it came back, and cried out huskily, in a tone of great alarm, "That traveling priest is not in the house;—he is gone! But that is not the worst of the matter. He has taken the body of our aruji; and I do not know where he has put it."

At this announcement the head of the aruji—distinctly visible in the moonlight—assumed a frightful aspect: its eyes opened monstrously; its hair stood up bristling; and its teeth gnashed. Then a cry burst from its lips; and—weeping tears of rage—it exclaimed, "Since my body has been moved, to rejoin it is not possible! Then I must die! . . . And all through the work of that priest! Before I die I will get at that priest!—I will tear him!—I will devour him! . . . *And there he is*—behind that tree!—hiding behind that tree! See him!—the fat coward!" . . .

In the same moment the head of the aruji, followed by the other four heads, sprang at Kwairyo. But the strong priest had already armed himself by plucking up a young tree; and with that tree he struck the heads as they came—knocking them from him with tremendous blows. Four of them fled away. But the head of the aruji, though battered again and again, desperately continued to bound at the priest, and at last caught him by the left sleeve of his robe. Kwairyo, however, as quickly gripped the head by its topknot, and repeatedly struck it. It did not release its hold; but it uttered a long moan, and thereafter ceased to struggle. It was dead. But its teeth still held the sleeve; and, for all his great strength, Kwairyo could not force open the jaws.

With the head still hanging to his sleeve he went back to the house, and there caught sight of the other four rokuro-kubi squatting together, with their bruised and bleeding heads reunited to their bodies. But when they perceived him at the back door all screamed, "The priest! the priest!"—and fled, through the other doorway, out into the woods.

Eastward the sky was brightening; day was about to dawn; and Kwairyo knew that the power of the goblins was limited to the hours of darkness. He looked at the head clinging to his sleeve—its face all fouled with blood and foam and clay; and he laughed aloud as he thought to himself: "What a miyage! the head of a goblin!" After which he gathered together his few belongings, and leisurely descended the mountain to continue his journey.

Right on he journeyed, until he came to Suwa in Shinano; and into the main street of Suwa he solemnly strode, with the head dangling at his elbow. Then women fainted, and children screamed and ran away; and there was a great crowding and clamoring until the torite (as the police of those days were called) seized the priest, and took him to jail. For they supposed the head to be the head of a murdered man who, in the moment of being killed, had caught the murderer's sleeve in his teeth. As for Kwairyo, he only smiled and said nothing when they questioned him. So, after having passed a night in prison, he was brought before the magistrates of the district. Then he was ordered to explain how he, a priest, had been found with the head of a man fastened to his sleeve, and why he had dared thus shamelessly to parade his crime in the sight of the people.

Kwairyo laughed long and loudly at these questions; and then he said, "Sirs, I did not fasten the head to my sleeve: it fastened itself there—much against my will. And I have not committed any crime. For this is not the head of a man; it is the head of a goblin;—and, if I caused the death of the goblin, I did not do so by any shedding of blood, but simply by taking the precautions necessary to assure my own safety." . . . And he proceeded to relate the whole of the adventure—bursting into another hearty laugh as he told of his encounter with the five heads.

But the magistrates did not laugh. They judged him to be a hardened criminal, and his story an insult to their intelligence. Therefore, without further questioning, they decided to order his immediate execution—all of them except one, a very old man. This aged officer had made no remark during the trial; but, after having heard the opinion of his colleagues, he rose up, and said, "Let us first examine the head carefully; for this, I think, has not yet been done. If the priest has spoken truth, the head itself should bear witness for him. . . . Bring the head here!"

So the head, still holding in its teeth the koromo that had been stripped from Kwairyo's shoulders, was put before the judges. The old man turned it round and round, carefully examined it, and discovered, on the nape of its neck, several strange red characters. He called the attention of his colleagues to these, and also bade them observe that the edges of the neck nowhere presented the appearance of having been cut by any weapon. On the contrary, the line of severance was smooth as the line at which a falling leaf detaches itself from the stem. . . . Then said the elder, "I am quite sure that the priest told us nothing but the truth. This is the head of a rokuro-kubi. In the book *Nan-ho-i-butsu-shi* it is written that certain red characters can always be found upon the nape of the neck of a real rokuro-kubi. There are the characters: you can see for yourselves that they have been painted. Moreover, it is well known that such goblins have been dwelling in the mountains of the province of Kai from very ancient time. . . . But you, sir," he exclaimed, turning to Kwairyo—"what sort of sturdy priest may you be? Certainly you have given proof of a courage that few priests possess; and you have the air of a soldier rather than of a priest. Perhaps you once belonged to the samurai class?"

"You have guessed rightly, sir," Kwairyo responded. "Before becoming a priest, I long followed the profession of arms; and in those days I never feared man or devil. My name then was Isogai Heidazaemon Taketsura, of Kyushu: there may be some among you who remember it."

At the utterance of that name, a murmur of admiration filled the courtroom; for there were many present who remembered it. And Kwairyo immediately found himself among friends instead of judges—friends anxious to prove their admiration by fraternal kindness. With honor they escorted him to the residence of the daimyo, who welcomed him; and feasted him, and made him a handsome present before allowing him to depart. When Kwairyo left Suwa, he was as happy as any priest is permitted to be in this transistory world. As for the head, he took it with him —jocosely insisting that he intended it for a miyage.

And now it only remains to tell what became of the head.

A day or two after leaving Suwa, Kwairyo met with a robber, who stopped him in a lonesome place, and bade him strip. Kwairyo at once removed his koromo, and offered it to the robber, who then first perceived what was hanging to the sleeve. Though brave, the highwayman was startled: he dropped the garment, and sprang back. Then he cried out, "You!—what kind of a priest are you? Why, you are a worse man than I am! It is true that I have killed people; but I never walked about with anybody's head fastened to my sleeve. . . . Well, Sir Priest, I suppose we are of the same calling; and I must say that I admire you! . . . Now that head would be of use to me: I could frighten people with it. Will you sell it? You can have my robe in exchange for your koromo; and I will give you five ryo for the head."

Kwairyo answered, "I shall let you have the head and the robe if you insist; but I must tell you that this is not the head of a man. It is a goblin's head. So, if you buy it, and have any trouble in consequence, please to remember that you were not deceived by me."

"What a nice priest you are!" exclaimed the robber. "You kill men, and jest about it! . . . But I am really in earnest. Here is my robe; and here is the money;—and let me have the head. . . . What is the use of joking?"

"Take the thing," said Kwairyo. "I was not joking. The only

joke—if there be any joke at all—is that you are fool enough to pay good money for a goblin's head." And Kwairyo, loudly laughing, went upon his way.

Thus the robber got the head and the koromo; and for some time he played goblin priest upon the highways. But, reaching the neighborhood of Suwa, he there learned the real history of the head; and he then became afraid that the spirit of the roku-ro-kubi might give him trouble. So he made up his mind to take back the head to the place from which it had come, and bury it with its body. He found his way to the lonely cottage in the mountains of Kai; but nobody was there, and he could not discover the body. Therefore he buried the head by itself, in the grove behind the cottage; and he had a tombstone set up over the grave; and he caused a Segaki-service to be performed on behalf of the spirit of the rokuro-kubi. And that tombstone—known as the Tombstone of the Rokuro-Kubi—may be seen (at least so the Japanese storyteller declares) even unto this day.

V

The Third World and Beyond

If one rummages about in the literature of the supernatural on an international scale long enough, an incontrovertible fact emerges. No matter how different peoples may be from place to place, no matter how remote from one another they may be in matters physical and cultural, when it comes to the supernatural, they are more related than not.

So far we have more or less rambled along on a leisurely tour of the realm, partially in time, partially in space. Ultimately we shall find our way to the more familiar surroundings of our own Western world. Until we get there, however, it would seem only proper to spend some time in some of the less familiar places, Armenia being one of the first that comes to mind. Early Armenian manuscripts contain their fair share of fanciful material, but one of the more interesting, if brief and fragmentary examples concerns a horrible demon called the Al. According to the tale, Saint Peter, Saint Paul, and their friend Silas were once traveling together and one day came upon a man seated in the sand alongside the road. His hair resembled writhing serpents, his eyebrows were brass, and his eyes were balls of glass. Furthermore, his face was more pallid than snow, his teeth were iron fangs, and protruding from his mouth as well were hideous tusks, like those of a wild boar. Contemplating him, they asked, "Who art thou, foul, infernal, and dreadful demon?" to which he replied, "I am the evil Al. I crouch upon the mother with child. I singe off her ears, rip out her liver, and strangle both her and her child. Our fare is the flesh of babes and the livers of pregnant women. We steal unborn infants from the womb and carry them off to our king. We dwell in the corners of houses, in stables, and in the abyss."

The Al should certainly sound relatively familiar by now, for we've found monsters very much like him elsewhere, both in appearance and in appetite. The following short tale from Africa, however, is unique in a way, for it concerns a were-hyena.

In a Nyasaland village there lived a girl who refused to have anything to do with a single suitor coming her way. At last a handsome stranger, who came from a far-off land, aroused her passions, and, after obtaining the consent of her parents, agreed to marry her. What she did not know was that her husband-to-be was a hyena, masquerading as a human.

Several days after the wedding had taken place, the girl prepared to leave her native village and return with her new husband to his home. Her younger brother, however, suspected that there was something evil about his new brother-in-law and asked the newlyweds if he could accompany them on their journey.

When his request was turned down, the youth merely waited until the couple had departed, at which time he began to follow them. By crouching low and hiding in the tall grass whenever he came too close, the brother had no difficulty in keeping up his pace. Finally, when he felt that they had gone too far to send him back, he revealed himself to the surprised couple. But instead of being allowed to remain in their company, even grudgingly, the lad was driven back by his sister's husband with curses and severe blows. Dodging as best he could, he pretended to go back, but in reality he dropped out of sight and continued following them in secret.

When the couple finally reached the village of the bridegroom, they were unaware that the young brother was still with them. The youth, after approaching some of the villagers, was allowed to remain, and was given a place to sleep among the chickens. He remained awake, however, and waited until after dark. Then he crept out to see what was going on outside. At first he believed the village to be deserted, for there was not a single man in sight, but then he saw the reason for this. There, in the center of the village, was what appeared to be a convention of hyenas. They formed a ring around the hut in which his sister slept, and chanted, "She is our game, and we will eat her when she is fat enough."

His suspicions confirmed, he slipped back into the henhouse and waited until morning. Then, when the hyenas had once again resumed their human shapes, he went to his sister and told her what he had seen and heard the night before. Refusing to listen to him, she became very angry and ordered him to leave. But when it grew dark he returned to his sister's side and asked her to allow him to prove the truth of his words. When she consented, he tied a piece of string to one of her toes. He unrolled it and took the other end with him.

Late that night when the hyenas began to dance again, the boy pulled on the string and woke his sister up. This time she was able to see for herself and recognize the dire peril of her situation.

The next day the young brother borrowed an adze from one of the hyena-men, explaining that he wanted to make himself a toy top. Instead he fashioned a magical wooden bowl. When it was finished he and his sister climbed into it, and when he chanted a certain incantation it began to rise up in the air. Thus, despite the angry pursuit of the hyenas, the two were carried safely back to their home village.

« »   « »   « »

Perhaps on the surface the were-hyena story seems radically different from the tales of metamorphosis with which we are more familiar. From the standpoint of basic theme, the story is virtually identical to those in the European tradition. A human being is in danger of being destroyed—in this case eaten—by a supernatural creature capable of shape-shifting. The human is ultimately saved by the intervention of another human who employs magic or supernatural means with which the shape-shifter is unable to cope. The chief difference between this African story and the standard werewolf tale is that here the hyenas were essentially animals capable of changing themselves into men, rather than men capable of changing themselves into animals.

Although geographically European, this next story concerning a were-bear is appropriate at this point because of the contrast it offers to the hyena tale. Thematically, the were-bear story is closer to later European werewolf traditions, for it involves witchcraft and skulduggery of the basest kind. It was written by Sir Walter Scott, who was retelling the story from an ancient Norse saga, *The History of Hrolfekraka*, which places the characters and events on a chronological par with Beowulf.

Hringo, King of Upland, had an only son, called Biorno, the most beautiful and most gallant of the Norwegian youth. At an advanced period of life, the king became enamored of a "witch-lady" whom he chose for his second wife. A mutual and tender affection had, from infancy, subsisted betwixt the youth Biorno and Bera, the lovely daughter of an ancient warrior. But the new queen cast upon her stepson an eye of incestuous passion; to gratify which she prevailed upon her husband, when he set out on one of those piratical expeditions, which formed the summer campaigns of a Scandinavian monarch, to leave the prince at home.

In the absence of Hringo, she communicated to Biorno her impure affection, and was repulsed with disdain and violence. The rage of the weird stepmother was boundless. "Hence to the woods!" she exclaimed, striking the prince with a glove of wolf-skin; "Hence to the woods! Subsist only on thy father's herds; live pursuing and die pursued!"

From this time the prince Biorno was no more to be seen and the herdsmen of the king's cattle soon observed that astonishing devastation was nightly made among their flocks by a black bear of immense size and unusual ferocity. Every attempt to snare or destroy this animal was found vain; and much was the unavailing regret for the absence of Biorno, whose one delight had been in extirpating beasts of prey.

Bera, the faithful mistress of the young prince, added her tears to the sorrow of the people. As she was indulging her melancholy, apart from society, she was alarmed by the approach of a monstrous bear, which was the dread of the whole country. Unable to escape, she waited its approach in expectation of instant death; when to her astonishment, the animal fawned upon her, rolled himself at her feet, and regarded her with eyes, which, in spite of the horrible transformation, she still recognized as the glances of her lost lover. Bera had the courage to follow the bear to his cavern, where, during certain hours, the spell permitted him to resume his human shape.

Her love overcame her repugnance at so strange a mode of life, and she continued to inhabit the cavern of Biorno, enjoying his society during his periods of freedom from enchantment. One day, looking sadly upon his wife, "Bera," said the prince, "the end of my life approaches. My flesh will soon serve for the repast of my father and his courtiers. But do thou beware lest either the threats or entreaties of my diabolical stepmother induce thee to partake of the horrid banquet. So shalt thou safely bring forth three sons who shall be the wonder of the North."

The spell now operated, and the unfortunate prince sallied forth from the cavern to prowl among the herds. Bera followed him weeping, and at a distance. The clamor of the chase was now heard. It was the old king, returned from his piratical excursions, who had collected a strong force to destroy the devouring animal which ravaged his country. The poor bear defended himself gallantly, slaying many dogs, and some huntsmen. At length, wearied out, he sought protection at the feet of his father. But his supplicating gestures were in vain, and the eyes of paternal affection proved more dull than those of love. Biorno died by the lance of his father, and his flesh was prepared for the royal banquet.

Bera was recognized and hurried into the queen's presence. The sorceress, as Biorno had predicted, endeavored to prevail upon Bera to eat of what was then esteemed a regal dainty. Entreaties and threats being vain, force was, by the queen's commands, employed for this purpose, and Bera was compelled to swallow one morsel of the bear's flesh. A second was put into her mouth, but she had the opportunity of putting it aside. She was then dismissed from her father's house.

Here, in the process of time, she was delivered of three sons, two of whom were affected as variously in person and disposition, by the share their mother had been compelled to take in the feast of the king. The eldest from his middle downwards resembled an elk, whence he derived the name Elgfrod. He proved a man of uncommon strength, but of savage manners, and adopted the profession of a robber. Thorer, the second son of Bera was handsome and well shaped, saving that he had the foot of a dog; from which he obtained the appellation of Houndsfoot. But Bodvear, the third son, was a model of perfection in mind and body. He revenged upon the necromantic queen the death of his father, and became the most celebrated champion of his age.

« »   « »   « »

The witch-queen of the old Norse tale must bring back shuddery recollections of childhood fairytales, with their wicked witches, who, when examined in the harsh light of critical analysis, can only be regarded as cannibals of the most blatant voracity. Since cannibalism, implicit or explicit, is one of the strongest taboos in any society, stories in which the subject is an ingredient tend often to be among the most horrifying.

What provides even more food for thought, however, is the fact that so many stories containing this particularly loathsome element—cannibalism—involve *villainesses* rather than villains, and not only in the West, as this Middle Eastern tale * so readily indicates.

Many years ago, a young man from Baghdad named Ali married a beautiful girl, who for the first weeks of marriage seemed like all other women. But by the third week Ali began to notice something strange about his bride. She never ate her eve-

---

* So reminiscent of the story of Sidi Nouman, in *The Thousand and One Nights*.

ning meal with him. When he asked her about this, she replied that she had grown out of the habit of eating too much as a result of having grown up amidst poverty.

Awakening late one night unexpectedly, Ali observed that his wife was not in bed beside him. He rose up and began looking for her, but to his dismay, she was nowhere to be found in the house. As the hours passed, his concern increased until he was nearly frantic with worry. Finally, just after the first light of dawn began streaming through the windows, Ali saw his wife stealthily making her way to the house from the street. Going back to bed, he feigned sleep, resolving to do nothing until he could learn more about her mysterious nocturnal behavior. So, despite the fact that he was burning with jealous curiosity, he waited until nightfall. When it was time to retire he behaved quite normally and went to bed as if he did not suspect a thing. Gradually he went through the motions of falling asleep, and sure enough, as soon as it appeared to his bride that he was dead to the world, she rose noiselessly from the bed, threw a cloak over her shoulders, and slipped quietly from the house.

Now feverish with suspicion, Ali jumped out of bed, dressed, and cautiously followed his unsuspecting wife. To his horror, she made her way through the darkest, most disreputable streets of the city and headed directly to a cemetery that lay just beyond the outskirts of Baghdad. It was a place avoided by prudent men after dark, for it was reputed to be haunted by ghouls and other unclean spirits.

Taking the greatest of care to conceal himself, Ali watched his wife light an oil lamp and enter a tomb. Creeping closer to see what she was doing in the murky recesses of the vault, he was horrified to see that she was in the company of several ghouls. There they were, gathered about the reeking remains of a freshly buried corpse, which they tore to bits with grunts of demonic delight. As they divided up the jagged chunks of decaying human flesh, their eyes and fangs gleaming with anticipation, poor Ali, sickened with terror and revulsion, stumbled from the recesses of his hiding place and hurried home as fast as he could go.

The next day he pretended that everything was normal again until the evening meal. But when, as usual, his wife refused to eat, he could contain his emotions no longer. Springing to his feet in a rage he cried, "So, you prefer to save your appetite for a feast of corpse flesh!"

Turning pale, she got up from the table and left the room without saying a word. Fearing her vengeance, Ali went to bed that night clutching a sharp, gleaming dagger in order to be prepared for the eventual confrontation. For nearly an hour nothing happened; then about midnight he heard a rustling sound. His heart began pounding furiously and he grasped the hilt of his weapon, prepared to strike at the instant of any attack. But he had not anticipated the ferocity with which he was to be assaulted, for suddenly his wife leaped upon him like a wild beast. Snarling as she straddled him like a horse, she dug her claws into his throat and rasped, "Now, dog of a husband, suffer the fate that your prying deserves!" With that she ripped his throat open and began sucking the blood as it spurted out.

But fortunately he was on his guard. Mustering every ounce of his strength, he sprang up and plunged the dagger into her breast, knocking her to the floor mortally wounded. Then rushing from the room, leaving a trail of blood from his torn throat, Ali awakened his servants, who came to his aid and tended his wound.

By morning the wife was dead and by nightfall she was in her grave. Had she been an ordinary mortal, however, that would have been the end of her. But three days later, at the stroke of midnight, she appeared again in Ali's bedroom and, shrieking balefully, lunged for his throat, determined to achieve now what she had failed to accomplish before. Ali, being unarmed and unprepared could do nothing but flee.

Shaken to the core by what had happened the night before, he arranged to have his wife's grave opened on the following day. When it was done the witnesses gasped at the horrible sight that greeted their eyes. Appearing perfectly lifelike, as if she were only asleep, the girl's lips were half open and red with fresh blood that dripped down her cheeks and drenched her coffin. The lid was slammed down, a guard was posted, and Ali led the company to the house of the dead woman's father. Reluctantly he agreed to tell them the truth.

Once, he explained, his daughter had been a human being, but she had become interested in magic, sorcery, and necromancy. In time she was possessed by a demon, who eventually consumed her and assumed her shape. By day she appeared to be a normal human, but by night she assumed the form of a ghoul, sometimes haunting places of the dead to devour the flesh of corpses, other times preying upon the living. The old man, too afraid for his own safety to say anything, had permitted her to remain and pass as his daughter. Ali, upon hearing of this, consulted a holy man. Together they returned to the grave, opened it again, and found the body lifelike as before. After rites of exorcism were performed, the body was cremated, thus putting an end to the demon forever.

« » « » « »

One hardly requires a dissertation at this point to see the similarities between this Middle Eastern concept and the European vampire tradition. A story that is distinctly different, but in which a female plays the heavy, is the following tale of Bengali origin. Geographically speaking, this means that it comes from the part of the world known as Bangladesh now. The flavor, consequently, is physically evocative of India, but culturally of Islam. Yet, despite all its exotic seasoning, it has a universal quality to it known everywhere in the world.

Mohammed Bux and the Demon
ADAPTED BY BERNHARDT J. HURWOOD

Many years ago there were two boon companions named Mohammed Bux and Amir Khan. Although the younger man, Mohammed Bux, was in the habit of visiting his friend frequently, he never returned the favor. It was not that he was an ingrate, quite the contrary; he deeply appreciated the warm reception he always received. There was another reason. Mohammed Bux had the misfortune of being married to an irascible shrew who had the tongue of a serpent and the soul of a horseradish. Thus on the day he learned that his friend Amir Khan was coming for a visit, his heart began to pound and he feared for the worst. But, being a brave man, Mohammed Bux approached Fazal Noor, his wife, and said, "My dear, Amir Khan is coming here with his sons. Since you are highborn and know what is proper, I trust you will extend to them the hospitality they deserve. I have visited their household many times and have always been treated with the deepest respect."

"Very well," she snapped, "have no fear. You shall not be disgraced on my account. But take care not to arouse my anger or you will have ample cause to regret it."

When the guests arrived they were led into a luxurious chamber filled with rich tapestries, thick carpet, and soft cushions. As soon as Fazal Noor was ready she sent the servant forth from the kitchen with dishes of succulent food. But alas, Mohammed Bux and his three guests had barely begun to eat when it became apparent that there would not be enough to go around. At first Mohammed Bux was sorely distressed, for he feared the consequences should his wife become irritated. But since he did not wish to seem a niggardly host he ordered his servant to fetch another helping. Obeying her master, she disappeared from the room and soon returned with another helping, which was eagerly devoured by the four men. As they were still hungry, Mohammed Bux again dispatched the servant to the kitchen—this time quaking inwardly as he gave the order.

When the servant reached the kitchen and told Fazal Noor what her husband wanted, she went into a frenzy. Uttering dreadful curses, she began rolling her eyes fiercely and stamping her feet. Then, seizing whatever objects she could reach, she began to hurl them against the walls, upon the floor, and at the terrified servant, who cringed in the corner. When nothing was left but a large clay pot, the enraged virago seized it and charged into the dining chamber like a maddened water buffalo. Leaping at her husband, she dashed the earthen vessel over his head, shattering it into a thousand pieces. Raising his hands in astonishment and pain, the poor man discovered that the rim was still intact and hanging about his neck like the yoke of an ox. Amir Khan, who had become rigid with amazement, relaxed and tried to sooth Mohammed Bux.

"Be of good heart, my friend," he said, "all women are afflicted with bad tempers. Such things happen to me, too. Come, let us take a walk and refresh ourselves."

Mohammed Bux needed no urging after such an unpleasant experience and quickly agreed to the suggestion. When they had gone some distance from his house he stopped and began pleading with Amir Khan to do away with Fazal Noor. Amir Khan stroked his beard reflectively and then replied, "Although I believe it is sinful for a man to get blood on his hands and needlessly, he must certainly help a friend in such dire distress as yours."

"Allah be praised!" cried Mohammed Bux, and he leaped into the air with joy. Then, at the recommendation of Amir Khan, he returned at once to his house.

Early the next morning Amir Khan summoned his eldest son and gave him the following instructions.

"Akbar, my son, listen closely and do exactly as I bid you. Go to the house of Mohammed Bux and convince his wife that you wish her to accompany you to a wedding celebration. Then lure her to some deserted spot and make certain that she never returns to plague my friend."

The young man did as he was told, went to the house of Mohammed Bux, and extended the "invitation" to Fazal Noor. She was reluctant to accept at first, for she recalled all too clearly how she had disgraced her husband at dinner the night before. Finally, however, after some coaxing, she agreed to accompany young Akbar Khan. After dressing herself in the finest silks and jewels, she was prepared for the journey. Akbar Khan led the way, while Fazal Noor and Mohammed Bux followed closely behind. They traveled for hours until they were deep in the midst of a thick and shadowy forest. The air was filled with the cries of wild beasts and the frightful wails of disembodied spirits. When it was nearly noontime they came to a clearing near a well. There they paused to rest and Fazal Noor went over to draw some water. An instant after she bent over the edge, Akbar Khan gave a single mighty push and shoved her into the well.

Now as it happened, the well had been dry for many years for it was the dwelling place of a fierce and loathsome demon. However, when Fazal Noor fell down the long shaft she landed directly on his back, frightening him nearly out of his wits. Furthermore, after she landed, since she remained firmly in the same spot, the demon was convinced that she was some dreadful monster even more terrible than himself. Shaking with fear, he roared in anguish and demanded to know who straddled his back so fearlessly. With a wit as sharp as her tongue, Fazal Noor replied, "I am the devil's own sister, and though you are merely a miserable demon I am in love with you."

"What do you mean?" asked the startled demon.

"I mean what I say," replied the wily shrew. "I saw you once from a distance and was smitten by your charms. I began searching for you and finally discovered where you live. That is why I came here to you."

The demon, in truth an ugly wretch, was so flattered by her honeyed words that he was completely hoodwinked.

"In that case, will you marry me?" he asked eagerly.

"Of course I'll marry you," said Fazal Noor, "if you will promise me one thing."

"Anything," answered the demon, blushing a fiery red.

"Oh, it is really nothing," said Fazal Noor demurely. "You must permit me to smite you on the head with my slipper a hundred times each morning."

When he heard this the demon was horrified and he changed from red to a brilliant green. But when he gazed at her beauty —which was not inconsiderable—and at the smallness of her feet, he foolishly consented.

Thus they were married and they lived together in the well for some time. It did not take long, however, for the demon to grow weary of his daily beatings. Besides, his lacerated head began to give him perpetual pain. But when some insects laid their eggs in his wound his suffering increased to boundless measure. To make matters worse, when he went to visit his relatives they derided him, saying, "What kind of demon are you, allowing a woman to abuse you so cruelly?"

Before long, smarting under the stings of contempt on one side and of torture on the other, the wretched demon became exceedingly melancholy. Finally his distress became utterly unbearable. Departing from his abode one day, he changed himself into human form and fled to the inner precincts of a mosque where it was prohibited for women to enter. Only then did he consider himself safe from the malevolence of Fazal Noor.

By a coincidence Mohammed Bux had become a dervish and lived in the very same mosque with a group of other holy men. The demon, of course, did not know who he was and, approaching Mohammed Bux, made the following proposition.

"Brother, if every day you and the others will beg an extra share of food for me in the village, I shall do all of your work here in the mosque. I shall sweep, clean, and carry water."

Mohammed Bux and the other dervishes thought the matter over, and on deciding that it was fair, agreed to the terms. By day they would go among the villagers with their begging bowls and at night they would return to the mosque. But alas, when it came time for the evening meal, the demon seized all the food, devoured it voraciously, and left not a scrap for the others. After several days their bellies began to growl and they grew weak from hunger. Taking the demon aside, Mohammed Bux said to him, "It pains me to say this, brother, but I do not believe you are a man. Verily, the manner in which you gobble up everything in sight leads me to believe you are a djinn or some other kind of evil spirit."

"Nonsense," replied the demon with a loud belch, "I am as human as you."

"I don't believe you," persisted Mohammed Bux. "No man eats the way you do. I insist that you tell me the truth."

At this the demon sighed and said, "Very well. I shall confess. You are right, I am a demon. But please—please do not divulge my secret! I am in the throes of desperation and I have taken refuge here from my wife, who is the most vexatious shrew in all the world."

With that he launched into his complete tale of woe. He explained how he had dwelt happily in his well for hundreds of years until the devil's own sister, Fazal Noor, came to persecute him. Upon hearing this Mohammed Bux was filled with wonder.

"My dear friend," he said, "I know exactly what manner of suffering you have endured, for I too was once married to this selfsame creature. However, now that you have revealed your identity, are you not afraid that she may find you?"

The demon turned pale and began to tremble visibly. Between chattering teeth he cried out mournfully, "For the love of Allah, do not divulge the truth! Do whatever you will, but keep her from me. Promise me this one thing and I shall see to it that you marry the sultan's daughter."

With that the demon disappeared from sight, leaving an astonished Mohammed Bux. Remaining invisible until he got to the sultan's palace in the capital city, the demon entered the chamber of the princess and took possession of her body. Naturally, to all outward appearances she became a raving maniac. Despite her beauty, which was like unto the beauty of a celestial houri, she became fearsome and dangerous. Her handmaidens had to flee, for their lives were in danger. The sultan summoned the wisest philosophers, sorcerers, physicians, and astrologers to cure her, but it availed him nothing. Whenever the learned men came into the poor girl's presence the demon caused her to perform acts of mischief and violence. Sometimes she pulled off their turbans and flung them out the window. Other times she threw the men to the floor with superhuman strength, or twisted their noses, or seized their beards. She even threw handfuls of pepper into their faces. Tired of such ill treatment, the wise men refused to come any more, lest they be subject to further indignities.

When Mohammed Bux heard of this he knew that it was time to act. Traveling to the capital city, he went to the sultan and said, "Your highness, I shall exorcise the demon who is plaguing the princess, provided that you agree to grant me her hand in matrimony." The sultan was more than pleased, for Mohammed Bux was a personable and handsome man. When they entered the princess's room she was writhing on the floor, frothing at the mouth, and snarling like an angry tigress. The sultan's attendants drew back in terror, but Mohammed Bux strode boldly to the girl, bent down, and touched her gently on the shoulder. Instantly she rose to her feet and prostrated herself before the newcomer. There were gasps and sighs among the onlookers. Even the sultan was awestruck by the spectacle. Then, lifting the girl to her feet, Mohammed Bux glared solemnly into her eyes and intoned sonorously, "Demon, cease tormenting this poor girl. Set her free and depart. If you fail to obey I shall imprison you forever."

Unfortunately the demon was no longer inclined to keep the promise he had made, for demons are notorious liars. He told Mohammed Bux firmly that he was satisfied where he was, and that he had no intention of leaving. Without hesitation, Mohammed Bux leaned over and whispered into the ear of the princess.

"My friend," he said, "if you know what is good for you you will flee. That she-viper, Fazal Noor, is in the palace."

Upon hearing such terrible news the demon within caused the princess to vibrate like the tongue of a serpent. Then with a fearful shriek she collapsed to the floor in a faint. When she arose to her feet and opened her eyes it was plain to see that she was rid of her tormentor once and for all. The sultan was beside himself with delight. He proclaimed a full week of rejoicing and, true to his word, arranged for the wedding of his daughter to Mohammed Bux at once.

Unfortunately the demon did not leave the vicinity. After several months had passed he appeared one day before Mohammed Bux and said, "Listen closely to what I am about to tell you. Through my efforts the sultan has heaped great riches on you and adopted you as his own son. I, on the other hand, remain miserable and homeless. I have seen the daughter of the Grand Vizier and have made up my mind to possess her for as long as it pleases me. However, I will not tolerate any meddling from you this time. If you do not obey me I shall tear out your entrails, rip your flesh to pieces, then crush your bones to dust and scatter it to the winds."

With these words the demon vanished and flew directly to the villa of the Grand Vizier. Arriving unseen at his destination, the demon floated through a keyhole into the chamber of the unfortunate girl in the form of a perfumed mist. Detecting what she believed to be merely a pleasant scent in the air, the Vizier's daughter inhaled the demon with a single deep breath. Uttering a piteous scream, she fell to the floor, where she writhed and moaned and rolled her eyes frantically. Her handmaidens fled in terror and reported the dreadful event to her father, who came at once to see what he could do. When he saw his beloved child thrashing about like a maddened cobra he wept with grief. Following the example of the sultan, the old man sent for wise men, physicians, and sorcerers, but all to no avail.

In final desperation he flung himself at the feet of his master and begged him to dispatch Mohammed Bux, in order that he might cure the wretched girl. The sultan immediately called his son-in-law and commanded him to exorcise the demon from the afflicted maiden. Fearing what might happen to him should he attempt to obey, Mohammed Bux said, "Your highness, I cannot do what you ask of me. Allah granted me the power only once, when I drove the fiend from my beloved wife. Should I attempt such a thing again I would fear for my life."

The sultan grew very annoyed at these words and drew himself up to his full stature. With his beard bristling and his eyes flashing he pointed a long finger at the young man and said, "Hear me well, son-in-law, and do as I command! If you drive this demon from the Vizier's daughter you will attain even greater glories and riches than you now have. But should you fail, you will certainly keep an appointment with the executioner."

Seeing that he was absolutely without choice in the matter, Mohammed Bux went directly to the Grand Vizier's household. When the demon saw who had come, he issued forth from the girl's nostrils and confronted his old acquaintance with a ferocious glare. He grew until he stood a full ten feet high; then he advanced with outstretched arms that had claws like gleaming scimitars. Blood-red saliva dripped from his gaping mouth, which revealed three rows of razor-sharp fangs.

"Wait!" cried Mohammed Bux. "I come not to molest you. I shall keep my word until I die. I have a message for you of the most dire urgency."

These words mollified the demon slightly and he shrunk to a less terrifying size, agreeing at the same time to listen. Looking over his shoulder as though in a state of great agitation, Mohammed Bux lowered his voice and whispered to the demon, "Listen, the last time I told you that Fazal Noor was in the palace, I was only jesting. But now, alas, she has really come. She has learned of your presence here and even now is in the great hall below."

Upon hearing this the demon turned yellow, then green, then purple with fright. His eyes bulged and smoke began curling out of his ears.

"For the love of Allah," he cried, "get rid of her! Send her anywhere, but do not let her find me. Grant me this one favor and I swear I shall leave this place forever!"

Immediately Mohammed Bux left the chamber and went downstairs, where he remained for several minutes. Then he returned and told the trembling demon that he was out of danger —for the time being. The demon heaved a great and mighty sigh, saying, "I shall keep my word this time. Where I am going she will never find me. Good-by forever!"

In an instant he was gone and the Grand Vizier's daughter, who had fallen into a swoon, recovered her senses. The maiden's father wept tears of joy. The sultan was delighted and declared three days of feasting. Great honors were showered upon Mohammed Bux, and when his father-in-law died, he ascended to the throne, ruling wisely and happily for many years.

« »   « »   « »

The unfortunate demon who was hoodwinked by Mohammed Bux and tormented by Fazal Noor could hardly be regarded in retrospect as having had an overabundance of intelligence. This cannot be said of the demons in the Hindu pantheon of supernatural entities. As concise an account of representative Indian demons as can be found is the following extract from an obscure book on vampirism published some years ago:

136

In ancient India the vetala, a vampire-like spirit or demon, lurked in dark places and ill-omened spots, particularly where human remains were found. There they entered corpses and, animating them, went about their business. They were not inimical to humans in all cases. . . . The Indians had other vampirish demons, however, who were far more malicious than the vetala. The rakshasas not only animated dead bodies, and ate human flesh, they perpetrated all sorts of mischief such as interfering with religious rites. They were said to be ugly and deformed, and colored either yellow, blue or green [conceivably the demon encountered by Mohammed Bux was related to the rakshasas]. Their eyes were especially terrible to behold, being long, hideous slits. Besides eating human flesh, they also ate horses, a trait that in ancient times must have been exceedingly bothersome to those who had to depend on them for transportation. Any poor unfortunate who was scratched by the nails of a rakshasa was doomed, for such a scratch was considered to be poisonous. In spite of all their unpleasant qualities, even these demons were not thought to be all bad. They were said to be exceedingly wealthy and on occasion when they took a liking to a human being they were capable of making him rich beyond his wildest dreams.

The most gruesome and horrible of Indian vampires was not a vampire in the ordinary sense, she was Kali, the goddess of plagues, destruction, and violent death. She is depicted in Indian mythology as a dark woman with long flowing hair and four arms. In statues and drawings she holds a sword in one arm, a severed head in the second; with the other two she beckons to her worshipers. Her adornments are as hideous as her nature. She wears dangling corpses for earrings and a necklace of human skulls. Kali's face is horrible to contemplate. Her eyes are blood-red and her tongue hangs drunkenly out of her mouth.

The head that Kali brandishes belongs to Raktavija, chief of the army of demons. In a furious battle between gods and demons, according to myth, Kali attacked this archdemon and smote him with every weapon at her disposal. Each drop of his blood generated a thousand giant demons as powerful as Raktavija himself. Kali ultimately defeated her enemy by drinking all of his blood. Then, glutted and sated by victory, she embarked on a wild dance of joy that caused the entire earth to tremble.

For the benefit of those who are laboring under the misapprehension that Thuggee (or the cult of Kali, whose devotees have been variously known as Thugs, Phansigars, or Deceivers) no longer exists, let it be pointed out that even as late as the nineteen-seventies ritual killings attributed to present-day followers of the goddess continue to occur. But since such matters belong to the world of reality, we will forsake them—here, at least—in favor of our present arcane pursuits, and before departing from India take a parting look at one more, especially gruesome variety of demon. It turns up in the story of Nischayadatta, in the seventh book of a classic, the *Kathásaritságara*. In the story, the hero, traveling in the company of four pilgrims, finds it necessary to spend the night in a deserted temple of Shiva, one of the supreme deities of the Hindu pantheon. The temple is haunted, however by a Yakshiní, a terrible female demon, who transforms men by spells into beasts, after which she devours them. In the circumstances, the five men sit up watchfully beside a fire, around which they have traced a circle of ashes. Then, at midnight, the demon-sorceress arrives, dancing and playing upon a flute made of a dead man's bone. Fixing her piercing eyes on one of the men, she commences to execute a wild dance as she mutters an incantation. Out of the doomed man's head a horn emerges. He loses control of himself, leaps up, and leaps into the flames. Then the Yakshiní seizes his partially burnt corpse and devours it. After destroying and consuming the second and third pilgrims in exactly the same manner, she then turns her attention to the fourth. But then she hesitates and places her flute on the ground. Instantly the hero snatches it up and begins to play, dancing in frenzied imitation of the Yakshiní about the demon herself, at the same time fixing his eyes upon her as he repeats the words of her own incantation. Thus deprived of her power, she submits to Nischayadatta, and becomes his slave forever afterward, effectively ending her demonic career.

One of the great classics of Sanskrit literature is deeply interwoven with the demon lore of India, and it deals with the life and adventures of a semi-mythical hero, King Vikramaditya, whose place is roughly equivalent to that of Haroun Al Raschid among the Arabs, and King Arthur in the west. There is ample evidence to support the fact that he actually lived, and it was during his reign, in his court at Ujjain or Ujjayan, located in central India, that the so-called nine gems of Sanskrit literature flourished.

Of him Sir Richard Burton, the great scholar-adventurer, wrote: "He acted in his own dominion with justice, he chastised foreign foes with rigor, he behaved generously to Brahmins, and he avoided favoritism amongst his friends. In war he never slew a suppliant, a spectator, a person asleep, or undressed, or anyone that showed fear."

It is not surprising that Burton, whose translation of *The Thousand and One Nights* is by far the best, should have taken it upon himself to translate as well the epic dealing with the great king's life. It would be impossible to include the work here in full because it encompasses an entire book. But since it is such a superb example, not only of classical Indian literature, but of one that so embodies Indian supernatural tradition, this book would be incomplete without at least a few of its highlights.

Burton called his translation *Vikram and the Vampire*, explaining that this shortened version of the great king's name was not uncommon in general usage, and along with the historical information, he gave his readers the usual colorful and lively Burton narrative.

According to tradition, he said, Vikram was a grandson of the god Indra, ruler of heaven and master of lightning, thunder, and storm. There are a number of versions of the story dealing with the king's ascension to his throne; the point at which we become concerned is when he decides to take a leave of absence, as it were, and to wander about the world in disguise for a few years in order to learn firsthand what it is like. Before taking his leave, however, Vikram places his brother, Bhartari, on the throne as regent. Through a series of events that are secondary to the main story, Bhartari decides to abandon the worldly life in order to go off and become a yogi, and by so doing he leaves the throne at Ujjain vacant. The god Indra then dispatches a giant div, or demon, named Prithwi Pala to guard the city and defend it until its lawful master returns, for in Indian mythology Indra was also regarded as the protector of earthly monarchs. It is at the point of the king's return that we pick up the Burton narrative.

In less than a year the valorous Raja Vikram became thoroughly tired of wandering about the woods half dressed: now suffering from famine, then exposed to the attacks of wild beasts, and at all times very ill at ease. He reflected also that he was not doing his duty to his wives and children; that the heir-apparent would possibly make the worst use of parental absence; and finally, that his subjects, deprived of his fatherly care, had been left in the hands of a man who, for aught he could say, was not worthy of the high trust. He had also spied out all the weak points of friend and foe. Whilst these and other equally weighty considerations were hanging about the Raja's mind, he heard a rumor of the state of things spread abroad; that Bhartari, the regent, having abdicated his throne, had gone away into the forest. Then quoth Vikram to his son, "We have ended our wayfarings, now let us turn our steps homewards."

The gong was striking the mysterious hour of midnight as the king and the young prince approached the principal gate. And they were pushing through it when a monstrous figure rose up before them and called out with a fearful voice, "Who are ye, and where are ye going? Stand and deliver your names!"

"I am Raja Vikram," rejoined the king, half choked with rage, "and I am come to mine own city. Who are thou that darest to stop or stay me?"

"That question is easily answered," cried Prithwi Pala the giant, in his roaring voice; "the gods have sent me to protect Ujjayani. If thou be really Raja Vikram, prove thyself a man: first fight with me, and then return to thine own."

The warrior king cried, "Sadhu!" wanting nothing better. He girt his girdle round his loins, summoned his opponent into the empty space beyond the gate, told him to stand on guard, and presently began to devise some means of closing with or running in upon him. The giant's fists were large as watermelons, and his knotted arms whistled through the air like falling trees, threatening fatal blows. Besides which the Raja's head scarcely reached the giant's stomach, and the latter, each time he struck out, whooped so abominably loud, that no human nerves could remain unshaken.

At last Vikram's good luck prevailed. The giant's left foot slipped, and the hero, seizing his antagonist's other leg, began to trip him up. At the same moment the young prince, hastening to his parent's assistance, jumped viciously upon the enemy's naked toes. By their united exertions they brought him to the ground, when the son sat down upon his stomach, making himself as weighty as he well could, whilst the father, climbing up to the monster's throat, placed himself astride upon it, and pressing both thumbs upon his eyes, threatened to blind him if he would not yield.

Then the giant, modifying the bellow of his voice, cried out—

"O Raja, thou has overthrown me, and I grant thee thy life."

"Surely thou art mad, monster," replied the king, in jeering tone, half laughing, half angry. "To whom grantest thou life? If I desire it I can kill thee; how, then, dost thou talk about granting me my life?"

"Vikram of Ujjayani," said the giant, "be not too proud! I will save thee from a nearly impending death. Only hearken to the tale which I have to tell thee, and use thy judgment, and act upon it. So shalt thou rule the world free from care, and live without danger, and die happily."

"Proceed," quoth the Raja, after a moment's thought, dismounting from the giant's throat, and beginning to listen with all his ears.

The giant raised himself from the ground, and when in a sitting posture, began in solemn tones to speak as follows:

"In short, the history of the matter is, that three men were born in this same city of Ujjayani, in the same lunar mansion, in the same division of the great circle described upon the ecliptic [i.e. the zodiac], and in the same period of time. Youf, the first, was born in the house of a king. The second was an oilman's son, who was slain by the third, a yogi, or anchorite, who kills all he can, wafting the sweet scent of human sacrifice to the nostrils of Durga, goddess of destruction [another of the names by which Kali is known]. Moreover, the holy man, after compassing the death of the oilman's son, has suspended him head downwards from a mimosa tree in a cemetery. He is now anxiously plotting thy destruction. He hath murdered his own child. . . ."

"And how came an anchorite to have a child?" asked Raja Vikram, incredulously.

"That is what I am about to tell thee," replied the giant. "In the good days of thy generous father, Gandharba-Sena, as the court was taking its pleasure in the forest, they saw a devotee, or rather a devotee's head protruding from a hole in the ground. The white ants had surrounded his body with a case of earth, and had made their home upon his skin. All kinds of insects and small animals crawled up and down the face, yet not a muscle moved. Wasps had hung their nests to its temples, and scorpions wandered in and out of the matted and clotted hair; yet the hermit felt them not. He spoke to no one; he received no gifts; and had it not been for the opening of his nostrils, as he continually inhaled the pungent smoke of a thorn fire, man would have deemed him dead. Such were his religious austerities.

"Thy father marveled much at the sight, and rode home in profound thought. That evening, as he sat in the hall of audience, he could speak of nothing but the devotee; and his curiosity soon rose to such a pitch, that he proclaimed about the city a reward of one hundred gold pieces to anyone that could bring to court this anchorite of his own free will.

"Shortly afterwards, Vasantasena, a singing and dancing girl more celebrated for wit and beauty than for sagesse or discretion, appeared before thy sire, and offered for the petty inducement of a gold bangle to bring the anchorite into the palace, carrying a baby on his shoulder.

"The king, hearing her speak was astonished, gave her a betel leaf in token that he held her to her promise, and permitted her to depart, which she did with a laugh of triumph.

"Vasantasena went directly to the jungle, where she found the pious man faint with thirst, shriveled with hunger, and half dead with heat and cold. She cautiously put out the fire. Then, having prepared a confection, she approached from behind and rubbed upon his lips a little of the sweetmeat, which he licked up with great relish. Thereupon she made more and gave it to him. After two days of this generous diet he gained some strength, and on the third, as he felt a finger upon his mouth, he opened his eyes and said, 'Why has thou come here?'

"The girl, who had her story in readiness, replied: 'I am the daughter of a deity, and have practiced religious observances in the heavenly regions. I have now come into this forest!' And the devotee, who began to think how much more pleasant is such society than solitude, asked her where her hut was, and requested to be led there.

"Then Vasantasena, having unearthed the holy man and compelled him to purify himself, led him to the abode which she had caused to be built for herself in the wood. She explained its luxuries by the nature of her vow, which bound her to indulge in costly apparel, in food with six flavors, and in every kind of indulgence [in India, at the time Burton wrote, there was still a monastic order devoted to the pursuit of pleasure]. In course of time the hermit learned to follow her example; he gave up inhaling smoke, and he began to eat and drink as a daily occupation.

"At length Kama began to trouble him [the Hindu equivalent of Eros or Cupid, from which the title of the *Kama Sutra* is derived]. Briefly the saint and saintess were made man and wife, by the simple form of matrimony called the Gandharbavivaha [nonceremonial mutual consent], and about ten months afterwards a son was born to them. Thus the anchorite came to have a child.

"Remained Vasantasena's last feat. Some months passed: then she said to the devotee her husband, 'Oh saint! let us now, having finished our devotions, perform a pilgrimage to some sacred place, that all the sins of our bodies may be washed away, after which we will die and depart into everlasting happiness.' Cajoled by these speeches, the hermit mounted his child upon his shoulder and followed her where she went—directly into Raja Gandharba-Sena's palace.

"When the king and the ministers and the officers and the courtiers saw Vasantasena and her spouse carrying the baby, they recognized her from afar. The Raja exclaimed, 'Lo! this is the very singing girl who went forth to bring back the devotee.' And all replied: 'O great monarch! thou speakest truly; this is the very same woman. And be pleased to observe that whatever things she, having asked leave to undertake, went forth to do, all these she hath done!' Then gathering around her they asked her all manner of questions, as if the whole matter had been the lightest and the most laughable thing in the world.

"But the anchorite, having heard the speeches of the king and his courtiers, thought to himself, 'They have done this for the purpose of taking away the fruits of my penance.' Cursing them all with terrible curses, and taking up his child, he left the hall. Thence he went to the forest, slaughtered the innocent, and began to practice austerities with a view to revenge that hour, and, having slain his child, he will attempt thy life. His prayers have been heard. In the first place they deprived thee of thy father. Secondly, they cast enmity between thee and thy brother, thus dooming him to an untimely end. Thirdly, they are now working thy ruin. The anchorite's design is to offer up a king and a king's son to his patroness Durga, and by virtue of such devotional act he will obtain the sovereignty of the whole world!

"But I have promised, O Vikram, to save thee, if such be the will of Fortune, from impending distruction. Therefore hearken well unto my words. Distrust them that dwell amongst the dead, and remember that it is lawful and right to strike off his head that would slay thee. So shalt thou rule the universal earth, and leave behind thee an immortal name!"

Suddenly Prithwi Pala, the giant, ceased speaking, and disappeared. Vikram and his son then passed through the city gates, feeling their limbs to be certain that no bones were broken, and thinking over the scene that had occurred.

We are now informed how the valiant King Vikram met with the vampire.

It was the spring season when the Raja returned, and the Holi festival [the Hindu Saturnalia] caused dancing and singing in every house. Ujjayani was extraordinarily happy at the return of her ruler, who joined in her gladness with all his kingly heart. The faces and dresses of the public were red and yellow with gulal and abir—perfumed powders—which were sprinkled upon one another in token of merriment. Musicians deafened the citizens' ears, dancing girls performed till ready to faint with fatigue, the manufacturers of comfits made their fortunes, and the Nine Gems of Science celebrated the auspicious day with the most long-winded odes. The royal hero, decked in regal attire, and attended by many thousands of state palanquins glittering with their various ornaments, and escorted by a suite of a hundred kingly personages, with their martial array of the four hosts, of cavalry, elephants, chariots, and infantry, and accompanied by Amazon girls, lovely as the suite of the gods, himself a personification of majesty, bearing the white parasol of dominion, with a golden staff and tassels, began once more to reign.

After the first pleasures of return, the king applied himself unremittingly to good government and to eradicating the abuses which had crept into the administration during the period of his wanderings. . . .

« »   « »   « »

During this period of intensive reform, King Vikram receives a rich merchant who commences showering him with priceless gifts. The man's persistence is such that Vikram's suspicions are understandably aroused. Why, he wonders, should this man be so generous with his wealth? He finally reveals himself to be Shanta-Shil, a sorcerer, explaining that if Vikram will assist him in the performance of certain tasks, he, Shanta-Shil, will become master of the Eight Powers of Nature. The king assents, and is instructed by the sorcerer to meet him at a specified time and place, armed, but accompanied by no one but his son. Again we return to the Burton translation.

« »   « »   « »

The valiant Vikram . . . retired into an inner apartment, to consult his own judgment about an adventure with which,
for fear of ridicule, he was unwilling to acquaint even the most
trustworthy of his ministers.

In due time came the evening moon's day, the 14th of the dark
half of the month Bhadra. As the short twilight fell gloomily on
earth, the warrior king, accompanied by his son, with turban-
ends tied under their chins, and with trusty blades tucked under
their arms ready for foes, human, bestial, or devilish, slipped out
unseen through the palace wicket, and took the road leading to
the cemetery on the river bank.

Dark and drear was the night. Urged by the furious blast of
the lingering winter rains, masses of bistre-colored cloud, like the
forms of unwieldy beasts, rolled heavily over the firmament plain.
Whenever the crescent of the young moon, rising from an horizon sable as the sad Tamala's hue, glanced upon the wayfarers, it
was no brighter than the fine tip of an elephant's tusk protruding
from the muddy wave. A heavy storm was impending; big drops
fell in showers from the forest trees as they groaned under the
blast, and beneath the gloomy avenue the clayey ground gleamed
ghastly white. As the Raja and his son advanced, a faint ray of
light, like the line of pure gold streaking the dark surface of the
touchstone, caught their eyes, and directed their footsteps towards the cemetery.

When Vikram came upon the open space on the river bank
where corpses were burned, he hesitated for a moment to tread its
impure ground. But seeing his son undismayed, he advanced
boldly, trampling upon remnants of bones, and only covering his
mouth with his turban end.

Presently, at the further extremity of the smashana, or burning
ground, appeared a group. By the lurid flames that flared and
flickered round the half-extinguished funeral pyres, with remnants of their dreadful loads, Raja Vikram and Dharma Dhwaj
could note the several features of the ill-omened spot. There was
an outer circle of hideous bestial forms; tigers were roaring, and
elephants were trumpeting; wolves, whose foul hairy coats blazed

with sparks of bluish phosphoric light, were devouring the remnants of human bodies; foxes, jackals, and hyenas were disputing over their prey; whilst bears were chewing the livers of children. The space within was peopled by a multitude of fiends. There were the subtle bodies of men that had escaped their grosser frames prowling about the charnel ground, where their corpses had been reduced to ashes, or hovering in the air, waiting till the new bodies which they were to animate were made ready for their reception. The spirits of those that had been foully slain wandered about with gashed limbs; and skeletons, whose moldy bones were held together by bits of blackened sinew, followed them as the murderer does his victim. Malignant witches with shriveled skins, horrid eyes and distorted forms, crawled and crouched over the earth; whilst specters and goblins now stood motionless, and tall as lofty palm trees; then, as if in fits, leaped, danced, and tumbled before their evocator. The air was filled with shrill and strident cries, with the fitful moaning of the storm-wind, with the hooting of the owl, with the jackal's long wild cry, and with the hoarse gurgling of the swollen river, from whose banks the earth-slip thundered in its fall.

In the midst of all, close to the fire which lit up his evil countenance, sat Shanta-Shil, the yogi, with the banner that denoted his calling and his magic staff planted in the ground behind him. He was clad in the ocher-colored loin-wrap of his class; from his head streamed long tangled locks of hair like horsehair; his black body was striped with lines of chalk, and a girdle of thigh bones encircled his waist. His face was smeared with ashes from a funeral pyre, and his eyes, fixed as those of a statue, gleamed from this mask with an infernal light of hate. His cheeks were shaven, and he had not forgotten to draw the horizontal sectarian mark. But this was of blood; and Vikram, as he drew nearer, saw that he was playing upon a human skull with two shank bones, making music for the horrid revelry.

Now Raja Vikram, as has been shown by his encounter with Indra's watchman, was a bold prince, and he was cautious as he was brave. The sight of a human being in the midst of these terrors raised his mettle; he determined to prove himself a hero, and feeling that the critical moment was now come, he hoped to rid himself and his house for ever of the family curse that hovered over them. For a moment he thought of the giant's words, "And remember that it is lawful and right to strike off his head that would slay thee." A stroke with his good sword might at once and effectively put an end to the danger. But then he remembered that he had passed his royal word to do the devotee's bidding that night. Besides, he felt assured that the hour for action had not yet sounded.

These reflections having passed through his mind with the rapid course of a star that has lost its honors [the stars being men's souls raised to the sky for a time proportioned to their virtuous deeds on earth], Vikram courteously saluted Shanta-Shil. The yogi briefly replied, "Come sit down, both of ye." The father and son took their places, by no means surprised or frightened by the devil dances before and around them. Presently the valiant Raja reminded the devotee that he was come to perform his promise, and lastly asked, "What commands are there for us?"

The yogi replied, "O king, since you have come, just perform one piece of business. About two kos [four miles] hence, in a southerly direction, there is another place where dead bodies are burned; and in that place is a mimosa tree, on which a body is hanging. Bring it to me immediately."

Raja Vikram took his son's hand, unwilling to leave him in such company; and, catching up a firebrand, went rapidly away in the proper direction. He was not certain that Shanta-Shil was the anchorite who, enraged by his father, had resolved his destruction; and his uppermost thought was a firm resolve "to breakfast upon his enemy, ere his enemy could dine upon him." He muttered this old saying as he went, whilst the tom-toming of the anchorite upon the skull resounded in his ears, and the devil-crowd, which had held its peace during his meeting with Shanta-Shil, broke out again in an infernal din of whoops and screams, yells, and laughter.

The darkness of the night was frightful, the gloom deepened till it was hardly possible to walk. The clouds opened their fountains, raining so that you would say they could never rain again. Lightning blazed forth with more than the light of day, and the roar of the thunder caused the earth to shake. Baleful gleams tipped the black cones of the trees and fitfully scampered like fire-flies over the waste. Unclean goblins dogged the travelers and threw themselves upon the ground in their path and obstructed them in a thousand different ways. Huge snakes, whose mouths distilled blood and black venom, kept clinging around their legs in the roughest part of the road, till they were persuaded to loose their hold either by the sword or by reciting a spell. In fact there were so many horrors and such a tumult and noise that even a brave man would have faltered, yet the king kept on his way.

At length having passed over, somehow or other, a very difficult road, the Raja arrived at the smashana, or burning place pointed out by the yogi. Suddenly he sighted the tree where from root to top every branch and leaf was in crimson flame. And when he, still dauntless, advanced towards it, a clamor continued to be raised and voices kept crying, "Kill them! Kill them! Seize them! Seize them! Take care that they do not get away! Let them scorch themselves to cinders! Let them suffer the pains of Patala [Hell]!"

Far from being terrified by this state of things the valiant Raja increased in boldness, seeing a prospect of an end to his adventure. Approaching the tree he felt that the fire did not burn him and so he sat there for a while to observe the body, which hung, head downwards, from a branch a little above him.

Its eyes, which were wide open, were of a greenish-brown, and never twinkled; its hair was also brown, and brown was its face —three several shades which notwithstanding, approached one another in an unpleasant way, as in an overdried coconut. Its body was thin and ribbed like a skeleton or a bamboo framework, and as it held on to a bough, like a flying fox, by the toe-tips, its drawn muscles stood out as if they were ropes of coir. Blood it appeared to have none, or there would have been a decided determination of that curious juice to the head; and as the Raja handled its skin, it felt icy cold and clammy as might a snake. The only sign of life was the whisking of a ragged little tail much resembling a goat's.

Judging from these signs the brave king at once determined the creature to be a baital *—a vampire. For a short time he was

* Synonymous with vetala.

puzzled to reconcile the appearance with the words of the giant, who informed him that the anchorite had hung the oilman's son to a tree. But soon he explained to himself the difficulty, remembering the exceeding cunning of yogis and other reverend men, and determining that his enemy, the better to deceive him, had doubtless altered the shape and form of the young oilman's body.

With this idea, Vikram was pleased, saying, "My trouble has been productive of fruit." Remained the task of carrying the vampire to Shanta-Shil the devotee. Having taken his sword, the Raja fearlessly climbed the tree, and ordering his son to stand away from below, clutched the vampire's hair with one hand, and with the other struck such a blow of the sword, that the bough was cut and the thing fell heavily upon the ground. Immediately on falling it gnashed its teeth and began to utter a loud wailing cry like the screams of an infant in pain. Vikram, having heard the sound of its lamentations, was pleased, and began to say to himself, "This devil must be alive," then nimbly sliding down the trunk, he made a captive of the body, and asked, "Who art thou?"

Scarcely, however, had the words passed the royal lips, when the vampire slipped through the fingers like a worm, and uttering a loud shout of laughter, rose in the air with its legs uppermost, and as before suspended itself by its toes to another bough. And there it swung to and fro, moved by the violence of its cachinnation.

"Decidedly this is the young oilman!" exclaimed the Raja, after he had stood for a minute or two with mouth open, gazing upwards and wondering what he should do next. Presently he directed Dharma Dhwaj not to lose an instant in laying hands upon the thing when it next might touch the ground, and then he again swarmed up the tree. Having reached his former position, he once more seized the baital's hair, and with all the force of his arms—for he was beginning to feel really angry—he tore it from its hold and dashed it to the ground, saying, "O wretch, tell me who thou art?"

Then, as before, the Raja slid deftly down the trunk, and hurried to the aid of his son, who, in obedience to orders, had fixed his grasp upon the vampire's neck. Then too, as before, the vampire, laughing aloud, slipped through their fingers and returned to its dangling place.

To fail twice was too much for Raja Vikram's temper, which was right kingly and somewhat hot. This time he bade his son strike the baital's head with his sword. Then, more like a wounded bear of Himalaya than a prince who had established an era, he hurried up the tree, and directed a furious blow with his saber at the vampire's lean and calfless legs. The violence of the stroke made its toes loose their hold of the bough, and when it touched the ground, Dharma Dhwaj's blade fell heavily upon its matted brown hair. But the blows appeared to have lighted on ironwood—to judge at least from the behavior of the baital, who no sooner heard the question, "O wretch, who art thou?" than it returned in loud glee and merriment to its old position.

Five mortal times did Raja Vikram repeat this profitless labor. But so far from losing heart, he quite entered into the spirit of the adventure. Indeed he would have continued climbing up that tree and taking that corpse under his arm—he found his sword useless—and bringing it down, and asking it who it was, and seeing it slip through his fingers, six times sixty times, or till the end of the fourth and present age, had such extreme resolution been required.

However, it was not necessary. On the seventh time of failing, the baital, instead of eluding its capturer's grasp, allowed itself to be seized, merely remarking that "even the gods cannot resist a thoroughly obstinate man." [The vampire's speech alludes specifically to prayer. In a footnote to the original Burton translation, it is explained in the following quotation from the poet Robert Southey that appeared in the preface to his poem "Curse of Kehama": "In the religion of the Hindus there is one remarkable peculiarity. Prayers, penances, and sacrifices are supposed to possess an inherent and actual value, in one degree depending upon the disposition or motive of the person who performs them. They are drafts upon heaven for which the gods cannot refuse payment. The worst men, bent upon the worst designs, have in this manner obtained power which has made them formidable to the supreme deities themselves." To this Burton himself adds, "Moreover, the Hindu gods hear the prayers of those who desire the evil of others. Hence when a rich man becomes poor, his friends say, 'See how sharp are men's teeth!' and, 'He is ruined because others could not bear to see his happiness!' "] And seeing that the stranger, for the better protection of his prize, had stripped off his waistcloth and was making it into a bag, the vampire thought proper to seek the most favorable conditions for himself, and asked his conqueror who he was, and what he was about to do.

"Vile wretch," replied the breathless hero, "know me to be Vikram the Great, Raja of Ujjayani, and I bear thee to a man who is amusing himself by drumming to devils on a skull."

"Remember the old saying, mighty Vikram!" said the baital with a sneer. "That many a tongue has cut many a throat. I have yielded to thy resolution and I am about to accompany thee, bound to thy back like a beggar's wallet. But hearken to my words ere we set out upon the way. I am of a loquacious disposition, and it is well nigh an hour's walk between this tree and the place where thy friend sits, favoring his friends with the peculiar music which they love. Therefore, I shall try to distract my thoughts, which otherwise might not be of the most pleasing nature, by means of sprightly tales and profitable reflections. Sages and men of sense spend their days in the delights of light and heavy literature, whereas dolts and fools waste time in sleep and idleness. And I purpose to ask thee a number of questions, concerning which we will, if it seems fit to thee, make this covenant:

"Whenever thou answerest me, whether compelled by Fate or entrapped by cunning into so doing, or thereby gratifying thy vanity and conceit, I leave thee and return to my favorite place and position in the siras-tree, but when thou shalt remain silent, confused, and at a loss to reply, either through humility or thereby confessing thine ignorance, and impotence, and want of comprehension, then will I allow thee of mine own free will, to place me before thine employer. Perhaps I should not say so; it may sound like bribing thee, but—take my counsel, and mortify thy pride, and assumption, and arrogance, and haughtiness, as soon as possible. So shalt thou derive from me a benefit which none but myself can bestow."

Raja Vikram, hearing these rough words, so strange to his royal ear, winced; then he rejoiced that his heir-apparent was not near; then he looked round at his son Dharma Dhwaj, to see if he was impertinent enough to be amused by the baital. But the first glance showed him the young prince busily employed in pinching and screwing the monster's legs, so as to make it fit better into the cloth. Vikram then seized the ends of the waistcloth, twisted them into a convenient form for handling, stooped, raised the bundle with a jerk, tossed it over his shoulder, and bidding his son not to lag behind, set off at a round pace towards the western end of the cemetery.

The shower had ceased, and, as they gained ground, the weather greatly improved.

The vampire asked a few indifferent questions about the wind and the rain and the mud. When he received no answer he began to feel uncomfortable, and he broke out with these words: "O King Vikram, listen to the true story which I am about to tell thee."

« »   « »   « »

At this point the vampire launches into a series of involved tales, not unlike those of Scheherazade in *The Thousand and One Nights*. They are totally unrelated to the life of the king, but each ends on a controversial note with which the vampire hopes to entrap his royal captor. Despite all of his efforts to induce Vikram to speak, the baital fails—which brings us to the conclusion of the story as written by Sir Richard Burton.

« »   «   « »

At Raja Vikram's silence the baital was greatly surprised, and he praised the royal courage and resolution to the skies. Still he did not give up the contest at once.

"Allow me, great king," pursued the demon, in a dry tone of voice, "to wish you joy. After so many failures you have at length succeeded in repressing your loquacity. I will not stop to inquire whether it was humility and self-restraint which prevented your answering my last question, or whether it was mere ignorance and inability. Of course I suspect the latter, but to say the truth of your condescension in at last taking a vampire's advice, flatters me so much, that I will not look too narrowly into cause or motive."

Raja Vikram winced, but maintained a stubborn silence, squeezing his lips lest they should open involuntarily.

"Now, however, your majesty has mortified, we will suppose, a somewhat exacting vanity, I also will in my turn forgo the pleasure which I had anticipated in seeing you a corpse and in entering your royal body for a short time, just to know how queer it must feel to be a king. And what is more, I will now perform my original promise, and you shall derive from me a benefit which none but myself can bestow. First, however, allow me to ask you, will you let me have a little more air?"

Dharma Dhwaj pulled his father's sleeve, but this time Raja Vikram required no reminder: wild horses or the executioner's saw, beginning at the shoulder, would not have drawn a word from him [the son's action here refers to a point immediately after the vampire's last story, when the king almost forgot himself and allowed a non-committal "ahem" to escape his lips]. Observing his obstinate silence, the baital, with an ominous smile, continued:

"Now give ear, O warrior king, to what I am about to tell thee, and bear in mind the giant's saying, 'A man is justified in killing one who has a design to kill him.' The young merchant Mal Deo, who placed such magnificent presents at your royal feet, and Shanta-Shil the devotee-saint, who works his spells, incantations, and magical rites in a cemetery on the banks of the Godaveri River are, as thou knowest, one person—the terrible yogi, whose wrath your father aroused in his folly, and whose revenge your blood alone can satisfy. With regard to myself, the oilman's son, the same yogi, fearing lest I might interfere with his projects of universal dominion, slew me by the power of his penance, and has kept me suspended as a trap for you, head downwards from the siras-tree.

"That yogi it was, you now know, who sent you to fetch me back to him on your back. And when you cast me at his feet he will return thanks to you and praise your valor, perseverance, and resolution to the skies. I warn you to beware. He will lead you to the shrine of Durga, and when he has finished his adoration he will say to you, 'O great king, salute my deity with the eight-limbed reverence.' "

Here the vampire whispered for a time and in a low tone, lest some listening goblin might carry his words if spoken out loud to the ears of the devotee Shanta-Shil.

At the end of the monologue a rustling sound was heard. It proceeded from the baital, who was disengaging himself from the dead body in the bundle, and the burden became sensibly lighter upon the monarch's back.

The departing baital, however, did not forget to bid farewell to the warrior king and his son. He complimented the former for the last time, in his own way, upon the royal humility and the prodigious self-mortification he had displayed—qualities, he remarked, which never failed to ensure the proprietor's success in all the worlds.

Raja Vikram stepped out joyfully, and soon reached the burning-ground. There he found the yogi, dressed in his usual habit, a deerskin thrown over his back, and twisted reeds instead of a garment hanging round his loins. The hair had fallen from his limbs and his skin was bleached ghastly white by exposure to the elements. A fire seemed to proceed from his mouth, and the matted locks dropping from his head to the ground were changed by the rays of the sun, to the color of gold or saffron. He had the beard of a goat and the ornaments of a king; his shoulders were high and his arms long, reaching to his knees: his nails grew to such a length as to curl round the ends of his fingers, and his feet resembled those of a tiger. He was drumming upon a skull, and incessantly exclaiming, "Ho, Kali! Ho, Durga! Ho, Devi!"

As before, strange beings were holding their carnival in the yogi's presence. Monstrous asuras, giant goblins, stood grimly gazing on the scene with fixed eyes and motionless features. Rakshasas and messengers of Yama, fierce and hideous, assumed at pleasure the shapes of foul and ferocious beasts. Nagas and bhutas, partly human and partly bestial, disported themselves in throngs about the upper air, and were dimly seen in the faint light of the dawn. Mighty daityas, Brahma-daityas, and pretas, the size of a man's thumb, or dried up like leaves, and pisachas of terrible power guarded the place. There were enormous goats, vivified by the spirits of those who had slain Brahmans; things with the bodies of men and the faces of horses, camels, and monkeys; hideous worms containing the souls of those priests who had drunk spiritous liquors; men with one leg and one ear, and mischievous bloodsucking demons, who in life had stolen church property. There were vultures, wretches that had violated the beds of their spiritual fathers, restless ghosts that had loved low-caste women, shades for whom funeral rites had not been performed, and could not cross the dread Vatarani stream [the Hindu Styx], and vital souls fresh from the horrors of Tamisra, or utter darkness, and the Usipatra Vana, or sword-leaved forest. Pale spirits, alayas, gumas, baitals, and yakshas, beings of a base and vulgar order, glided over the ground, amongst corpses and skeletons animated by female fiends, dakinis, yoginis, hakinis, and shankinis, which were dancing in frightful revelry. The air was filled with supernatural sights and sounds, cries of owls and jackals, cats and crows, dogs, asses, and vultures, high above which rose the clashing of the bones with which the yogi sat drumming upon the skull before him, and tending a huge caldron of oil whose smoke was of blue fire. But as he raised his long lank arm, silver-white with ashes, the demons fled, and a momentary silence succeeded to their uproar. The tigers ceased to roar and the elephants to scream; the bears raised their snouts from their foul banquets, and the wolves dropped from their jaws the remnants of human flesh. And when they disappeared, the hooting of the owl, and ghastly "ha! ha!" of the curlew, and the howling of the jackal died away in the far distance, leaving a silence still more oppressive.

As Raja Vikram entered the burning-ground, the hollow sound of solitude alone met his ear. Sadly wailed the wet autumnal blast. The tall gaunt trees groaned aloud, and bowed and trembled like slaves bending before their masters. Huge purple clouds and patches and lines of glaring white mist coursed furiously across the black expanse of firmament, discharging chains and lozenges and balls of white and blue, purple and pink lightning, followed by the deafening crash and roll of thunder, the dreadful roaring of the mighty wind, and the torrents of plashing rain. At times was heard in the distance the dull gurgling of the swollen

156

river, interrupted by explosions as slips of earth-bank fell head-
long into the stream. But once more the yogi raised his arm and
all was still: nature lay breathless, as if awaiting the effect of his
tremendous spells.

The warrior king drew near the terrible man, unstrung his
bundle from his back, untwisted the portion which he held,
threw open the cloth, and exposed to Shanta-Shil's glittering eyes
the corpse, which had now recovered its proper form—that of
a young child. Seeing it, the devotee was highly pleased, and
thanked Vikram the Brave, extolling his courage and daring
above any monarch that had yet lived. After which he repeated
certain charms facing towards the south, awakened the dead
body, and placed it in a sitting position. He then in its presence
sacrificed to his goddess, the White One, all that he had ready by
his side—betel leaf and flowers, sandalwood and unbroken rice,
fruits, perfumes, and the flesh of man untouched by steel. Lastly,
he half filled his skull with burning embers, blew upon them till
they shot forth tongues of crimson light, serving as a lamp, and
motioning to the Raja and his son to follow him, led the way to a
little fane of the Destroying Deity, erected in a dark clump of
wood, outside and close to the burning-ground.

They passed through the quadrangular outer court of the temple, whose piazza was hung with deep shade. In silence they cir-
cumambulated the small central shrine, and whenever Shanta-Shil
directed, Raja Vikram entered the sabha, or vestibule, and struck
three times upon the gong, which gave forth a loud and warning
sound.

They then passed over the threshold, and looked into the
gloomy inner depths. There stood Smashana-Kali, the goddess in
her most horrid form. She was a naked and very black woman,
with half-severed head, partly cut and partly painted, resting on
her shoulder; and her tongue lolled out from her wide yawning
mouth; her eyes were red like those of a drunkard; and her eyebrows were of the same color: her thick coarse hair hung like a
mantle to her heels. She was robed in an elephant's hide, dried
and withered, confined at the waist with a belt composed of the
hands of the giants whom she had slain in war: two dead bodies
formed her earrings, and her necklace was of bleached skulls. Her

four arms supported a scimitar, a noose, a trident, and a ponderous mace. She stood with one leg on the breast of her husband, Shiva, and she rested the other on his thigh. Before the idol lay the utensils of worship, namely dishes for the offerings, lamps, jugs, incense, copper cups, conchs, and gongs; and all of them smelt of blood.

As Raja Vikram and his son stood gazing upon the hideous spectacle, the devotee stooped down to place his skull-lamp upon the ground, and drew from out his ocher-colored cloth a sharp sword which he hid behind his back.

"Prosperity to thine and thy son's for ever and ever, O mighty Vikram!" exclaimed Shanta-Shil, after he had muttered a prayer before the image. "Verily thou hast right royally redeemed thy pledge, and by virtue of thy presence all my wishes shall presently be accomplished. Behold! The sun is about to drive his car over the eastern hills, and our task now ends. Do thou reverence before this my deity, worshiping the earth through thy nose, and so prostrating thyself that thy eight limbs [i.e., temples, nose, chin, hands, and knees] may touch the ground. Thus shall thy glory and splendor be great; the Eight Powers and the Nine Treasures shall be thine, and prosperity shall ever remain under thy rooftree."

Raja Vikram, hearing these words, recalled suddenly to mind all that the vampire had whispered to him. He brought his joined hands open up to his forehead, caused his two thumbs to touch his brow several times, and replied with the greatest humility, "O pious person! I am a king ignorant of the way to do such obeisance. Thou are a spiritual preceptor: be pleased to teach me and I will do even as thou desirest."

Then the yogi, being a cunning man, fell into his own net. As he bent down to salute the goddess, Vikram, drawing his sword, struck him upon the neck so violent a blow, that his head rolled from his body upon the ground. At the same moment Dharma Dhwaj, seizing his father's arm, pulled him out of the way in time to escape being crushed by the image, which fell with the sound of thunder upon the floor of the temple.

A small thin voice in the upper air was heard to cry, "A man is justified in killing one who has the desire to kill him." Then glad shouts of triumph and victory were heard in all directions. They proceeded from the celestial choristers, the heavenly dancers, the mistresses of the gods, and the nymphs of Indra's Paradise, who left their beds of gold and precious stones, their seats glorious as the meridian sun, their canals of crystal water, their perfumed groves, and their gardens where the wind ever blows in softest breezes, to applaud the valor and good fortune of the warrior king.

At last the brilliant god, Indra himself, with the thousand eyes, rising from the shade of the parigat tree, the fragrance of whose flowers fills the heavens, appeared in his car drawn by yellow steeds and cleaving the thick vapors which surround the earth —whilst his attendants sounded the heavenly drums and rained a shower of blossoms and perfumes—bade the king Vikramajit the Brave ask a boon. The Raja joined his hands and respectfully replied, "O mighty ruler of the lower firmament, let this my history become famous throughout the world!"

"It is well," rejoined the god. "As long as the sun and moon endure, and the sky looks down upon the ground, so long shall this thy adventure be remembered all over the earth. Meanwhile rule thou mankind."

Thus saying, Indra retired to the delicious Amrawati [his heavenly residence, built by Wishwa-Karma, the architect of the gods]. Vikram took up the corpses and threw them into the caldron which Shanta-Shil had been tending. At once two heroes started into life, and Vikram said to them, "When I call you, come!"

With these mysterious words, the king, followed by his son, returned to the palace unmolested. As the vampire had predicted, everything was prosperous to him, and he presently obtained the remarkable titles, Sakaro, or foe of the Sakas, and Sakadhipati-Vikramaditya.

And when, after a long and happy life spent in bringing the world under the shadow of one umbrella, and in ruling it free from care, the warrior king Vikram entered the gloomy realms of Yama, from whom for mortals there is no escape, he left behind him a name that endured amongst men like the odor of the flower whose memory remains long after its form has mingled with the dust.

« »   « »   « »

After such a soaring, triumphant ending, it seems downright anti-climactic to return to anything less dramatic than Sir Richard Burton's flamboyant translations. But before moving on to one of Asia's more remote regions, consider this colorful pair of south-eastern demons as described in the vampire book mentioned earlier.

In Malaya the belief in demons is quite widespread, but only two of them are worth mentioning here because of their similarity to the Western vampire. The first is called the langsuir or langsuyar [mentioned earlier]. She appears as a beautiful woman wearing a flowing green robe. Her nails are long, tapering, and sharp, and she has jet-black hair that flows down to her ankles. In the back of her neck there is a hole through which she sucks the blood of children. She is believed to have once been a beautiful woman, who, when her child was stillborn, was so overcome with grief that she flew off into the jungle and became a demon. In addition to the blood of children she has an inordinate fondness for fish, and she often lurks near rivers so that she may steal from unsuspecting fishermen. She can be rendered harmless if she is captured, provided her captors follow the proper procedure. First her nails and hair must be cut short and the hair stuffed into the hole in her neck. Then she will become quite tame and behave as an ordinary woman. Women are in danger of becoming langsuirs after death if they die in childbirth, or immediately afterwards. To prevent this the mouth of the dead woman is filled with glass beads, eggs are placed in her armpits, and needles in the palms of her hands. By taking these precautions she cannot flap her arms to fly or open her mouth to shriek, and she will rest in her grave peacefully.

The second Malayan demon worth mentioning here is the penanggalan. She is one of the most repulsive vampires in the world, and like so many others she favors young children as victims. According to legend, she was once an old woman. One day while in the act of performing a religious duty, sitting at the time on the edge of a large vat of vinegar, she was suddenly startled by the appearance of a strange man. She jumped up so suddenly that she kicked herself under the chin with great violence and in the process separated her head from her body. With that the head and its dangling entrails flew away to a treetop and lived forever after as a malicious demon. Another account of the penanggalan's origin tells that once she was a woman who devoted herself to the study of witchcraft and black magic. She had a devil for a private tutor who taught her everything she wished to learn. Finally when her studies were completed, she was able to separate her head from her body at will and fly about seeking victims whose blood she could suck. It is also believed that after she has satiated herself with the blood of her victims, the penanggalan's intestines are bloated and distended. Therefore, when she returns to her house, in order to return to her body, she must soak her entrails in a large jar of vinegar so that they will shrink and fit properly. Since she favors children, especially newborn infants, elaborate precautions are taken by superstitious Malayans when babies are born. Thorns are strung up around the windows and doors so that if she enters the house, she will catch her intestines on them and become hopelessly entangled. It is very important for those who believe to protect themselves from this she-vampire, for it is feared that if any blood or other liquid drips from her onto a living person the result will be dreadful sores and severe illness.

Alien as this demon and the beliefs surrounding her sound, consider that in Europe, even today, superstitious peasants living in remote and backward regions still protect their homes against evil spirits by hanging up assorted talismans consisting of such items as briars, buckthorns, crucifixes, garlic, and horseshoes. And in America, what about the hex signs that adorn barns in Pennsylvania Dutch country?

Difficult though it may be to accept, the fact remains that the supernatural has its roots in reality. As the American theologian Tryon Edwards once put it, "Superstitions are for the most part shadows of great truths." This brings us directly to four curious little tales of demons taken from the lore of one of Asia's least hospitable regions, Siberia.

1.

There once lived a brave man named Itje, whose parents had been eaten by a horrible monster named Tunegusse. At the time, Itje escaped to a southern desert, where he grew to manhood among distant relations. When he had grown to his full size, he determined to return to his home in the north and liberate his people from the demon Tunegusse. Although he succeeded in killing the giant man-eater, it kept on being reborn again and again. Itje decided, therefore, to build a great fire which would consume the monster's body to ashes. Unfortunately the corpse resisted the flames. Even after the ashes began to cool, the demon's jaw snapped open and shut, grinding together with dreadful sounds. Then its disembodied voice shrieked out that, even though burnt to dust, it would continue to torment the human race. With that a great gust of wind picked up the ashes and scattered them into the air, and from the ashes arose swarms of mosquitoes, which continue to suck the blood of mankind until this very day.

2.

At one time there lived a malevolent water demon named Andalma-Muus. By seizing men with his long, powerful tongue he would drag them down to the depths of the ocean and devour them. A demigod named Tyurun-Nuzykay finally announced that he was powerful enough to rid the earth of this dreadful monster. With that he descended from the heavens, entered the womb of a virgin, and was born as a man on earth.

One day, while he was still a child, he was running along the seashore and he chanced to see the tongue of the demon rise from the water and come toward him. The youthful stalwart, however, was equal to the ordeal. Seizing the monster's tongue in his hands, he pulled with all his strength. The ensuing struggle was so fierce that the very earth was in danger of sinking into the ocean. But to prevent such a holocaust, the young godling began to drink up the sea. With huge gulps he drank and drank until the water sank to the ankles of the demon. Then the hero grabbed his enemy's feet, dragged him from the ocean, and howling with fury, beat him to death against the rocks. This onslaught against the fiend was so ferocious that its blood gushed out and its entrails were smeared as far as the eye could see. From this the rocks derived their many colors, but when Tyurun-Nuzykay cut the giant into tiny pieces, they gave birth to all the noxious biting insects that even now plague man in every corner of the earth.

3.

Two sisters once lived together in a hut that lay in an isolated part of the forest. One day while the eldest was away, a man-eating demon came and began to pursue the younger woman about the house. At first she succeeded in avoiding him, and saved herself by locking herself up in a stout oaken cupboard. The crafty demon, however, then resorted to trickery. He not only persuaded the poor thing to come out of hiding, he caused her to stick out her tongue, which he tore from her mouth with a triumphant howl. The shock was so great that it overcame her and she died.

Later, when the older woman returned and discovered the evil that had befallen her sister, she swore an oath of revenge. For a long while afterward she searched the forest, in order to find the dwelling place of the demon. Finally she came upon four sinister storehouses, one of which reeked of death. Cautiously entering, she discovered that it was piled high with severed human hands. Furthermore, from the roof hung countless human tongues suspended by tiny hooks. One she recognized as belonging to her sister, so she took it down, wrapped it in a soft kerchief, and left as quickly as she could.

Some time later, in the deepest part of the forest, she finally came upon the house of the demon. Fortunately, he was not at home, and his sister, who was good at heart, promised to help in destroying him when he returned. Shortly after darkness had fallen the fiend returned with a freshly killed corpse which he greedily devoured before retiring. Then, while he snored unsuspectingly, the two women crept up to him and smashed him to pieces with heavy mallets. Then, scattering the fragments every which way, they chanted, "Man-eater, thou feedest thyself on human flesh, may thy flesh and thy bones become small insects, which, like thee, shall eat human blood."

Suddenly an ear-shattering humming noise was heard, followed by a great shuddering among the pieces. From the smallest ones arose the gnats, from the next size came mosquitoes, and from the largest, all manner of flies and beetles. Soon a mighty cloud of buzzing insects ascended and blotted out the sky until they spread out over the entire face of the earth.

4.

A man once lived peacefully with his sister in a little hut on the edge of the forest. One day when he came home from his daily hunting he noticed that his sister's belly seemed slightly swollen. He suspected at once that she had secretly lain with some stranger. Saying nothing to her, and pretending that he had not noticed her condition, he behaved in his usual manner. The next day, however, before going off to hunt, he spread a ring of fine ashes completely around the house. When he returned the next day he could hardly believe what he saw. There in the ashes were the unmistakable tracks of a huge tiger. Despite these strange signs, the man kept his suspicion to himself until it became obvious that his sister was with child. One night, a short time later, as she lay in her bed singing softly to herself, the hunter chanced to overhear the words. He stopped to listen more carefully and he heard, "I have lain with the tiger, he is my mate, his spirit dwells within me and you cannot kill me. But if you chop off my little finger, I shall die."

Hesitating no longer, he seized his longest knife and plunged it into his sister's breast. Then he cut off her little finger and waited until she was dead. After that he built a huge pyre of logs and threw the body into it. As it burned more fiercely the fire took on an eerie glow. Then a great shower of sparks began to rise. But when the brother looked more closely he saw that they were not sparks, but evil spirits in the shape of hideous birds and insects, which flew from the fire and disappeared into the darkness.

« »   « »   « »

Since it is virtually impossible to think of Siberia without at least a fleeting consideration of Russia, it would seem that this is the logical point at which to embark on the Slavonic leg of our excursion through the supernatural. The Russians, being neither completely Asian, completely European, nor exactly a perfect blending of the two, are a deep and complex people whose literature—and especially their supernatural literature—is thoroughly unique.

It has all the trappings of the occult that are found everywhere else, to be sure. There are witches, demons, and ghosts, vampires, werewolves, and ghouls. But such baneful horrors notwithstanding, there are still more, a mordaciously savage variety being homicidal corpses that rise from their graves at night like vampires, then rampage among the living with the ferocity of Attila and his barbarian hordes.

It is that distinctive national quality, however, which renders Russian stories so different, even when they contain familiar themes. In one story, for example, we find an element immediately recognizable to anyone who has ever read "Jack and the Beanstalk." An old peasant plants a cabbage plant that grows to such gargantuan heights that its top disappears in the clouds. The wonders he discovers up above are truly miraculous, but when his wife tries to climb up to see for herself she slips, falls, and is smashed to pieces. The old fellow, disconsolate at this turn of events, is approached by a fox, whose role immediately reminds us of the Japanese variety, the only difference being that he retains his vulpine form. The fox assures the old peasant that he can piece the wife together again, and the man, anxious to see her repaired, promises his complete cooperation. Assuming the air of a physician, the fox demands that, along with the wife's fragments, a bag of oatmeal and a tub of butter be placed with him in the bathroom. He then warns the peasant not to look in until the process is completed. Now, if this were a West European story, the fox might very well patch the woman up again, perhaps backward, or even inside out, thereby requiring a whole series of complicated dealings to straighten matters out properly in the end. But no, this is a Russian story. So, when the old man is finally permitted to enter, he finds that the fox not only has eaten up his oatmeal and butter but has left nothing of the poor broken wife but a pile of white bones.

Perhaps the geographical location of Russia has a bearing on the nature of her folklore. Influenced over the centuries in turn by travelers from east and west, by pagans and Christians, friends and foes, merchants and adventurers, a rich tapestry was bound to emerge. Seasoned by the native Russian melodramatic nature, and zest for storytelling, the end result could be nothing but fabulous in the dictionary sense of the word. As proof of this, consider that even the Soviets have remained true to form. In the nineteen-twenties they circulated tales in some of their more backward regions to the effect that Lenin had originally been a bear! "The bear Lenin," they said, "lived for a long time in the virgin forest. There came a Russian general to the forest and tried to trap the bear. He placed a barrel of vodka in the forest, and

Lenin, having drunk it, became intoxicated. Thus he fell into the hands of the Russian general, who compelled him to wander about all over the world and to dance for him. Finally he escaped, became a man, and now he is revenging himself on all generals."

But now, back to the days of prerevolutionary Russia, to the time when superstition shared the throne of the czars. Although, as in the case of such tales as the one about the demon and the smith, which is included here, a note of whimsy and humor emerged, by far the most memorable of the Russian stories are bloodcurdling. Thus, to the Russian peasant, the freezing, dark, interminable night held terrors he knew in his heart and soul to be real as hunger, deadly as the flashing blade of a drunken cossack.

Imagine yourself huddled near a stove for warmth as icy winds outside whistle and lash at creaking walls and rattling windows, while mournful howling of distant wolves conjures up frightful images of yawning graves in lonely burial grounds, where creaking coffin lids disgorge demoniacal corpses and bloodthirsty vampires. Picture yourself shuddering, clutching some holy object for protection against demons or the evil spells of ugly witches—the dreaded baba yagas. Visualize yourself muttering fervent prayers that you will live to see another sunrise, unharmed by the accursed horrors of the night. Stories of the sort that follow, then, are the kind you will hear again and again, and repeat to your children and your grandchildren, and they in turn to those who follow them—if for no other reason than to be prepared for the inevitable confrontation.

The Dead Mother

In a little village there lived a husband and wife. Their life was happy, loving, and peaceful. All their neighbors envied them, and the very sight of them gave pleasure to honest people. But a dark cloud cast its shadow over their happiness, for shortly after the wife bore a son she died. The husband, unhappy moujik that he was, moaned and wept over his loss. But above all he was in despair about the infant. How was he to nourish it, how was he to bring it up without its mother? So he did the best he could, and hired an old woman to look after it. But a strange thing took place. All day long the baby would cry piteously, refusing all food, refusing to be soothed. But during a great part of the night it remained so silent that one would have thought that it wasn't there at all.

Unable to fathom the reason for this, the old woman decided one night to stay awake in hopes of getting to the bottom of the matter. Well, just at midnight, when all was quiet, she heard someone softly open the door and tiptoe to the cradle. The baby grew still as if it was being suckled.

The next night the same thing took place, and on the third night too. When she told the moujik about it he called together his kinsfolk and held counsel with them. They finally determined to do this: to keep awake on a certain night, and to spy upon who it was that came to suckle the infant. So when the appointed night came, they all lay down on the floor, and beside them they set a lighted taper hidden in an old earthen pot.

At midnight the door of the cottage slowly opened. As usual, the soft footsteps could be heard approaching the cradle, and as usual, the baby grew still. At that moment one of the kinsfolk suddenly brought out the light. There, as they looked on, their eyes wide with astonishment, the dead mother, clad in the very same clothes in which she had been buried, knelt down beside the cradle and suckled the child at her dead breast.

The moment the light shone in the cottage she rose up, gazed mournfully at her tiny son, and left the room without a sound, and without a word to anyone. All those present who saw her stood for a moment terror-struck, and when they finally looked upon the child, it was dead.

The Warlock's Corpse

There was once a moujik with three married sons, who was looked on by the people of his village as a koldun, or warlock. When he was on the brink of death, he gave orders that his sons' wives should keep a dead-watch over his corpse for three nights after he died, taking one night apiece. He also specified that his body be placed in the cold chamber beyond the living room, and that the wives of his sons should spin wool to make his body a caftan. Moreover, he ordered that no cross should be placed upon him, and that no crucifix be worn by the daughters-in-law. With that he breathed his last.

On the first night the eldest daughter-in-law took her seat beside him with some gray wool and began spinning. At midnight a sepulchral voice issued forth from the coffin. "Daughter-in-law, art thou there?"

She was terrified, but she managed to gasp out a reply, "I am."

"Art thou sitting?"

"I sit."

"Art thou spinning?"

"I spin."

"Gray wool?"

"Gray."

"For a caftan?"

"For a caftan."

And as her fingers trembled, he rose from his coffin and moved toward her, his dead eyes blazing like the fires of hell. "Daughter-in-law," he intoned as he shuffled nearer, "art thou there?"

"I am," she murmured, terror-stricken. And as he repeated his questions, she retreated to the corner with each answer, until she cringed there shivering, with no way to go as the dead man loomed nearer. So choked with fear was she that no prayer escaped her lips, and he strangled her where she crouched.

In the morning the sons removed her body, saddened, but unaware of what had passed in the night, and the next evening, in obedience to their father's dying request, they sent the second daughter-in-law to keep watch. To her the same horrible fate befell, and they found her strangled corpse in the morning.

The third daughter-in-law was sharper than the other two, and though she declared that she had taken off her cross, in reality she kept it on. She took her seat alongside the coffin and began to spin, muttering prayers to herself all the while.

At the stroke of midnight the hollow voice of the corpse called out from the coffin, "Daughter-in-law, art thou there?"

"I am," she replied.

"Art thou sitting?"

"I sit."

"Dost thou spin gray wool for a caftan?"

"I do."

And as he had on the other two nights, he rose from his coffin, bore down on the frightened girl, repeating his questions. But as he reached out to strangle her in the corner, as he had the others, she brandished her cross, and with a fearful moan he fell down dead.

Stepping cautiously around the body, she went over to the coffin and looked in. There lay an immense pile of money. The father-in-law had wanted to take it with him, or at least to make sure that only she with the wit and cunning to outdo him should get it.

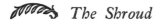 *The Shroud*

[*Note the similarity between this Russian tale and the Japanese "Legend of Yurei Daki."*]

In a certain village there was a lazy, slothful girl, who hated working but who loved to gossip and chatter away with her friends with no thought to doing anything useful herself. One day she took it into her head to invite the other girls of the village to a spinning party. As everyone knows, in all such villages, it is always the lazy one who gives the spinning feast, and the sweet-toothed ones who attend.

On the appointed night she got her spinners together; they spun for her, while she feasted and fed them. Among the things that they discussed was which of them was the boldest.

"I'm not afraid of anything," declared the lazy one.

"Well then," said one of the others, "if you're not afraid, go past the graveyard to the church, take down the holy icon from the door, and bring it here."

"Agreed," she replied. "But first each of you must promise to spin a full distaff for me."

She was delighted, for it was her idea to do nothing herself, but to get others to do it for her. So she went to the church, took down the icon, and brought it home. The others saw that she had indeed done as she had promised, for they recognized the icon as coming from the church door. But it had to be replaced, and it was now approaching midnight.

"The rest of you just go on spinning," said the girl. "I'm not afraid of anything; I'll take it back myself."

So she took the icon, returned to the church, and put it back where it belonged on the door. As she was passing the graveyard, she saw a corpse in a white shroud seated on a tombstone. The moon shone brightly, casting its pale light everywhere, causing everything to be visible. Going boldly up to the corpse, she snatched off its shroud and turned away. It held its peace, not uttering a word, for no doubt the time for it to speak had not yet come. And without turning back she went directly home.

"There," she said as she walked through the door. "I've taken back the icon, and what's more, here's a shroud I took away from a corpse."

A few of the girls were horrified, but the rest didn't believe a word she said and laughed.

After they had had a snack and were getting ready to go to sleep there came a tapping at the window. It was the corpse. "Give me back my shroud! Give me back my shroud!" it demanded.

"There, take it," offered the lazy one.

"No," replied the corpse, "take it back to where you got it!"

Just then the cocks began to crow, and the corpse disappeared from sight.

Next night, long after the other girls had gone back to their own houses, at the very same hour, just before dawn, the corpse returned and tapped angrily at the window. "Give me back my shroud!" it moaned. So the girl's parents opened the window and offered the dead man his shroud, but again he refused, saying, "No, let her take it back to where she got it."

And again, just at that moment the cocks began to crow and the corpse disappeared.

The next day, alarmed, the girl's father and mother sent for the village priest, told him the whole story, and begged him to help them. "Can't you perform a service," they asked, "to rid us of this frightful visitor?"

The priest thought for a while, then instructed them to send their daughter to church the next day.

Accordingly, on the following day the lazy girl went to church and the service began. A number of the villagers attended to participate, and just as they were nearly finished, a terrible whirlwind arose. The entire church trembled and everyone in the congregation was flung to the floor, but the girl was thrown down with even greater force. A bloodcurdling scream escaped from her lips; then all became silent again, and the whirlwind was gone. As for the girl, all that remained of her was a single braid of her hair.

The Two Friends

Many, many years ago there lived in a small village two young men. They were great friends and inseparable companions; in fact, they regarded one another as brothers. One day they made a mutual vow. Whichever of the two married first was to make certain that his comrade came to the wedding, even if the bachelor was dead.

About a year after this, one of the two fell ill and died. A few months later the survivor decided to get married. On the day of the wedding he gathered together all his relatives and friends and set off to get the bride. Now it happened that they had to drive past the cemetery in which the bridegroom's old friend lay in his grave. Remembering his old vow, the young man stopped the wedding procession and said, "I am going to my old comrade's grave. I shall ask him to come and enjoy himself at my wedding. He was a great friend, and I must keep my promise to him."

So he went to the grave and called aloud, "My dear comrade, I invite you to my wedding!"

Suddenly the earth began to tremble, the grave yawned, the dead man rose up and said, "Thank you, brother, for remembering your promise. And now, that we may take advantage of this happy occasion, enter my abode and we will drink a glass apiece."

"I cannot, my friend. The whole wedding procession has stopped outside, and everyone is waiting for me."

"Oh, come, brother," said the dead man imploringly. "Surely it won't take long to have a single drink."

Thus persuaded, the bridegroom jumped into the grave. The corpse poured two drinks, and they tossed them down as in times gone by. What the bridegroom did not know was that a hundred years passed by.

"Have another drink, dear friend," said the dead man. They drank again—and another hundred years passed.

"And now, dear comrade, let us have a third cup," insisted the dead man. "Then go in God's name and celebrate your marriage."

They drank the third cup—and a third hundred years passed away. With that the dead man took leave of his friend, the coffin lid fell shut, and the grave closed.

The bridegroom now looked around. Where the graveyard had been was now a piece of wasteland and desolation. There was no road; there was no wedding procession; there were no relatives. All around were tall weeds, nettles, and ruins.

He ran to the village, his heart pounding with alarm, but the village was not what it had been. The houses were different; the people were all strangers. Frantically he sought out the priest, another stranger, and told him everything that had happened. The priest searched through the old record books and found that, three hundred years before, a bridgegroom had gone to the cemetery on his wedding day and disappeared. His bride, after waiting an appropriate period of time, had married another man.

The Cossack and the Witch

Late one cold, dark night, a cossack rode into a village, reined in his horse at the last cottage, and cried out, "Hey, master! Will you put me up for the night?"

"Come in," came the reply, "if you don't fear death."

"What kind of answer is that?" thought the cossack as he tethered his horse in the stable. But after he had fed the beast and gone into the cottage, he saw that everyone there, men, women, and children, were all sobbing, crying, and praying to God. And when they had finished praying, they began putting on clean clothes.

"What are you crying about?" asked the cossack.

"You see," explained the master of the house sadly, "in our village Death stalks about at night. Into whatsoever cottage she glares, there, the next morning, all who lived must be put into coffins and carried off to the graveyard. Tonight it's our turn."

"Have no fear in this house, master!" declared the cossack. "Without God's will, no pig gets its fill!"

So while the people of the house lay down to sleep, the cossack stayed on the lookout and never closed an eye. At the stroke of midnight the front window opened. Beyond it a witch appeared, dressed all in white. She took a sprinkler, thrust her arm through the window, and was just about to begin sprinkling when the cossack suddenly slashed down a sweeping stroke with his saber and cut off her arm just below the shoulder. The witch howled, squealed, and yelped like a dog, then fled into the darkness. As for the cossack, he picked up the severed arm, hid it beneath his cloak, washed away the bloodstains, and lay down to sleep.

Next morning the master and mistress of the house awoke and, upon discovering that everyone in the household was alive and well, were delighted beyond expression.

"If you like," said the cossack, "I'll show you Death! Summon together all the Sotniks and Desyatniks [rural police] as quickly as possible; then we'll go through the village and look for her."

As soon as the Sotniks and Desyatniks had come together, they began searching from house to house. At first, no matter where they went, they could find nothing, until at last they came to the house of the village sacristan.

"Is your family all present?" asked the cossack.

"Yes, but one of my daughters is ill. She's lying on the stove there."

The cossack looked toward the stove. The girl was very ill indeed! One of her arms had been cut off. Upon seeing this he told what had taken place, and he proved it by bringing out the arm and showing it to everyone. For this the magistrate rewarded the cossack with a good sum of money and ordered the witch to be drowned.

The Dog and the Corpse

A thick-headed moujik went out hunting one day and took his favorite dog along. He trudged and trudged over forests and bogs, but could find no game. At last the darkness of night fell upon them. When it was nearly midnight they passed by an old graveyard, and there, at the crossroads, the moujik saw a hideous corpse standing before him in a white shroud. He was terrified and didn't know whether he should keep right on going or turn around and run.

"Whatever happens," he finally decided to himself, "I'll keep on going."

Ahead he went, with his dog trotting along at his heels. When the corpse saw the pair, it began to pursue them, its feet never touching the ground, and its shroud flapping ominously in the cold night air. When it caught up with them it rushed at the man with a fearsome shriek. But just then the dog seized the bare calf of its leg with his fangs and began struggling furiously. When the moujik saw the dog grappling with the corpse he was delighted to have escaped its bony clutches, and he ran toward home as fast as he could. The dog kept fighting with the corpse until the cock crowed, at which time it fell lifeless to the ground. Then the dog ran off in pursuit of his master, catching up with him just as he reached his house. Rushing angrily at him, the dog attacked with savage ferocity. So persistent was the creature's assault that it was all the moujik's family could do to prevent him from being slaughtered.

"Whatever has come over the dog?" asked the man's old mother. "Why on earth should he suddenly hate his master so?" But when she was told what had happened, she furrowed her brow, shook her head sadly, and said, "A very sad thing, my son. The dog is disgusted at you for not having gone to his aid. There he was, fighting the corpse all alone, only to learn that he was deserted by his master, who thought only of saving his skin. Now he will hold this grudge against you for the rest of his life."

Next morning, while the rest of the family was about, the dog remained perfectly quiet. But the moment his master appeared the hackles rose, he bared his teeth, and began snarling with rage.

The only thing the family was able to do was chain the dog up. Whenever the master was out of sight, he was a perfectly calm dog, but the moment the moujik appeared, or came near, he would snarl, growl, and bare his fangs. For no matter how much time passed, he would not forget how his master had deserted him in his moment of need. One day, breaking loose from his chains, the dog leaped at his master's throat, determined this time to finish him off, and the only way the moujik was able to save his skin was to kill the dog instead.

The Moujik and the Coffin Lid

A moujik was driving along one night with a cartful of clay pots. His horse became tired of pulling such a big load and unexpectedly came to a halt in front of a graveyard. The moujik unhitched the horse to let it graze for a while, and took the opportunity to get a little rest himself. He lay down atop one of the graves, but somehow was unable to fall asleep.

He lay there for some time. Suddenly the grave began to tremble, for it was opening beneath him. Feeling the motion, he sprang to his feet immediately, and watched wide-eyed as the grave gaped open and its occupant, a corpse wrapped in a white shroud, emerged with the coffin lid clutched in his hands. He paid no attention to the terrified man as he ran to the nearby church and laid the coffin lid at the door, after which he began walking toward the village. Being essentially a brave man, the moujik regained his composure. Besides, he was curious. He picked up the coffin lid, took it to his cart, and waited to see what would happen next.

In a little while the corpse returned and was just about to snatch up the coffin lid when he realized that it was gone. Frantically the corpse began searching, and, upon tracking it down to the moujik, demanded, "Give me back my coffin lid or I'll tear you to bits."

Brandishing a wicked-looking hatchet, the moujik replied, "Do you see this, you kolot? If there's any chopping to be done, I shall do it!"

With that the corpse changed his tune. "Please, my good fellow, give me back my lid."

"I'll give it to you when you tell me exactly what you've been up to."

"Well," answered the corpse reluctantly, "to tell the truth, I've been to the village, where I killed a couple of children."

"In that case," declared the moujik, "you had better tell me how they can be brought back to life."

The corpse hesitated, then finally said, "Cut off the left skirt of my shroud, take it with you to the house where the youngsters lie dead, and pour some live coals into a pot. Put the piece of shroud in with them, then lock the door. The boys will be revived by the smoke."

The moujik followed the corpse's instructions and returned the coffin lid to him. The dead man immediately returned to his grave and was just in the midst of climbing back in when the cocks began to crow. This prevented him from covering himself completely, and as the dawn rose, one end of the coffin lid remained sticking up out of the ground.

The moujik saw this and made a careful mental note of it. As the light of day increased, he rehitched his horse and drove back into the village. From inside one of the houses he heard loud cries of mourning. He went inside and there saw the two dead boys.

"Don't cry," he announced. "I can bring them back to life."

"If you do that," promised the father, "I'll give you half of everything I own."

With that the moujik did everything the corpse had told him to do, and accordingly the boys soon returned to life. The family was overjoyed, but instead of keeping the father's promise they seized the moujik and bound him with ropes, saying, "Oh, no, you villain, we're turning you over to the authorities. If you knew how to bring them back to life, then it must have been you who killed them in the first place!"

"What are you talking about?" cried the moujik. "In the name of God, I tell you that you are mistaken!"

With that he told them everything that had happened to him the previous night. Naturally, the news of this spread rapidly through the village, and soon all the townsfolk gathered in the churchyard. They found the grave that the moujik had spoken of, dug it up, and drove an aspen stake through the heart of the corpse so that it might never rise again. Realizing that the moujik had spoken the truth, they heaped praise and rewards on him before sending him on his way with great honor.

The Soldier and the Vampire

Once a soldier of the Czar went home on furlough. He trudged and trudged for many days, finally coming near to his native village. Not far from there lived a miller who had been the soldier's best friend in the days before his military service. Since it was along the way, the soldier decided to pay his old comrade a visit. Naturally, the miller was delighted and brought out food and liquor. The two men began drinking and eating and talking about old times. Soon they had completely lost track of time, and before they knew how late it was, darkness had fallen.

Realizing that he must be off, the soldier arose and announced that he must take his leave. But the miller exclaimed, "Spend the night here, my friend! It's late, and perhaps you might get into trouble if you venture out now."

"What do you mean?" asked the soldier.

"God is punishing us," replied the miller gravely. "A terrible warlock died here recently, and every night he rises from his grave as a vampire and wanders through the village. He does such dreadful things that even the bravest of us dare not go out after dark. Even you must beware of him."

"Not at all," said the soldier, smiling. "I belong to the Czar, and, as you know, the Czar's property cannot be drowned in water or burned in fire. So don't worry about me. Besides, I'm anxious to see my family as soon as I can."

With that he left the miller's house. Now it happened that the road he had to take home passed by the very graveyard in which the dreaded warlock lay buried. While passing, the soldier noticed what appeared to be a fire blazing on one of the graves. Deciding to investigate for himself, he vaulted the fence and approached it. When he was close enough to see, he saw that the warlock was sitting alongside the fire, calmly sewing his boots.

"Halloo, there!" cried the soldier.

The warlock looked up with a malignant scowl on his face and retorted, "What do you want here?"

"I want to see what you are up to."

Surprised at the soldier's boldness, the warlock threw his work aside and said, "Come with me, we shall go into the village and make merry tonight. There's a wedding going on; we'll find mountains of food and oceans of vodka."

"Fine," agreed the soldier. "Let's be on our way."

So they went to where the wedding party was in progress, and they were treated as honored guests. As the warlock had predicted, there were immense quantities of food and drink. He guzzled so much vodka, however, that he became frightfully drunk. He howled and roared, bared his fangs, and chased all the family and guests from the house. Then he cast a spell over the bride and groom which threw them into a deep sleep. With that he took out two vials and an awl. Piercing the hands of the newlyweds with the awl, he drew off enough blood to fill each vial. When he was finished he said, "All right now, let us be off."

Away they went, and soon the soldier asked, "Tell me, why did you draw those two vials of blood?"

"In order to kill the bride and groom," said the warlock. "Tomorrow morning no one will be able to awaken them. I am the only one who could possibly bring them back to life."

"How the devil could you manage that?"

"Oh, that's easy. All one has to do is cut each one of them in the heel, then just pour the blood from the vials back into the wounds. I have the groom's blood in my right pocket and the bride's in my left."

The soldier listened carefully without letting a word escape his attention. Then the warlock began boasting again. "I can do whatever I wish," he declared.

"I suppose," observed the soldier, "it would be absolutely impossible to get the better of you."

"Not at all," confided the warlock. "If anyone really wanted to get rid of me, all he would have to do would be to build a pyre of aspen wood and burn my body on it. Of course, he would have to watch very carefully while the fire was burning, for maggots and worms and venomous reptiles would creep out of my guts. Crows and magpies and jackdaws would come flying out of my breast. All of these would have to be caught and flung back onto the pyre. If so much as a single maggot were to escape, then there would be no help, for in that tiny vermin I should escape."

The soldier made a silent note of all these details in his head as he and the warlock kept walking and talking. Finally, when they arrived at the grave, the warlock said, "Well, my friend, now I must tear you to pieces, otherwise you might decide to reveal my secrets and be the end of me."

"Don't be ridiculous." The soldier sneered. "I serve God and the Czar. My person is inviolate."

The warlock threw back his head and laughed nastily. Then he gnashed his teeth and sprang at the soldier with a frightful roar. The soldier had no intention of being overcome quite that easily, so he drew his sword and began slashing at the warlock with broad, sweeping strokes. They struggled and fought fiercely until the soldier was ready to drop with exhaustion. "Oh God!" he thought to himself. "I'm almost lost, and for nothing!"

But gradually a rosy glow began creeping across the sky, and the cocks began to crow. A glassy look came into the warlock's eyes; he went limp and fell to the ground in a heap—a lifeless corpse until the following sundown.

After sheathing his sword, the soldier took the vials of blood from the monster's pockets and went straight home. His family was delighted to see him. They asked him if he had seen any disturbances during the night, but he replied that he had not.

"You are very fortunate," they said. "We have had terrible things going on here in the village. A warlock has taken to plaguing our peace."

They talked and feasted, and soon it was night again and they went to sleep. The next day when the soldier woke up he said, "I understand there was a wedding here in the home of one of our townsfolk."

"There was indeed," replied one of his relatives. "But the bride and groom died mysteriously."

"Where is the house?" asked the soldier.

They told him, and without saying another word he went to the place at once. When he got there he found the entire family and most of the neighbors gathered together and weeping profusely.

"Why are you mourning?" he asked them.

"Because the unhappy bride and groom have died," they explained.

"What would you give me if I brought them back to life?" asked the soldier.

"If you could do such a thing," they said, "we would give you half of our worldly goods."

At once the soldier did exactly as the warlock had instructed him, and in no time at all the young people were alive again. Instead of weeping, there was now great rejoicing in the household. The soldier was treated like one of the family and rewarded richly.

With that he left and went directly to the house of the local magistrate, telling him that if the villagers followed his instructions they would be able to rid themselves forever of the troublesome vampire warlock. His offer was received with great enthusiasm. The first thing he did was order the peasants to bring a hundred cartloads of aspen wood to the graveyard. There they dragged the warlock's body from his grave, placed it on a pyre, and set it afire. Meanwhile all those present formed a circle around the blaze with their brooms, shovels, branding irons, and pitchforks. Soon the pyre became completely enveloped in smoke and flames. The warlock began to burn. His corpse burst open, and out crept worms, snakes, and other loathsome reptiles. But the peasants were ready for the creatures. They caught them all and flung them into the fire, not allowing so much as a single maggot to escape. As for the crows, jackdaws, and magpies that flew from his breast, all were knocked down and burned. And so the warlock was thoroughly consumed. The soldier collected the ashes and strewed them to the winds, after which there was peace in the village.

Naturally, the hero received the gratitude of the entire community. He stayed at home for a while and enjoyed himself immensely, feasting, rejoicing, dancing, and making love to beautiful girls. When he went back to the service of the Czar, he was a rich man. Thus, after he had served his time in the army he was able to retire, come home, and live the rest of his life in peace, comfort, and contentment.

The Smith and the Demon

There was once a blacksmith whose six-year-old son was a sharp, smart lad. One day the old man went to church and noticed there a large painting of the Last Judgment. What particularly struck him was the figure of a terrible-looking black demon with horns and a long tail.

So taken was he with that demon that he went out and hired an artist to paint exactly such a fiend on the door of the smithy. Thereafter, whenever the blacksmith came to work in the morning he would look at the painted demon and say, "Good morning, fellow countryman." And with that he would start the fire in his furnace and commence the day's chores.

Well, the blacksmith lived in good accord with this demon for some ten years, but then he fell ill and died. His son, now a strapping youth of sixteen, succeeded to his place as head of the household and took the smithy into his own hands. But he was not disposed to show attention to the demon as his father had done. When he came to work in the smithy each day, he never said "Good morning." Instead of offering a kind word, he took the biggest hammer he had and thumped the demon three times on the forehead, after which he went to work. Then whenever one of God's holy days came around, he would go to church and offer each saint a candle; then he would come home, go up to the demon, and spit in his face.

Three years went by thus, the young blacksmith favoring the demon every morning with either a thumping or a spitting. The demon endured it and endured it, and at last found that he could stand it no longer. It was too much for him. "I've had quite enough of his insolent disrespect," he thought. "Suppose I just employ a little diplomacy and play a trick on him."

So the demon assumed the form of a youth and went to the smithy. "Good day, uncle," he said.

"Good day," replied the blacksmith.

"What would you say to taking me on as an apprentice," suggested the demon. "I would carry fuel for you, blow the bellows, and do anything you might require of me."

"Not a bad idea," said the smith. "Not a bad idea at all. Two are better than one."

So with that the demon began to learn the blacksmith's trade, and at the end of a month he knew more about it than his master and was able to do everything his master couldn't. It was a pleasure to see him work. There's no describing how satisfied his master was with him, or how fond he grew of him. The blacksmith trusted his assistant so thoroughly that he sometimes left him completely in charge of the smithy.

Well, it happened one day that the master was away from home and the demon was all by himself in the smithy. Early in the afternoon he saw an elderly countess driving by in her carriage, so he popped his head out the door and began shouting, "Hey, Excellencies! Please, step in here! We've opened up a new business, we transform the old into youths again."

Hearing this, the old lady jumped out of her carriage and hurried into the smithy as fast as she could go. "What's this you say?" she demanded. "Can you really do it?"

"If we didn't know our business," answered the demon, "we wouldn't go about inviting people in to grow young again."

"How much do you charge?" asked the countess.

"A mere five hundred rubles," said the demon.

"Here's the money, then," she said, reaching into her purse. "Make me into a young woman again."

Taking the money from her, the demon called to her coachman. "Go into the village," he ordered, "and bring me back two buckets full of milk."

And as soon as the carriage was gone, he took a huge pair of tongs, caught the old lady by the feet, and flung her into the forge before she could even utter a scream. She burned to a crisp until nothing remained but bare bones.

When the buckets of milk were brought to him, he emptied them into a large tub; then he collected all the bones and dumped them into the milk. He stirred vigorously for about three minutes, and at the end of that time the countess emerged—alive, young, and beautiful!

Well, overjoyed, she climbed into her carriage and drove home at once. Going straight to her husband to tell him the great news, she was taken aback when he stared at her as if she were a

184

stranger. Realizing how old and decrepit the count looked, she snapped at him, "Well, what are you staring at? I'm young and beautiful again, much too attractive to have an old husband like you. Go to the smithy and have them make you young too; otherwise I'll have nothing to do with you."

Clearly there was nothing the old count could do but follow her instructions. Besides, he rather liked the idea of becoming a young man again. But by the time he got to the smithy, the blacksmith had returned and was hard at work. There hadn't been a trace of the apprentice when he first got there, and though he had looked high and low for the lad, he was nowhere to be found. The old count, knowing nothing of all this, walked straight up to the blacksmith and demanded to be made young again.

"Are you out of your mind, Excellency?" said the smith. "How can I make a young man of you?"

"Never mind, you know all about it!"

"I know nothing of the kind!"

"You're lying, you filthy scoundrel! If you did it for my wife, you can do it for me. Besides, the way things stand now, if you don't, there won't be any living with the woman!"

"But I haven't even seen your good lady," insisted the smith.

"Your journeyman saw her, and as far as I'm concerned, it's all the same. If he did such a good job on her, then it stands to reason that you've got to be an old hand at the job. Now, come on, get to work, and if you don't I'll have my men rub you down with a birch-tree towel!"

So the smith had no choice but to try his hand at transforming the elderly count into a young man again. Pretending to give in, he excused himself on the grounds that he had to make elaborate preparations. Then, slipping outside, he held a private conversation with the count's coachman and asked him what had been done to the old lady, and when he learned, he shrugged his shoulders and said to himself, "Well, so be it, I'll do the same thing. If I fall on my face, I fall on my face. The way matters stand, I'm damned no matter what I do."

Re-entering the smithy, he stripped the old count naked, grabbed his legs with the tongs, popped him into the furnace, and began blowing the flames with the bellows. After the count had been burned to cinders, the smith took out the bones, flung them into the tub of milk, and began stirring as hard as he could. But after an hour no youthful count jumped out. Another hour passed, and nothing happened. He searched the tub and found nothing but charred bones.

As if matters weren't bad enough, at that moment a pair of messengers from the countess arrived to see how soon the young count would be ready. Being a truthful man, the unhappy smith declared that the count no longer lived.

Well, when the countess heard what had happened, that the smith had turned her husband into cinders instead of a youth, she was furious. Summoning her strongest servants, she ordered the unfortunate wretch dragged forthwith to the gallows and hanged. Wasting no time, they did exactly as they were told, and in less than an hour they had gone to the smith's house, seized him, and were dragging him to the gallows. All of a sudden, the young lad who had become the smith's journeyman appeared. "Where are they taking you, Master?" he asked, feigning innocence.

"They're going to hang me," replied the smith dejectedly, and with that he explained in detail all that had happened to him.

"Well then," said the demon, now revealing his true identity, "will you swear to me that you will never strike me with the hammer again, but that instead you will pay me the same respect your father always paid?"

"I swear," gasped the smith. "I swear by all the saints in Heaven and the Good Lord Himself! I swear! I swear!"

"In that case," whispered the demon, "the count will be alive again, and be young at that!"

So the demon hurried back to the smithy and shortly afterward returned, bringing the count with him and crying at the top of his voice, "Stop! Stop! Don't hang him! Here's your master, alive, well, and young again!"

Wide-eyed and open-mouthed, they untied the trembling smith and set him free as the count and countess rejoiced over their regained youth.

As for the smith, from that time forth he gave up spitting at

186

the demon and striking him with the hammer. The mysterious journeyman disappeared and was never seen again. The count and the countess embarked upon a new and prosperous life, and, for all anyone knows, may be living still.

« »   « »   « »

Not remote in the geographical sense, like Russia and many of the other places from which we have extracted so much material so far, British Columbia, touching both Canada and the United States physically, has a culture that is predominantly Western. Yet, as in so many other areas of the world, there coexists in the region an alien culture that was present long before the white man came.

To the Tahltan Indians of British Columbia, the dead lead an existence not at all unlike that of the living. The spirits of those who die go to dwell in the Land of the Ghosts, which lies deep in the heart of the earth. Upon occasion they return to the surface, where, if they are seen, they appear in the form of disembodied skulls that roll along the ground. No one wishes to see them, however, for their appearance heralds the coming of many deaths.

There are always exceptions, though, as in the case of the girl who became the bride of two ghosts.

She was a very pretty girl, and her father was a rich man as the Tahltans reckoned wealth, for he owned many slaves and a great deal of property. Late one night the girl was awakened from her sleep by a handsome stranger she had never seen before. He told her that he wanted her to marry him, adding that if she consented she must elope with him at once. She had no idea at the time that he was a ghost, to whom night was day, in direct reversal of the scheme of things as they are among the living. Being young and romantic, she agreed to go away with him and willingly accompanied him to the Land of the Ghosts beneath the earth, assuming it to be just another part of the country.

In the morning, when her parents awoke and found that she had disappeared, they searched everywhere for her, but to no avail. Deeply distressed, her father sent slaves to search further for her in the houses of his neighbors, assuming that she had eloped with one of them. But their efforts were fruitless, and it was finally concluded that she had run away.

When the girl arrived in the Land of the Ghosts, she became the wife not only of the man who had brought her, but of another as well. Her two husbands were very kind to her, and as they were skillful hunters she never went hungry. After some time the husbands came to her and said, "Perhaps you would like to visit your father one day."

"Yes," she replied.

"Very well," said the husbands. "Let us journey to the village of your birth and visit your people."

When the three of them arrived at her father's house, they stood outside the door. The neighbors saw and went to her father, saying, "Your daughter has returned." He invited her in and said that, if she had a husband, he too was welcome.

"I have two husbands," she said.

"So be it," replied her father. "Tell them that they are welcome in my house and invite them to come in."

As room was made for them in the house, the girl was seen entering with two skulls rolling behind her. Out of courtesy no one said anything, though they were filled with fear, and the father ordered his slaves to prepare food for all three visitors and to set places for them at the evening meal. Upon seeing the two skulls on either side of the girl, everyone present was so filled with fear that not a single one of the company could eat. The girl, on the other hand, could not see any skulls, only her two husbands, who appeared to her as two good-looking young men.

So while everyone else sat trembling, the girl and the two ghosts enjoyed their meal and conversed together in ordinary fashion as they always did. This, of course, only disturbed the others more, for they could not hear the words of the ghosts.

After dinner the girl asked her father if her husbands could borrow one of his canoes in order to go hunting. He consented and offered them one that was in the water of the river. When dawn came, which was night to the ghosts, they camped and rested. But at nightfall, which to them was day, they came rolling up to the house as they had when they first arrived. The girl was pleased to see them and, after talking to them, went to her father and told him that the canoe was filled with game for him. When he saw it, he was very pleased and ordered his slaves to carry it from the canoe to his house. When this was done, the girl said to her father, "My husbands must leave soon and they wish to know if you will permit me to go back with them to their home."

"Will you return again?" he asked.

"No, we shall never come back again," she replied.

"In that case, you must stay here when they return. But I will compensate them with much good property so that they may leave you in peace."

He then ordered his slaves to prepare a goodly heap of valuable things which he might give to the ghosts before they returned to rest for the day. When the sun rose again the following morning, the ghosts were gone, along with all the property that had been given to them.

After this the girl remained in the house of her father, but she thought a great deal about the Land of the Ghosts, for she had been so happy there. "It is a good place," she said. "It is a better place than here. The people are kind and they never fight or quarrel."

"I know this, my daughter," said her father. "But the people there are ghosts."

The girl refused to believe this, however, and she longed for the day that her husbands would return for her, as they had promised they would before they left. Shortly afterward she died, and when she arrived in the Land of the Ghosts it was like a homecoming. She was welcomed by her husbands and by her friends, and the Chief of the Ghosts promised her that she would never have to leave again. This pleased her greatly, for in the company of the living she had not known such happiness.

« »   « »   « »

The Tahltan Indian concept of a subterranean ghost land is not unlike that found among non-Western peoples in many other parts of the world. Not only are these beliefs in realms of the dead very much alike from people to people, as you have probably noticed, but they also bear a striking resemblance to those held by our cultural forebears of ancient Greece and Rome.

In Africa, for instance, we can find many examples of this familiar underworld concept among peoples who have probably never heard about ancient Greek mythology and who certainly know nothing of the Tahltan Indians. But that is only a minor aspect of the supernatural in Africa, for it includes magic, witchcraft, ghosts, goblins, demons, vampirism, and lycanthropy. Furthermore, because of the rich blend of many cultures in Africa, there exists a supernatural treasure trove that has barely been touched.

This situation is unique and bears explaining. To begin with, there has been an extensive cross-cultural exchange among Africans since ancient times. Unlike the Arabs and Europeans who came to that continent over the centuries, native Africans, regardless of what region they came from, were unbelievably broadminded (by our standards). Certainly they had their class hatreds, repressions, wars, and xenophobic outrages—all ordinary human failings. Indeed, in the West African kingdom of Dahomey, the selling of black Africans to white Europeans and Americans achieved the status of a major industry. Black Africans were not guiltless when it came to slaveholding, either. But in the realm of religion and the supernatural Africans differed radically from the foreigners who descended upon them.

Africans traditionally had great respect for the forces of nature and the gods who were inextricably involved with them. When Islam spread the word of Allah, Africa embraced Islam. When Christian missionaries spread the word of Jesus Christ, Africa embraced that word. But what neither the Arabs nor the Christians understood was that Africa had no intention of abandoning the old gods, the old beliefs, the old culture.

These ideas that were indigenous to Africa were perfectly workable; they had functioned for centuries and had developed in such a way that Africans were quite capable of absorbing new ideas and making them coexist with old ones. For example, when an Ibo went to live among the Yoruba he did not give up his gods; it would have been unthinkable—and foolish. Nevertheless, he had no intention of insulting the Yoruba gods, so he paid them their due respect. The Yoruba looked at things the same way. There was no point in taking chances and angering the Ibo gods. Understandably, then, over the ages there took place a vast cultural exchange next to which the Soviet-American program seems puny.

When Christianity came it made perfect sense to Africans to accept these new teachings. There was no doubt in their minds that the white men had strong magic and a mighty God. Not only was this God powerful, He had a son born of a virgin and legions of angels and saints to assist Him. What the missionaries could not get through their heads was that the Africans, though perfectly willing to accept Christianity, had no intention of accepting it to the exclusion of the old gods.

The monumental and frequently tragic misunderstandings that arose from this confrontation between unbending Christian zealots and millennia of African tradition left wounds that have yet to be healed. Nevertheless, the African talent for cultural blending produced fascinating results. Colored lithographs of religious scenes played a significant role. In time Africans began to recognize relationships between the old and the new that probably drove many a missionary to the bottle. For example, it became plain to anyone who could see that Moses of the Old Testament was the father of Damballah, the snake-god. The pictures proved it. Didn't Moses cast a rod to the ground and cause it to become a snake?

And there you have the essence of voodoo. The word is merely a corruption of the Yoruba term *vodun*, meaning "deity," which was mispronounced and misunderstood by the French. What we think of as voodoo, of course, is the blend of Afro-Catholicism that took root in Haiti. In other places such as Brazil, Cuba, Jamaica, etc., similar cults flourished and developed along parallel lines, having to this day considerable influence on the cultural life of the Americas. But since this is not a text in the field of cultural anthropology, it will be best at this point to return to the realm of supernatural tales.

A perfect example of the similarity in beliefs mentioned earlier is in this Dahomean tale of the girl who visited the market of the dead. It also explains why the dead may not be summoned at will.

There was once a woman who had a pair of twins, a boy named Zinsu and a girl, Dosi. The boy died, and the girl took to doing everything for her mother, including the marketing and the cooking.

One day while at the market, Dosi saw a hunter who was offering smoked meat for sale. Although he had a great deal of it, she bought it all from him because he was asking a good price. As she was making her way home with the meat, she met an old woman who told her that if she took the meat to another market nearby she could sell it at a very sound profit because they had no meat there. Dosi took the old woman's advice and found it to be very good indeed, for she sold all the meat for considerably more than she had paid the hunter.

When she got home that night and told her mother how much money she had made, the mother was very pleased and told her to do the same thing again when it was market day again. She had to wait for a time, for in the kingdom of Dahomey in those times the markets were open for periods of four days, and then they would close until the next time.

When the next market day came, Dosi went back, saw the same hunter, and bought his meat from him. She repeated this three days in a row, each time taking the meat to the other market and selling it for a good profit. At the end of the third day, however, when she came home with her money, Dosi found that her mother had died. Since she had accumulated a good deal of money by now, she called together all of her relatives and friends, bought a proper quantity of food and drink, and saw to it that her mother had a suitable funeral.

After her mother was buried, Dosi began trading at the markets again, and the next time she saw the hunter from whom she always bought the smoked meat she said, "I am alone now at home. I had only my mother, but now she is dead." Hearing this, the hunter said, "In that case, after the next market I will come home with you." And as he had said, on the day of the next market he appeared with all his possessions. He went home with her, became her husband, and now, when he brought meat home after hunting she would take it to the market and sell it for a good price.

One day, however, the young woman went to the market of the dead by mistake. To her amazement she saw an old woman there looking exactly like her grandmother, who had died long ago. When Dosi went over to greet her, she vanished from sight. This disturbed Dosi greatly, and when she got home she told her husband what had happened. After hearing her story, he said, "You must have gone to the market of the dead, but to make certain, go again next market day and see what happens."

On the next market day she went there again. To her joy she saw her dead brother, Zinsu. Eagerly she pushed her way through the crowd so that she might greet him, but when she called out, he too disappeared. Anxious to get home so that she could tell her husband what happened, Dosi was turning to leave, when she saw her mother. It so happened that she had a piece of meat left in the calabash she was carrying, and she wanted to give it to her mother, but when she called, "Mother!" the woman vanished, just as the others had.

When Dosi arrived home that night, she said nothing, but the next day she returned to the market, determined to find her mother, her grandmother, and her brother once again. When she finally found them, she offered her grandmother a piece of meat and said, "Why did you disappear when you saw me? It frightened me."

They would not tell her, but they warned her that she must tell no one that she had come to the market of the dead and spoken to them. She promised that she would say nothing, and when it was time to leave she went home. At first she said nothing to anyone, but it was such a great secret, she had to tell someone. So she went to her best friend and told her all about how she had gone to the market of the dead and seen her mother, her grandmother, and her brother. "That's a lie," scoffed the friend. "No one can see the dead. I'll come with you and see for myself."

Hearing this, Dosi became frightened. "No!" she said. "It is impossible, no one can come with me. I was not supposed to tell anyone about it and I am afraid." But her friend kept begging to be taken to the market of the dead, and so finally, on the next market day, Dosi took her along.

When they got there, Zinsu was the only member of the family that Dosi could find. He was very angry and he frowned. "You were forbidden to bring anyone here," he said. "For that, your friend must remain, even though you may go."

Hearing this, the other girl was terrified. She did not want to stay forever in the market of the dead, and she followed Dosi as she started to leave. But then Zinsu seized her and cut off her head.

Seeing what had happened, Dosi felt terribly sorry. "It's all my fault that you cut off her head," she said to Zinsu. "I brought her here, so I must stay too." And so she became one of the dead herself and never returned.

Now it so happens that this was long ago, and in those days when the living wanted to know where a dead person was, all they needed to do was whistle, and they could summon the dead. So when the family of Dosi's friend and her own husband began to miss the two young women, they began whistling. Nothing happened. They did not return, and ever since then no one else has returned either, and it is all because of Dosi, who went to the market of the dead.

« » « » « »

A strange tale involving a sojourn in an entirely different kind of underworld is the story of Maruwa. It comes from the Wachaga tribe, a Bantu people of East Africa, and its flavor is totally unlike the story of Dosi and the market of the dead.

Maruwa was a girl in her teens who had been assigned the task of standing watch with her little sister over a garden of ripening beans. One afternoon the heat became so fierce that Maruwa had to get a drink of water. So, leaving her sister alone for a little while, she went down to the Kiningo pool to cool off and take a drink.

While Maruwa was gone, a troop of chattering baboons overran the bean garden. As she was all by herself, the little sister was afraid to chase them away, and by the time Maruwa returned the entire crop of beans had been eaten. Overcome by guilt, and convinced that her father would beat her for her negligence, Maruwa burst into tears, ran back to the pool, and threw herself in, wailing with despair. Her little sister, equally frightened, ran home and told her mother what had happened. Hearing this, the mother seized her younger daughter by the hand and rushed from the house. When they reached the pool they saw that Maruwa was still floating.

"Come back, Maruwa," called her mother. "Never mind the beans, we'll plant some more!"

"I can't!" Maruwa wept disconsolately. "The baboons ate all the beans, and it's my fault, I don't dare come home."

So despite her mother's pleas, Maruwa kept refusing to come

out of the water, and finally she sank to the bottom. But when she got there, to her amazement, she found a village just like her own. There were people and animals and houses. When the people saw her they offered to give her food, but she felt so guilty that she refused to eat. They asked her what she wanted and said, "What do you eat at home?" To which she answered, "Bitter fruits and emetic leaves."

Nevertheless she remained with the people of the underworld and went to stay in the house of an old woman. She remained there for many days, refusing to eat the whole time. Living in the house with the old woman was a little girl who helped with the chores. One day as the child was about to go out and cut grass to feed the goats, the old woman said to Maruwa, "You may go with her if you wish to, but don't help her with the work." But Maruwa felt sorry for the girl and cut the grass for her, handing it to her just before they returned to the house. She did the same thing when the girl was sent out to gather firewood or draw water, so naturally after a time she came to grow very fond of Maruwa.

Then one day the little girl said, "You will have to leave here soon. Once they get accustomed to having you around, they'll begin mistreating you very badly."

"What can I do about it?" asked Maruwa.

Looking around to make sure that no one was listening, the little girl whispered, "Go to the old woman and tell her that you're homesick. Ask her if you may go home."

"Suppose she refuses?"

"You have nothing to fear if you do exactly as I say," the girl assured her. "If she asks, 'Shall I let you go through the manure or the burning?' say to her, 'Please, Mother, let me go through the manure.'"

Accordingly, when Maruwa got back to the house she did exactly as the girl had told her. The old woman took her out in back to the cattle stall and threw her in the manure pile. When she picked herself up and climbed out again, she discovered that she had returned to the upper world once more. Not only was she home, but she was perfectly clean and she was wearing beautiful beads, bangles, and golden chains.

She hurried to her parents' house as quickly as she could, but when she found that they were not home she hid in the cowpen in back. In time her mother came to get a calabash full of milk and was astonished to find Maruwa there.

"Maruwa!" she cried, reaching out to embrace her daughter, but the girl pulled back and exclaimed, "Don't touch me or my jewelry!" (For she feared the consequences of any such contact so soon after returning from the spirit world.)

Running back to the house, the mother called to her husband, "Hé! Mbonyo! Mbonyo! Come to the cow pen and get the milk calabash. Hurry!"

At first he did not want to come out, for he was reluctant to do something that was considered to be women's work. But on second thought he decided that she made the request for some special reason, so he came out, and when he saw his daughter, she warned him too to keep his distance. He was overjoyed to see her and he left at once to get a sheep, which he gave to her as a gift of welcome. Now she was able to come out into the open and be admired properly, so she emerged from the cowpen and proudly displayed all the fine adornments she had received in the spirit world beneath the Kiningo pool. The neighbors too came to admire her, and they were filled with wonder.

It so happened that a girl of Maruwa's age who lived nearby was jealous, for she wanted to have beautiful bangles, chains, and beads of her own. Having heard of how Maruwa had got them, she ran away and plunged to the bottom of the Kiningo pool. Unlike Maruwa, she ate all the food that the people there offered her, and when she was taken into the old woman's house, she did exactly as she was told. That is, she never lifted a finger to help the little girl with her chores of cutting grass for the goats, drawing water, and gathering firewood. One day the little girl said to her, "We are very poor here, and I think you had better ask the old woman to let you go home." She advised Maruwa's neighbor to ask in exactly the same way, but instead of suggesting that she request being sent back through the manure, she recommended the burning.

Unaware that the fire was hidden in her body, she slipped into the cowpen behind Maruwa's house as soon as she returned to the upper world. As it happened, Maruwa was the first person to see her, upon entering to get a calabash of milk. Knowing no better, the girl reached out to embrace her friend, and the instant they touched, fire burned out of her entire body. Shrieking with pain, she ran flaming from the cowpen to the nearest stream. But when she threw herself into the water the flames kept burning as hotly as ever. From river to river she went, screaming in anguish for release from her fiery agony, but no earthly waters had the capacity to extinguish the flames. Every stream she saw she begged fervently to help her, but not one of them did so. At last when she came to the Sere stream of Namuru she sank beneath its waters and died, which explains why those who know the story of her sad fate never drink there.

« »   « »   « »

Not all African ghost stories have such grim endings. Though the temptation is strong to delve deeper and deeper into the occult lore of that vast continent, the limitations imposed by space dictate otherwise. For a final tale embodying the dwelling-place-of-the-ghosts motif we move to the southeastern tip of Nigeria, where the Ekoi people live. The Ekoi tradition is richly endowed with magic, sorcery, divination, totemism, ghosts, and monsters —not exactly uncommon factors in Africa. But when you couple these things with other Ekoi traits such as their ready wit, superb imaginations, and love for a good yarn, you can be sure to find their folklore lively, original, and entertaining.

Their ghosts are both good and bad. They retain most of the traits they possessed while alive, and as a rule good ghosts always keep a close watch over bad ones in order to prevent them from doing harm to the living, a good arrangement indeed. They can also be very reasonable. For instance, Ekoi ghosts seem to have very good appetites, and it is not uncommon for them to come around looking for offerings of food. If a man inadvertently eats food that was intended for a ghost, the ghost tends to be reasonable about it and refrains from bringing harm to that man. But the person who deliberately goes about gobbling up food that was left for the ghosts is bound to pay for his indiscretion by meeting ultimately with an unpleasant fate.

Some of the most charming Ekoi ghost stories involve not only a village of ghosts but food; in the case of the following tale, tomatoes—their introduction into the world of the living, to be exact. It should be explained at this point that an old Ekoi funeral custom was to put on a play in honor of the deceased, in which everyone participated by singing and dancing and ceremonially feasting. And now for the story.

Long ago a man named Effa lived with his wife Akat and his mother. When the mother died they sent word to all the neighboring villages that the people were invited to come and participate in a play in honor of the deceased woman.

The mother's spirit went to dwell in a ghost village that was very far away, where there happened to be a ghost named Echi, who during his lifetime had known her and her family. For that reason he decided that he would like to journey back to Effa's village and take part in the ceremonies attending the old woman's death.

At the first village he came to on the way, he was asked by the chief, "What is your name?"

"When I travel," he said, "my name is Egut."

He then asked if they would loan him a hand, which they did before sending him on his way again. In the next village he asked the people if they would lend him a neck. They too were generous, and they granted his request. At the third village he borrowed a second hand, at the fourth a belly, at the fifth loins, and at the sixth and seventh, a foot apiece. At the eighth town he borrowed a machete, and at the ninth a gun.

When he arrived in the tenth village all the people were away except for a single woman. Coming to the door of her house to look at him, she was smitten by his handsome appearance, for she had no way of knowing that he was actually a ghost with borrowed parts from many bodies. When she invited the handsome stranger to stay with her for a few days, he agreed, for she happened to be a very beautiful woman. When she asked him his name he said, "My name is Nopp Amba."

From the house of the beautiful woman the ghost Echi went directly to the village of Effa, where the people were still performing the play in honor of the dead woman. They were delighted to welcome such a handsome stranger into their midst, and when they asked him his name, he said, "My real name is Echi." With that they returned to the ceremonial singing and dancing, but soon it became apparent that the ghost (whom no one recognized as such) surpassed them all.

More than any of the others, a woman named Atem noticed the grace of his dancing and the beauty of his voice, which, combined with his handsome appearance, made her fall in love with him. Recognizing her feelings at once, he said to her, "My name is Nopp Amba. Would you like to take me as your husband while I am here in your village?" Atem readily consented to this.

A few days later, when they had finished the rites in honor of the dead woman, Echi prepared to return to the village of the ghosts. Not wishing to be left behind, Atem pleaded with him to take her with him, but he said, "No, I cannot, for I am not permitted to have two wives."

From this a controversy arose, and a meeting of the entire village was called. It was decided that he had married the woman, and since she chose to go with him, he had to take her. Instead of challenging the decision, he bade the villagers farewell and set out on his journey back, taking the woman with him.

At the town from which he had borrowed the gun, he returned it. At the town from which he had borrowed the machete, he returned it. At the towns from which he had borrowed all the parts of his body, he returned what he had borrowed. When Atem saw what was happening she began weeping. "If I had known what sort of man you were, I would never have become your wife." But he continued, and less and less of him remained.

Finally Atem stopped and refused to go another step. "I want to go back home!" she demanded.

"You came of your own free will," replied the ghost. "Now there is no turning back."

After they had passed through the last of the towns, all that remained of Echi was a bare skull. But when they entered the village of the ghosts, and all the spirits came out to greet them, one ghost recognized Atem at once.

"This is my sister," she said. "She must come with me to my house."

That night all the ghosts gathered together so that they could kill Atem and devour her. But her sister, though herself a ghost, hid her and said, "Listen carefully to me, and you will be saved. Accept nothing that they offer you to eat, for if you do you will die. If you eat only what I give you, they cannot do you any harm." She then hid her sister and kept her from starving by feeding her tomatoes, a strange fruit she had never seen before.

Finally, when it was safe, Atem's sister took her by the hand, led her to the road out of the village of the ghosts, and sent her on her way with a bag of tomatoes to eat along the way. "When you get home," said the ghost sister, "Tell no one what you have seen among the ghosts." With that, Atem bade her sister farewell and hurried back to her own village.

When she got back to her house she became very ill, so she went to Nyopp the porcupine and asked him for a charm that would cure her. He agreed to help her and said, "Take all the tomatoes you have remaining and bury them in the soft earth behind your house. Then go to the edge of the town, where the road begins, and make a sacrifice of seven leaves, which you must lay on the ground."

Atem did exactly as she had been told. When the ghosts who had been chasing her, and who had caused her to feel ill, came and found the leaves, they began to count them.

"One, two, three, four, five, six . . ." they counted, but they could not count up to seven, so they ate the leaves and departed.

Until this time, when ghosts became hungry, all they needed to do was come into the villages and the houses and haunt them until the owners gave up what was demanded of them. But after the sacrifice of the seven leaves, they did not do this any more. There were also no tomatoes among the people before this, but when Atem brought them from her sister in the village of the ghosts, and buried them behind her house on the instructions of the porcupine, they grew and flourished, and from them sprang all the tomatoes that came afterward.

« » « » « »

If ever there was living proof that the peoples of the world have more in common than not, the similarities in ideas about the dead and about the survival of a spirit or soul provide it. There is certainly a vast gulf between the Africans whose stories you have just seen and the Indians in Mexico. Here are people whose traditions are a mixture of the indigenous and the imported; yet notice in the following story the conceptual similarities to the Tahltan, the Dahomean, the Wachaga, and the Ekoi.

The wife of a certain Indian living in Chiapas died, and he was overwhelmed with grief. For now there was no one to care for him, to comfort him, or to keep him from being lonely in the night. As time passed, his sadness increased, and like a man in a trance he would wander about to the houses of his neighbors, who felt sorry for him and who shared their gruel and tortillas with him.

One evening he went to the little cemetery where his wife lay buried, and, throwing himself upon her grave, he wept and cried out to her, "Where have you gone, *mi corazón!* Why did you leave me to suffer like this, alone and forgotten?" And as the tears of anguish streamed down his weatherbeaten cheeks he suddenly became aware that he was not alone. Looking up, he saw the figure of a man—perhaps it was God, he did not know. He looked like a *ladino*, a city-dweller, and he wore clean trousers and shirt of cloth.

"Why do you weep, *amigo?*" asked the stranger gently. "What is wrong?"

At first the poor man was too startled to speak, but at last he replied, "I weep because my wife is dead and I am so lonely that my heart is breaking."

"So," murmured the stranger, "you desire to see your wife. *Muy bueno!* I shall bring you to her. Now, do as I say. Close your eyes and keep them closed until I tell you to open them again." A few moments later he said, "Open your eyes."

When the man opened them he found himself in the underworld, standing before the Lord of Death. The *ladino* was nowhere to be seen, and the Lord of Death said, "If you wish to see your wife, proceed until you come to a river. On the bank you will find a horse which you must bring back to me."

He proceeded as he had been told, and in time he came to the river. But there was no horse in sight. All he could see was a multitude of women washing their hair and scrubbing clothes. Walking among them, the man searched high and low, but still he could find no horse, so sadly he returned to the Lord of Death and told him that only women were to be found on the riverbank.

"Return to the river," declared the Lord of Death. "Ask each of the women if she is a horse. The one who answers that she is will be your wife, and when you ask her your question she will become a horse. When this happens, tie her and bring her to me."

Again the man went back to the river. But this time he questioned each of the women as he had been instructed to do, until he found one who turned into a horse when she was asked. She had been wearing a ribbon in her hair, so he took it and tied it around her neck, but when she complained that it was too tight he took it off and tied her with the cotton belt he wore. Then he led her back to the Lord of Death.

On their way they passed a great well in which a roaring fire burned. Alongside the well was a heap of human bones. The man asked the horse which was really his wife what the meaning of these things was, and she said, "Every day I must go to the river to wash and gather firewood. When I do this I am in the shape of a woman. But then I am changed into the shape of a horse in order to carry the wood to the well of fire. At the well of fire I become nothing but bones, like the ones you see. Once I become a pile of bones, the Lord of Death throws me into the fire, where I remain until my bones are consumed to ashes, when I cry out that I have suffered enough for the day. I must suffer this punishment because you did not beat me while I lived with you up on the earth."

The Lord of Death permitted the woman to take her husband to her hut, which was exactly like those of the living above. She was also permitted to resume the shape of a woman again. When they were in the hut the wife gave her husband yellow corn and red beans to eat. "We are not permitted to eat white corn," she explained, "for it is really the brains of man. And we cannot eat black corn, for that is our burnt flesh, and we cannot eat black beans, for those are the pupils of our eyes."

When they had finished eating, the wife told her husband that she was tired and was going to sleep. "I will sleep on the bed," she said, "but you must sleep on the floor near the fire, for we are not permitted to sleep together and do the things we did when we were on the earth together." So he lay down on the floor near the fire, but after a while he felt a desire for his wife, and he went to the bed. But the moment he touched her he felt only bare bones without flesh.

In the morning his wife complained bitterly. "You should not have touched me. It was an evil thing. Now, just as my punishment was growing less, it will be increased because of what you have done."

It is not known how long the man remained in the underworld, for no one knows whether there are days or nights, years or months. In any case, the time came when the wife said to her husband, "You must return to the earth above now. You will die fifteen days after you get back, though, for you have come here and seen what no living man must see. It is too bad for you, because it had been written that you were not to die until you were old, but that is all changed now."

The man shrugged and replied, "It makes no difference to me, I don't want to live there by myself."

Then the *ladino* who had brought him below knocked at the door and said, "Are you ready?"

"I am ready."

"Good, then close your eyes just as you did before, and keep them closed until I tell you to open them again."

He did as he was told, and when the *ladino* commanded him to open them again he found himself back in the cemetery alongside the grave of his wife. He was alone, but he did not feel so bad any more, so he went home to his hut and slept. And just as his wife had said, in fifteen days he died and descended to the under-world forever.

« »   « »   « »

Understandably, tales of the supernatural coming from the cities have an entirely different flavor. The next one could very likely be a story from anywhere, but since it happens to be a tale of old Mexico City, this is the most logical place to tell it. It is a chiller containing all the elements of which nightmares are made, and it explains how an alley called Callejon del Padre Lecuona got its name.

The Confession

In the early eighteen-hundreds Mexico City was still very much an old-world place where many of the dingy back streets and al-leys were as nameless as the anonymous poor who lived and died in them. Padre Lecuona was a priest who happened to be liked and respected by rich and poor alike. Consequently he was never at a loss for companionship when he had time for himself. One of his best friends was a well-to-do property-owner whose home was the scene of a friendly game of cards almost every night of the week. As a rule, if there were no more pressing matters, the padre could be counted on to join in the game.

One stormy winter evening as he hurried through the stinging rain on his way to the house of his friend, he heard a voice that sounded like an old woman calling out to him from behind. "Padre, please, wait!" He stopped, turned, and peered through the darkness just in time to see an elderly bent figure swathed in ragged clothing emerge from the shadows. "You must hear a confession. It is urgent, we haven't a moment to lose!"

"Surely one of the good padres from this district can attend to this matter," he suggested.

"Oh no, Padre Lecuona," declared the old woman. "You see, he asks for you—and you only."

Thoroughly mystified, for he had no idea of who the woman was, the priest agreed to accompany her at once. Instead of speaking, she gathered her rebozo about herself, turned, and began heading in the opposite direction, leading along a dark, narrow, and twisting street. Finally, turning into a nameless alley that looked more like a river of mud, she proceeded to a dilapidated, darkened house and stopped before the door. The wood was half rotten in spots, the doorknob and lock appeared to be solid rust, and the hinges seemed ready to fall apart.

As he followed her in through the door a wave of fetid, musty air assailed his face and filled his nostrils. Halting in his tracks as the old woman lit a candle, Padre Lecuona peered about as soon as its dimly flickering light sprang into life. A rat scurried into the shadows and disappeared. The room was bare and windowless, the only exit being the door through which they had come. A decaying chair sagged forlornly against the far wall, and in the corner opposite it was a wooden box with a broken wine bottle on it. Dust and cobwebs were everywhere, and in another corner of the room lay a filthy straw pallet on which was stretched the still, emaciated form of a man.

Taking the candle from his guide, the padre went over to the pallet, knelt down beside it, and gently lifted the threadbare blanket covering the man. But it was no living figure lying there. How could it be? The skin was brown and leathery, stretched tightly over the bones; the face, its lips already drawn back in the hideous grimace of death, was but a skull covered with skin and a few wisps of matted hair.

"Mother of God!" gasped Padre Lecuona, clutching his crucifix and turning to the old woman. "This is no living man!"

"Hear him, Padre, please!" she begged, "He will confess!"

Then gently she lifted the flickering candle from his hand and retreated to the far side of the room, leaving him in near darkness. Suddenly the priest heard what sounded like a feeble rustling sound at his feet. It was impossible—yet as he peered down through the gloom he could see the emaciated figure on the pallet slowly rise to a sitting position. The hollow, sunken eyes retained the unblinking corpselike stare, and it was impossible to see if the lips actually moved. But there was no mistaking the weak, sepulchral voice as it croaked out the familiar words, "Forgive me, Father, for I have sinned. . . ."

What followed was the most incredible confession that Padre Lecuona had ever heard in his life. Pronouncing each syllable with painstaking care, the mysterious penitent related how many years before he had died violently without having had the opportunity to receive the last rites. Now, he said, through divine intercession, he had been permitted to return long enough to make his confession.

Convinced that he was listening to the words of a dying madman, the priest listened patiently to the entire outpouring and when it was finished gave absolution. There was a deep sigh, a slight rustling, and again the figure on the pallet looked like a mummified corpse. Suddenly the room began to darken. Whirling about, Padre Lecuona saw at once that the candle, resting on the box in the corner, was sputtering its last, and the old woman was gone. The door to the street was still ajar, so without further hesitation he hurried out into the street and closed the door behind him. As he pulled it shut he could have sworn that there was a force on the other side pushing it from inside.

Looking about for the old woman, Padre Lecuona was mystified to find that the alley was deserted, and after peering about in the dark he tried to look inside again, but the door would no longer open. Sighing, he shook his head and decided that there was no point in his remaining here any longer, and he set out to join his friends, determined to return the following day.

The streets were like troughs of mud, and the torrential rain drenched his face, driven as it was by high winds. It was a relief finally to enter the house of his friend with its light, warmth, and good fellowship. As his friends greeted him, Padre Lecuona reached into his pocket. His face was still wet with rain, and he wanted to dry it with his handkerchief. Then he remembered that he had dropped it when he was hearing the confession of the dying man. It was a very valuable handkerchief of handmade linen and lace. Seeing what the situation was, the host immediately summoned one of his servants and dispatched him to the place where it had been lost in order to retrieve it. Now, ordinarily, the padre would have insisted that the matter be forgotten, but he was anxious to know more about the man who had just confessed.

His friends, now curious to hear what had detained him, asked the priest what had caused him to be so late, and as they sat down at the table for their game, he said with a sigh, "I suppose it wouldn't be a violation of the confessional to tell you what happened. You see, I was summoned to give comfort to a dying man, and the poor soul was so demented he thought that he had been dead for many years, and that he had been given divine permission to return and confess. But surely you don't want to hear any more of this dreary talk. Come, let us begin our game, my dear friends."

About an hour later the servant who had gone to fetch the handkerchief returned with a strange story. He said that he had gone to the house as directed and that he had knocked on the door for half an hour with no answer. Finally a man who lived across the alley came to him and told him that the house was vacant and had been for many years.

The story was especially interesting to the host, for when he heard the exact location of the house, he realized that it was his property. "This is very strange indeed," he said. "I know for a fact that place has been empty for years, for the entire building is involved in a legal action." He questioned whether or not Padre Lecuona had been certain of the address, and when the priest replied with absolute assurance, he too became anxious to go there the next day and find out what was going on. Perhaps, he suggested, someone had broken in and was occupying the premises illegally.

The following day Padre Lecuona and his friend met and went together to the house where the strange confession had been made the night before. It made no sense whatsoever. The door looked as if it had not been opened for years. Cobwebs were stretched over it, even over the keyhole. The padre agreed that something was terribly wrong, yet something told him he had to go inside. Perhaps he was the one who was losing his mind. His friend had no objections to opening the door, however, and after inserting the rusty old key in the lock and turning it with considerable difficulty, he pushed the door open. The ancient hinges scraped as the door swung inward. Then, as the two men crossed the threshold, the fetid, tomblike atmosphere of the place enveloped them, but as they glanced around the room it was plain to see that, aside from the dust of many years, it was completely empty. Padre Lecuona was bewildered. He was certain that this was the room in which he had given absolution to the dying madman the night before, yet he could see that there was nothing in it. But if only to convince himself he went over to the corner where he thought he recalled having seen the dying man on the pallet. Like the rest of the room, the corner was empty. But lying there on the floor was his handkerchief. He gasped as he picked it up. A sharp pain shot through his chest as he staggered back toward the door, a wave of dizziness coming over him.

"Are you all right, Padre?" exclaimed his friend, a note of alarm in his voice.

"Yes, yes," replied the priest as he retreated from the room and back out into the street. "I'll be all right in a moment."

But he was not all right. That night he went into a state of delirium for no apparent reason and from no visible cause. He remained that way for several days before he died. As for the house, it was finally demolished, and behind one of the walls a skeleton was found. Was there any connection, you ask? *Quien sabe?*—as they say in Mexico.

« »   « »   « »

Anthropologists specializing in folklore categorize the myths, legends, and tales they collect according to theme and motif. One that is especially prevalent in Latin America and the Caribbean involves supernatural entities guarding hidden treasure. This is not surprising, because after Columbus's voyages of discovery there came a succession of adventurers bent more on plunder than on exploration—a fact all too well documented by history. Although much of the gold, silver, and other treasure found its way back to Europe, a great deal did not. We know, of course, about the vast shipments that went to the bottom of the sea, because they are still being discovered by enterprising present-day adventurers who occasionally stumble on lost fortunes. What we know very little about are the legendary caches said to have been buried by pirates who never returned for them, and which are supposedly still where they were hidden, waiting to be retrieved.

The following narrative is not about buried pirate treasure, but about gold said to have been hidden in a cave by the conquistadors centuries ago. Chances are you have never heard this story unless you are familiar with the place where this gold is still said to be. Whether this gold really exists, whether its supernatural guardians are actually there, is hard to say. Perhaps it is just another of those tales that people tell to entertain visiting gringos. At any rate, here it is, exactly as it was recorded on tape by an American architect, a former Peace Corpsman who had recently served in Colombia. The region he describes, incidentally, is located roughly twenty miles northwest of Cali as the crow flies, but on land . . .

A group of us from the Peace Corps were together on a two-week assignment as part of our training. In a sense it was like an outing. We were to find a small farm village where we could get to know the people, get accustomed to the life they lived, the food they ate, and so forth. We started from a town called Dagua, which is about an hour-and-a-half ride from Cali up into the mountains. It's basically the way-station on the main trucking route between Cali and the city of Buenaventura on the coast. It also supplies a lot of food to both cities. Dagua itself has probably less than five thousand people.

There were four of us, actually, and our assignment was to go to a smaller town farther up in the mountains to live with some very poor farmers—*campesinos*. We were supposed to spend three or four weeks there, observing their life style, where they sold their goods, who they sold them to—generally the whole life style of the people. The idea was for us to see exactly how the Peace Corps could get involved in a helpful way. Now, the town itself was a rather new settlement, almost like the Old West settlements in the United States. The farmers who had lived in the region had been given land through land redistribution approximately ten years before. There were small parcels of property scattered around through the region, so each farmer might have three or four plots, each one very small, but altogether enough to eke out a bare existence.

We went into the town and met one farmer and his wife. Actually there was no place for us to stay because the houses are tiny little stone huts with thatched roofs, no plumbing, and we actually ended up sleeping in a one-room schoolhouse on the benches. We would spend most of the day wandering around the countryside. We began by bringing in our bedrolls and having toast and coffee, then going out and seeing people, before coming back in the evening. Of course, there was no electricity, so we'd sit around and talk till eight o'clock or so, playing guitars by candlelight, and getting to know the hosts. Actually, the whole idea of this was for us to become really proficient in Spanish.

One night after the first few days, while we were joking about gold and the Spanish conquistadors coming through, the old farmer sort of hinted that there was gold in the region. I shouldn't call him old; he was probably no more than forty-five or fifty, but thin and tough, gnarled and strong, a delightful man to talk to or to hear sing—and how he worked! Well, when we pressed him about the gold, he got very vague and then he wouldn't talk about it any more.

This went on for some time, and more and more we got the idea that up in the mountains, near one of his little parcels of land, which happened to be the center of a crater that he shared with another man, was a cave. Now in this cave was not necessarily so much gold, but old armor, and cutlases, and equipment left behind by the Spaniards. But the gold was there—at least, that was the impression we got. The trouble was that when he got to this point he was obviously not very anxious to say anything more about it. Well, all that did was arouse our curiosity. We wanted to go; we wanted to go and visit the cave! Finally he said it was haunted and that he didn't want to talk about it. His wife didn't like the idea of his talking about it either.

We kept thinking about this, naturally, so on our evenings between guitar songs we kept pressing him, and little by little more of the story came out. It seems that one of the village girls, actually the daughter of the mayor, had apparently found some of this gold a few years back. She had brought it home and hidden it under the floorboards in her house. The way they learned about it was that several days later they found her dead on the floor over the gold, and there was absolutely no apparent reason for her death. They put two and two together, after having noticed that the floorboards had been pried loose. What we didn't understand was why they connected her death with the gold, and that surprised him. He looked at us as if we should know. It wasn't good gold, he said; it was ungodly gold and gave off a gas of some kind, an odor that would kill anybody who took it. What impressed me was the matter-of-fact way in which he made the statement. It was *truth* as far as he was concerned. Well, after that we talked a little more about this, and it seemed that the only way anyone could get the gold without being killed was to take all of it. You had to take every gram! If you didn't take it all, the odor or the curse attached to it, if you prefer, would take your life.

Once we knew the story we mentioned it to some of the other

villagers we met—the town was very small, it didn't have more than fifteen men in it. Well, they were very upset. The very fact that we had even heard about this scared them, and they said that we should definitely stay away from that place, not go anywhere near it! We were respected gringo guests and liked by the people; we were having good times drinking *aguardiente* and beers and singing together; we shouldn't be playing around with gold.

But we kept badgering José, our host, to take us to this cave and show us the gold. There was another thing we wondered about. I remember saying, "Look, you're poor, why don't you go and take it all away?" And he said, "Oh, I tried to, a long time ago." Apparently, when he was a boy he had heard the legend and wanted to be daring or, as he put it, *macho*, so he and a couple of *compañeros* took two donkeys and went up to the mountain looking for the cave, and he said they saw it. Then he explained that there was another belief about the cave, that it was guarded by werewolves. They weren't like any werewolves I ever read about; they were what you might think of as wolflike spirits who would look at intruders and hypnotize whomever they saw—and I'm using the word "hypnotize" very freely here, because the Spanish expression he used was a little beyond me. But if you looked into their eyes you'd be paralyzed. He even gave me the proper stance to use up there. You had to keep your eyes averted, and you could get them out of your way if you hit them with a metal implement; a rake or a scythe would do. When we asked him what they looked like, he said he hadn't actually seen one. So now we were really curious because after all, he had gone right up to the cave! What had happened to prevent him from going in? He told us that apparently the donkeys saw the werewolves, because one of them dropped dead on the spot, and he said when that happened he knew everything he had heard about the cave and the gold was true, and that they so feared for their lives they ran away, and he finished by saying he had never gone back to the spot to this day.

You have to picture what the conditions were like when he told us about this. Visualize, if you can, darkness—absolute silence, like nothing you've ever experienced in North America, in a stone hut—sitting on a dirt floor or the beds. There weren't enough chairs. He was sitting on one chair and someone else on the other, tiny little chairs, like babies' chairs, because they're hand-carved, and there's not enough wood around there to make them too big. There was this utter darkness and the flickering candles, and he was explaining to us that this thing really scared him. The donkey died! He lost a donkey, and they just ran the hell out of there as fast as they could, and even after twenty or thirty years he hadn't gone near the spot. Not only that, he said that other people had had similar experiences.

But we wanted to see it. We used all our persuasive powers on him. "You don't have to go in yourself, José," we said. "We just want to go see the place." It was actually terribly unfair, because we were the gringos, we were the guests, and we were to be pleased. If you ask a South American where the laundry is, and he doesn't know, he's very likely to tell you, "A block over there," and point in a specific direction, just so you won't be disappointed.

So the next to the last day before we left, we finally persuaded him to take us up at least to see his farmland—the part that was near the cave. We got all set in our hiking boots, and our knapsacks and canteens, and we set off at about 4:30 in the morning. We had to get an early start because even though it wasn't a big mountain it was quite steep and strewn with rocks and wild-growing thorny plants. It took about three hours just to get up to the crater, and after we had walked around a while we asked José when we were going to see the cave. Then he led us around the mountain, pretty much in the general direction he had pointed out from below. But remember, there weren't any paths. We were climbing over rocks, under trees, and through underbrush. It was really a hard climb, but he kept leading us on around for a good two hours more.

By now we were all getting tired. Besides, as far as we could see, it seemed as though he was taking us away from the direction he had indicated from below when we were still on the way up. But he insisted that we were going in the right direction, and at about this point something came up that whetted our appetites even more than ever. He showed us the strangest rock any of us had ever seen. It was about three feet in diameter, black and smooth, and almost perfectly spherical in shape. It was cloven in two, probably by lightning. José told us that it had been discovered there some years ago, and then he showed us that if we got way down on the ground and looked along the cleavage at the right angle, so that the sun reflected in a certain way, there was a cross. It was in white, and although it looked at first as though it had been scratched in, when you looked more closely you could see that that wasn't the case at all. But it wasn't as though it had been chalked on either, because when you looked at it directly you couldn't see a thing, and if it had been chalked on, and had managed to withstand the elements for all that time, it would have been visible no matter which way you looked at it. As I said, though, you had to sight it at a very special angle. And to make the thing even more weird, it was a Maltese cross, not the sort of thing you were likely to find in South America, and it was big, about two feet across. Nobody knew where it came from; apparently archaeologists had come up and looked at it without being able to offer any explanation for it. Of course, I'm not so certain what he meant exactly by archaeologists. They could have been anyone from the university in Cali. So the thing was a complete mystery, and as I said, it just made us that much more anxious to see the cave.

We knew we were fairly close to it now, but it was also increasingly apparent that José was becoming more and more frightened. He seemed to become more anxious and he began driving us through what I can only say now makes me think of the briar patch in the old Br'er Rabbit story. It was just an immense undergrowth of gnarled branches and huge thorns— above you, below you, all around, up, down. We had to scramble along on our hands and knees, and José was going faster and faster, trying to get ahead of us, which of course he, knowing how to get through there, did without any great difficulty. Then all of a sudden he was down on the foot of the mountain, yelling at us to hurry out of the thicket because it was time to go home. Obviously we had gotten too close to the cave and he hadn't wanted us to get any nearer, so he got us down that mountain as fast as he could before it was too late. As far as he was concerned, our lives were really in jeopardy, and the only thing he could do was save us from ourselves.

He was very apologetic about it afterwards, he even seemed a little sad about it, but we knew by then that we had gone as far as we should—too far, probably—so from then until we left we didn't push the matter any further. All we knew was that everybody in the village was afraid of *something* up there. It had killed a girl, they all knew it had! Even the local priest, who was dead against what he regarded as foolish local superstitions, acknowledged the presence of something unknown and incredibly evil up there, an evil that had to be avoided at all costs.

« »   « »   « »

Remote as the mountains of Colombia may seem, they are practically next door compared to the legendary islands of the South Pacific. And certainly no tour of the supernatural could be complete without at least a glimpse of the other world of Polynesia.

The Maori of New Zealand and other Pacific Islands have as rich a supernatural tradition as any people on earth. It is such a beautiful tradition that in many ways it seems a shame that they had to be enveloped by the modern world. When the stars guided their ancestors across the waters of the ocean they were not just bright points in the skies, but heavenly bodies with which the great navigators had personal relationships. The Maori had similar relationships with the rest of nature as well. Sharks and whales were their friends; mountains sent messages for them via clouds and thunder; birds, too, served as messengers from time to time. But most wonderful of all were the deeds of protective atuas or deities, the appearances of wairuas or souls of living and dead, who were not feared but welcomed, and, of course, the skills of the tohungas, or priests.

Although we think of the Maori tohunga essentially as a priest, traditionally he was far more than that. The word means "expert," and in addition to the duties associated with religion, he was also a magician, an astrologer, a historian, a poet, and when necessary a warrior. He was also a navigator and a physician. To give an inkling of how superb their knowledge of astronomy was, consider this excerpt from the teachings of the Hawaii tohungas: "If you sail for the Kahiki [Tahiti] groups you will discover new constellations and strange stars over the deep ocean. When you arrive at the Piko o Wakea [the Fquatorial regions] you will lose sight of Hokupaa [the North Star], and then Newe, the Southern Cross, will be the southern guiding star, and the constellation of Humu will stand as a guide above you." The latter referred to the constellation Aquila.

The Tohungas, of course, were not the only ones among the Maori who possessed great skills, especially in the case of the supernatural. The following story, which appeared in the *Polynesian Journal*,* gives a striking example of this fact.

> . . . Many years ago a Yankee whaling vessel called in at the island (Ahuahu, an earlier name of Mangaia, the most easterly island of the Cook group), and a Portuguese harpooner, who had trouble with the captain, deserted and hid himself in the bush. The people had taken a fancy to him and refused to give him up, so finally the captain was obliged to sail without the man. From all accounts, this harpooner must have been a good chap; when he proved that he was no common white waster, the chief gave him a bit of land, and a girl of a good family for a wife. . . . I think it was tools he needed, or some sort of gear for his house he was building; at any rate, when another whaler touched, he told his wife that he was going on a voyage to earn some money, and that he might be gone a year. There was a kind of agreement current in the Pacific, in those days, whereby a whaling captain promised to land a man at the point where he had signed him on. Well, the harpooner sailed away, and, as might have been expected, his wife never saw him again; but here comes the odd part of the story. The deserted wife, like so many of the Ahuahu women, had an ancestor who kept her in touch with current events. Being particularly fond of her husband, she indulged in a trance, from time to time, to keep herself informed as to his welfare. Several months after his departure the tragedy occurred—described in detail by the obliging and sym-

pathetic dweller in the marae. It was a kind of vision, as told to me, singularly vivid for an effort of pure imagination—the open Pacific heaving gently, and supplied by a light air; two boats from rival vessels pursuing the same whale; the Portuguese harpooner, standing in the bows of one, erect and intent upon his chase, his iron the first by a second of time to strike. Then came a glimpse of the two boats foaming side by side in the wake of the whale; the beginning of the dispute; the lancing and death-flurry of an old bull sperm; the rising anger of the two harpooners as the boats rocked gently beside the floating carcass; the treacherous thrust; the long red blade of the lance standing out between the shoulders of the Portuguese.

The woman awoke from her trance with a cry of anguish: her husband was dead—she set up a widow's tangi [lamentation]. One might have thought it an excellent tale, concocted to save the face of a deserted wife, if the same vessel had not called at Ahuahu within a year, to bring the news of the husband's death under the exact circumstances of the vision.

The widow's story illustrates how ordinary Maori, not necessarily concerned primarily with supernatural affairs are perfectly at ease in the supernatural milieu. There are innumerable Maori stories about living persons whose wairuas leave their bodies from time to time, sometimes performing errands that could not be undertaken in the flesh, other times communicating with the wairuas of the deceased or with various supernatural beings. But despite the psychic powers attributed to the Maori in general, they seem pale when compared to the awesome gifts of the tohungas.

Maori tradition and history abounds with accounts of tohungas' deeds. These range all the way from fire-walking, which has been witnessed by countless Europeans and other foreigners, to the striking dead of a bird in flight merely by the recitation of a specific karakia, or incantation. It is too bad that most Europeans who visited the Maori in the days before they were so extensively converted to Christianity refused to accept what they were told and sometimes even observed themselves. This narrow-mindedness prevented them from conducting investigations that might have led to some fascinating answers.

Illustrative of this is the anecdote of a missionary's encounter with an old tohunga of his aquaintance some time before the turn of the century. The tohunga's name was Tuhoto, and he lived on the island of Mokoia. The missionary was determined to convert the old man for purely practical reasons. He had an immense following among his people, and if he were to embrace Christianity it would be a simple matter to persuade them to abandon their old faith as well. The missionary made a special trip to Mokoia and devoted his maximum efforts to the cause of converting Tuhoto. At last the tohunga looked the missionary in the eye and said, "If you can do this, I will become a convert." With that he picked up a dried and withered leaf from a ti plant, held it out at arm's length, and uttered a short karakia. Before the very eyes of the missionary the leaf turned green and fresh, as if it had just been plucked. Realizing that he was no match for Tuhoto, he left the island, declaring afterward that what he had seen was nothing more than a trick performed by means of mass hypnotism. Perhaps it was just that, but regardless of what it was, the thought that lingers is this: what a beautiful world we would be living in if somehow we had been converted to the faith of the Maori instead of they to ours.

An even more fabulous story concerning a tohunga is the account of adventures experienced by Te Kere, a tohunga of legendary stature, who died in 1901 at the age of one hundred. His full name was Te Kere-ngatai-erua, and he was said to be descended from a union between a human being and an atua.

When he was a young man, Te Kere decided that he wanted to visit some of the strange, far-away places he had heard pakehas, or strangers, describe. So he shipped out on a whaler in order to fulfill that wish. Unfortunately the voyage proved to be a disastrous one, for because of adverse winds, bad weather, and poor hunting, the crew finally found itself on the verge of starvation.

The only man in the crew with whom Te Kere had managed to make friends was the cook, by virtue of the fact that he spoke a little Maori. One night the cook came to Te Kere in a state of nervous agitation. In whispered tones he told the young man that his life was in danger. In order to keep from starving, the white men were going to kill him and eat him. Te Kere was so terrified that he locked himself up in his cabin and wept tears of bitter despair. To make matters worse, he could hear the sounds of the pakeha sailors waiting outside his door to seize him the moment he came out.

Suddenly, as he had finally begun to abandon hope for himself, he became aware that his cabin was becoming flooded with light. An atua appeared and ordered him to leave the cabin and go up on deck. The atua unlocked the door and caused all the pakeha sailors to fall into a deep sleep, except for the cook who had been Te Kere's friend. For having been so kind to him, Te Kere offered the man all his money, which he refused, although he was finally prevailed upon to accept five pounds. This sum he tied to an oar with a scarf as he told Te Kere to tie the rest around his waist, which the youth did.

When this was done the atua told Te Kere to jump overboard, upon which the cook threw the oar with the five pounds tied to it in after him. Seizing it, Te Kere managed to keep afloat.

When morning came, Te Kere could see nothing but open sea, and he was concerned, for the gold he carried in his pockets was weighing him down. Taking off his trousers, he let them sink under the water. Soon after this a taniwha (or benevolent sea-monster) was sent to him by the atua, and it carried Te Kere to a sacred rock known as Motu-kakaho, which, though in the middle of the salt sea, was surrounded with fresh water.

The next day some Ngapuhi Maoris who had been out on an all-night fishing expedition found Te Kere's trousers and the oar floating in the water. Not long after that they came near to the rock where the taniwha had placed him, and when he saw them he waved his shirt to attract their attention. At first they did not want to go near for fear of violating the sanctity of the place, but Te Kere finally prevailed upon them to rescue him, and they did, at which time he told them everything that had happened to him.

Writing in the *Polynesian Journal* in 1937, a man who had known Te Kere, T. W. Downes, wrote:

> . . . As a lad I remember three of his meeting houses, each said to have been ninety-nine feet long; one was at Awakino, another at Awahuri, and the third at Kakariki. Te Kere's atua still at times reveals himself to some members of the family. When Raungaiti died about 1923, he had previously buried Te Kere's bible and a manuscript book of whakapapa (genealogies). His daughter Karanga was anxious to find these, and one night the atua appeared before her in the form of a kawau [a kind of small cormorant that is crested during the mating season] and opened its wings; on these wings, as on the pages of an open book, she saw Te Kere's name written. The kawau then flew to a certain tree, and the next day, by digging under this tree, the books were found.

The mention of genealogies is quite important, for among the Maori the keeping of detailed family records going back to distant times is a very important matter. The custom of reciting whakapapa to one another in groups is a social tradition that has enabled historians to piece together a great deal of information about the Maori past. It also plays a part in the following story about a particular Maori ghost.

Early in the last century a chief of the Ngati-kahungunu people of the northeast coast of New Zealand was paying a visit to the Ngati-awa of Taranaki on the northwest coast.

During his visit a Ngati-awa warrior assaulted a woman of the tribe and murdered her husband. It was not the first violent crime he had committed against his own people, so they decreed that he must die. Nothing was done, however, to carry out this sentence of death because everyone was afraid of him. Consequently he became worse than ever insofar as his general behavior was concerned.

Upon learning of this situation the visiting chief, who had recently bought a new gun, offered to carry out the execution on behalf of the tribe, an offer that was readily accepted with profound relief.

That might have been the end of the matter, for everyone was glad to be rid of the scoundrel—everyone except for one person, a woman who had been in love with him. She immediately began making trouble, demanding to know what right a stranger had to slay a Ngati-awa. It had been none of his affair. She admitted that the dead man had deserved death, and that had he been killed by a member of his own people it would have been tika, or correct.

Little by little she swung the Ngati-awa around to her way of thinking, and they decided to take the life of the man who had killed the warrior for them. They were happy that he had done it, but this involved a matter of deep principle. The Ngati-kahungunu chief, however, got wind of their talk and, deciding to let discretion be the better part of valor in this instance, he slipped away without offering any farewells. A war party went after him, but he had covered his tracks well and was not seen by them again.

Afterward at a tribal gathering it was decided that a kanga, or curse, be laid on this man and his family. Its terms were simple. The first of his descendants to visit Taranaki would die.

In time almost everyone forgot about the kanga. This means nothing, however, for it is said by the Maori that a kanga never dies. It may slumber for many years, but a single word can awaken it.

Nearly a century later a great-granddaughter of the chief upon whom the kanga had been laid was invited to an important hui, or social gathering, being given by a group of Ngati-awa at Taranaki. All might have gone smoothly, for everyone was having a wonderful time at the hui, but one day before her visit was over, she was sitting around with a group of women, reciting whaka-papa. When the young woman had finished her recitation, an old woman with a long memory recalled the kanga and jumped to her feet. "What right have you to come here, since the kanga on your family has never been lifted?" she demanded. "You have dared to come, but you will never leave!"

Despite the fact that she knew nothing of the kanga, she was dead within two weeks. Some were skeptical and suggested that she had been poisoned, for she experienced severe abdominal pains when she died. Others, however, were certain that it was the kanga that had killed her.

« »   « »   « »

This was not the last of her, though, for she had been very happily married to a man who lived at Anatohia Bay. Shortly after her death in 1901 her wairua was seen returning to the house by many different people. In the year 1917, a European surveyor, who knew nothing of her story, happened to be a guest in that house, and on one rainy day he saw an unfamiliar young Maori woman emerge from the room opposite that in which he was staying. The room she left, by the way, was a kind of trophy room in which the family kept their most valued heirlooms and other precious possessions. It should also be mentioned that in the room, occupying a place of honor, was a beautiful feather cloak, to which the man assumed was attached a story.

On the surface there was nothing unusual in his seeing a visitor in the house, but he had never seen this young woman before, and he casually asked his hostess who she was when she did not turn up for lunch.

"Oh, we have no visitors today," she said. "It is much too wet to travel."

"But I know I saw her," he insisted. "She was a young Maori woman, and she came out of the mat room across from my room, then she turned and headed for the kitchen."

"Oh, many people have seen her," replied the hostess calmly, "but she never comes to the kitchen."

The reply struck him as rather odd, but he said nothing more about the matter at the time. Later in the afternoon his hostess took out a photograph and showed it to him, asking him if he recognized it. At first he did not, but on second glance he saw that it was a picture of the young woman he had seen coming from the mat room, and he said so. That was when the hostess told him the whole story, explaining that the feathered cloak had belonged to the girl in the picture, and that she was the victim of the kanga laid upon her great-grandfather so long ago.

Rather than leave the Maori with recollections of a curse, we shall bid them farewell on another note with a verbatim account by a New Zealander named F. E. Maning, who relates an intensely emotional experience he had in the eighteen-sixties. The pakeha referred to in the text, by the way, is Maning himself.

A young chief who had been very popular and greatly respected in his tribe had been killed in battle; and, at the request of several of his nearest friends, the tohunga had promised on a certain night to call up his spirit to speak to them, and answer certain questions they wished to put. The priest was to come to the village of the relations, and the interview was to take place in a large house common to all the population. This young man had been a great friend of mine; and so, the day before the event, I was sent for by his relations, and told that there was an opportunity to converse with my friend once more. I was not much inclined to bear a part in such outrageous mummery, but curiosity caused me to go. Now it is necessary to remark that this young man was in advance of his times and people in many respects. He was the first of his tribe who could read and write;

and, amongst other unusual things for a native to do, he kept a register of deaths and births and a journal of any remarkable event which happened in the tribe. Now, this book was lost. No one could find it, although his friends had searched unceasingly for it, as it contained many matters of interest, and also they wished to preserve it for his sake. I also wished to get it, and had often inquired if it had been found, but had always been answered in the negative. The appointed time came, and at night we all met the priest in the large house I have mentioned. Fires were lit, which gave an uncertain flickering light. The priest retired to the darkest corner. All was expectation, and the silence was only broken by the sobbing of the sister, and other female relations of the dead man. They seemed to be, and indeed were, in an agony of excitement, agitation, and grief. This state of things continued for a long time, and I began to feel in a way surprising to myself, as if there was something real in the matter. The heartbreaking sobs of the women, and the grave and solemn silence of the men, convinced me that to them at least, this was a serious matter. I saw the brother of the dead man now and then wiping the tears in silence from his eyes. I wished I had not come, for I felt that any unintentional symptom of incredulity on my part would shock and hurt the feelings of my friends extremely; and yet, whilst feeling thus, I felt myself more and more near to believing in the deception to be practiced. The real grief, and also the general undoubting faith, in all around me, had this effect. We were all seated on the rush-strewn floor; about thirty persons. The door was shut; the fire had burnt down, leaving nothing but glowing charcoal. The room was oppressively hot. The light was little better than darkness; and the part of the room in which the tohunga sat was now in perfect darkness. Suddenly, without the slightest warning, a voice came out of the darkness.

"Salutation!—salutation to you all!—salutation! salutation to you, my tribe!—family, I salute you!—friends, I salute you;—friend, my pakeha friend, I salute you."

The high-handed daring imposture was successful; our feelings were taken by storm. A cry expressive of affection and despair, such as was not good to hear, came from the sister of the dead chief, a fine, stately, and really handsome woman of about five and twenty. She was rushing with both arms extended into the dark, in the direction from whence the voice came. She was instantly seized round the waist and restrained by her brother by main force, till, moaning and fainting, she lay still on the ground. At the same instant another female voice was heard from a young girl who was held by the wrists by two young men, her brothers.

"Is it you?—is it you? *truly* is it you?—aue! aue!—they hold me, they restrain me; wonder not that I have not followed you; they restrain me, they watch me, but I go to you. The sun shall not rise, the sun shall not rise, aue! aue!"

Here she fell insensible on the rush floor, and with the sister was carried out. The remaining women were all weeping and exclaiming, but were silenced by the men, who were themselves nearly as much excited, though not so clamorous. I, however, did notice two old men, who sat close to me, were not in the slightest degree moved in any way, though they did not seem at all incredulous, but quite the contrary. The spirit spoke again.

"Speak to me, the tribe!—speak to me, the family!—speak to me, the pakeha!"

The "pakeha," however, was not at the moment inclined for conversation. The deep distress of the two women, the evident belief of all around him of the presence of the spirit, the "darkness visible," the novelty of the scene, gave rise to a state of feeling not favorable to the conversational powers. Besides, I felt reluctant to give too much apparent credence to an imposture, which at the very same time, by some strange impulse, I felt half ready to give way to.

At last the brother spoke—"How is it with you?—is it well with you in *that* country?"

The answer came—(the voice, it is to be remembered, was not the voice of the tohunga, but a strange melancholy sound, like the sound of the wind blowing into a hollow vessel)—"It is well with me—my place is a good place."

The brother spoke again—"Have you seen——, and——?" (I forget the names mentioned).

"Yes, they are all with me."

A woman's voice from another part of the room anxiously cried out—"Have you seen my sister?"

"Yes, I have seen her."

"Tell her my love is great towards her and never will cease."

"Yes, I will tell."

Here the woman burst into tears and the pakeha felt a strange swelling of the chest, which he could in no way account for.

The spirit spoke again. "Give my large tame pig to the priest [the pakeha was disenchanted at once], and my double-gun."

Here the brother interrupted—"Your gun is a manatunga [keepsake], I shall keep it."

He is also disenchanted, thought I, but I was mistaken. He believed, but wished to keep the gun his brother had carried so long. An idea now struck me that I could expose the imposture without showing palpable disbelief.

"We cannot find your book," said I. "Where have you concealed it?"

The answer instantly came, "I concealed it between the tahuhu [ridgepole of a house] and the thatch, straight over as you go in at the door."

Here the brother rushed out—all was silence till his return. In five minutes he came back *with the book in his hand.*

I was beaten, but made another effort. "What have you written in that book?" said I.

"A great many things."

"Tell me some of them."

"Which of them?"

"Any of them."

"You are seeking for some information, what do you want to know? I will tell you." Then suddenly—"Farewell, O tribe! farewell, my family, I go!"

Here a general and impressive cry of "Farewell" arose from everyone in the house.

"Farewell," again cried the spirit, *from deep beneath the ground!* "Farewell," again *from high in the air!* "Farewell," once more came moaning through the distant darkness of the night. "Farewell!"

I was for a moment stunned. The deception was perfect. There was a dead silence—at last. "A ventriloquist," said I!—"or —or—*perhaps* the devil."

I was fagged and confused. It was past midnight; the company broke up, and I went to a house where a bed had been prepared for me. I wished to be quiet and alone; but it was fated there should be little quiet that night. I was just falling asleep, after having thought for some time on the extraordinary scenes I had witnessed, when I heard the report of a musket at some little distance, followed by the shouting of men and the screaming of women. Out I rushed. I had a presentiment of some horrible catastrophe. Men were running by, hastily armed. I could get no information, so went with the stream. There was a bright flame beginning to spring up at a short distance, and everyone appeared going in that direction. I was soon there. A house had been set on fire to make a light. Before another house, close at hand, a dense circle of human beings was formed. I pushed my way through, and then saw, by the light of the flaming house, a scene which is still fresh before me. There, in the veranda of the house, was an old gray-bearded man; he knelt upon one knee, and on the other he supported the dead body of the young girl who had said she would follow the spirit to the spirit land. The delicate-looking body from the waist upward was bare and bloody; the old man's right arm was under the neck, the lower part of his long gray beard was dabbled with blood, his left hand was twisting his matted hair; he did not weep, he *howled*, and the sound was that of a heathen despair, knowing no hope. The young girl had secretly procured a loaded musket, tied a loop for her foot to the trigger, placed the muzzle to her tender breast, and blown herself to shatters. And the old man was her father, and a tohunga. A calm voice now spoke close beside me. "She has followed her rangatira," it said. I looked round, and saw the famous tohunga of the night. . . .

This story is tragedy, or I don't know what tragedy is, and the more tragic because, in every particular, literally true, so if you cannot find some pity for the poor Maori girl who "followed her Lord to spirit land," I shall.

VI

*The Other Worlds
of the West*

In Western Europe, the Americas, and anywhere else predominantly Western in the cultural sense, there is still a lively interest in ghosts, haunts, disembodied spirits, and the occult in general. But aside from the occasional eccentric among us who is unable to account for seemingly inexplicable phenomena, there are few who devote much serious attention to such subjects as vampirism, lycanthropy, or demonology. Yet they play so significant a part in our heritage that they have left an indelible imprint on much of our personalities, and certainly upon our literature.

As might be expected, our Western concepts of the vampire, the werewolf, and the demon are directly related to older beliefs handed down and passed on from other peoples. Changes and adaptations were influenced by such mundane factors as geography, climate, flora, and fauna. We could hardly expect Europeans to evolve any complex beliefs related to such animals as hyenas, tigers, or leopards, yet where wolves were a common enemy it stood to reason that supernatural beliefs about them would flourish. As for vampires and demons, depending on similar variables of time, place, and physical conditions, a wide spectrum of fascinating beliefs was born, nurtured, and able to grow and spread like mushrooms, always changing, adapting, and becoming enriched as centuries passed. Invariably these beliefs were inextricably enmeshed with religion. Thus, in those countries where Roman Catholicism was dominant, Roman Catholic teachings and thought became the matrix for folklore and superstition, whether or not the Church gave tacit approval. On the other hand, where the Orthodox Church held sway, its practices formed the foundations. To a lesser degree even a third body of beliefs arose among European Jews, beliefs that were a curious blend of ancient demonology, local folklore, and orthodox Christianity.

Since this intriguing potpourri of beliefs that often clashed, sometimes agreed, and always fomented hurricanes of controversy constitutes the rock foundation of all modern supernatural fiction, it deserves some attention here. Besides, in more cases than not we find in documented fact more hair-raising narratives than in most fiction, and more startling situations than in the majority of dramas.

Take the case of the real-life Dracula. Yes, there really was such a person, although there was hardly anything supernatural about him. He was Vlad IV, the Voivode, or Governor of Walachia, a medieval principality located in what is today southern Rumania. He inherited his voivodeship in the year 1455, when his father was overthrown by the Turks, who installed him as their puppet ruler. Among other things, he was a knight of the Order of the Dragon, an order founded in 1408 by King Sigismund of Hungary, whose official insignia was a double gold chain with a coiled dragon. Now, according to the law, all members of the order were forbidden to appear in public without wearing their dragon emblems on pain of being fined a sum equivalent to the cost of five masses. The significance of all this becomes more apparent when we learn that Vlad very rapidly developed into what could best be described as a spiritual ancestor of Hitler, Stalin, and all other genocidal butchers to follow. His favorite method of dealing with those who displeased him gave rise to the name bestowed upon him by historians—Vlad the Impaler.

As proof of the fact that faces often belie personalities, his portrait, which hangs in the Hungarian National Museum, reveals a handsome man; on the other hand, the artist who painted it may have feared to portray his subject otherwise. The *Encyclopedia Britannica* says of him: "The stories of his savage ferocity exceed belief. He is said to have feasted amongst his impaled victims." A more tolerant and recent writer, Stephen Csabai, declared:

> How much should be discounted, and how much believed, in these chronicles and chap books is difficult to determine. For the figure

of Dracula becomes more and more terrible, and the detailed accounts of his misdeeds more and more circumstantial. The ingenuity of his tortures was on a level with that of the old kings of Persia; without going into all the horrors that he is supposed to have perpetrated, it may be said that one receives the impression of a human monster, taking actual pleasure in the infliction of the most appalling tortures on people who, in most cases, seem to have done nothing to merit them. Whether he did actually wash his hands in blood before a meal as is recounted; whether he really "had innumerable persons chopped up like cabbage," shot out of guns, or torn to pieces by hounds, we need not perhaps inquire. In the absence of a more serious charge, it is related that he once impaled a peasant's wife because she had made her husband's shirt too short.

The name Dracula actually evolved quite simply. Early in Vlad's career, his unfortunate subjects began calling him Dracul, a dialect word used as synonymous with devil or dragon, stemming, of course, from the Latin *draco*—and the emblem of the knightly order to which he belonged. In all probability, then, when British novelist Bram Stoker sought a name for the dreadful vampire count in his classic novel, he looked for one that had the most horrible possible reputation attached to it, and certainly he couldn't have made a better choice.

As for the supernatural aspect of the vampire as we think of it, there are a number of facets. For those who adhered to the Eastern Orthodox Church there was no problem insofar as belief was concerned. The vampire, or vrykolakas (as it is still called in Greek) came into being via several routes. The most innocent road to vampirism involved being the victim of a curse, i.e., "May the earth not receive you!" The result of such a curse, especially efficacious if hurled by a priest, was that after death its recipient would not decay in the grave, thereby leaving the biblical injunction, "Dust to dust," unfulfilled. Red-haired individuals were also regarded as potential candidates for the fate of vampire, for no other reason than that their coloring was the same as that held by tradition to be Judas Iscariot's. Still another category of unwitting vampire was made up of those born on Christmas Day. Referred to as kallicantzaros, they were believed to commit certain vampirish deeds even during their lifetimes, and the rationale behind this belief was that they were being punished because their mothers had had the temerity to conceive on the same day as the Virgin Mary. In addition to all of the preceding, virtually anyone who had lived the life of a heretic or general evil-doer was a potential vampire after death.

One of the earliest descriptions of the Greek vampire was written by a Vatican scholar and theologian named Leone Allacci, who published a treatise on Greece in the year 1645, in which he declared, "No plague more terrible or more harmful to man can well be thought of or conceived. The name has been given him from a vile filth. βουρκα means black mud, not any kind of mud, but feculent mud that is slimy and oozing with excrementious sewerage so that it exhales a most noisome stench. λακκοs is a ditch or cloaca in which foulness of this kind collects and reeks amain."

The Roman Catholic Church held views on bodily decomposition that were diametrically opposite to those of the Greek Orthodox Church. Vatican theologians contended that only the saintly escaped bodily decay after death. This created a problem, for there had to be an explanation for the vampire, who, though far from being a saint, nevertheless managed to avoid the ravages of decay. Dom Calmet even went so far as to make reference to the Greek ideas on the subject, saying, "The belief of modern Greeks [i.e., eighteenth-century Greeks], who will have it that the bodies of the excommunicated do not decay in their tombs or graves, is an opinion which has no foundation, either in antiquity, in good theology, or even history. The idea seems to have been invented by the modern Greek schismatics, only to authorize and confirm them in their separation from the church of Rome."

Such opinions, however, still did not explain vampires within the framework of Catholic teaching. Scholars therefore conducted massive investigations and finally arrived at the only possible satisfactory answer. Basing their conclusions upon statements made by Saint Thomas Aquinas, they declared that the Devil was quite capable of forming bodies out of thin air and then giving them any shape or form he chose. This clearly established vampires as the handiwork of the Evil One. Taking the subject one step further within the framework of Catholic teaching, theologians easily settled the matter once and for all. Since nothing could exist without the permission of God, then vampires obviously existed with His permission. The only way to eliminate vampires, then, was to apply to Heaven for the withdrawal of that permission. There were regular methods of bringing this about, the easiest being the proper performance of prescribed ceremonies such as exorcisms, and the proper application of holy symbols such as crucifixes.

What is especially interesting in retrospect is the fact that epidemics of vampirism were reported more often during times of plague than in ordinary times. When we consider the traditional use of garlic as a protection against vampires, and the extraordinary stench that would arise during plague years as a result of the abnormal quantity of unburied bodies that were present, it is easy for us to get some insight into some of the origins of these beliefs.

Although most of the best-known accounts of vampirism are strictly fictional, there are those which, when originally set down on paper, were reported as actuality. The following extract is just such an account. It describes in detail two cases as related by a man named Weinrichius, one firsthand, and the other once or twice removed. What makes it interesting, however, is that it is one of the earliest of such accounts in English, coming from the pen of the seventeenth-century Cambridge Platonist philosopher Henry More. Specifically, it is from his book *An Antidote against Atheism*, published in 1653.

A certain Shoemaker in one of the chief Towns of *Silesia*, in the year 1591, *September* 20, on a Friday betimes in the morning, in the further part of his house, where there was adjoining a little Garden, cut his own throat with his Shoemaker's knife. The Family, to cover the foulness of the fact, and that no disgrace might come upon his Widow, gave out that he died of an Apoplexy, declined all visits of friends and neighbours, in the meantime got him washed, and laid Linens so handsomely about him, that even they that saw him afterwards, as the Parson, and some others, had not the least Suspicion but that he did die of that disease; and so he had an honest Burial, with a funeral Sermon, and other circumstances becoming one of his rank and reputation. Six weeks had not past, but so strong a rumour broke out, that he had not died of any disease, but had laid violent hands upon himself, that the Magistracy of the place could not but bring all those that had seen the corps, to a strict examination. They shuffled off the matter as well as they could at first, with many fair Apologies, in behalf of the deceased, to remove all suspicion of so heinous an act: but it being pressed more home to their Conscience, at last they confessed he died a violent death, but desired their favour and clemency to his widow and children, who were in no fault; adding also, that it was certain but that he might be slain by some external mishap, or, if by himself, in some irresistable fit of phrency or madness.

Hereupon the Councel deliberate what is to be done. Which the Widow hearing, and fearing that they might be determining something that would be harsh, and to the discredit of her Husband, and herself, also being animated thereto by some busie bodies, makes a great complaint against those that raised these reports of her Husband, and resolved to follow the Law upon them, earnestly contending that there was no reason, upon mere rumours and idle defamations of malevolent people, that her Husband's body should be digged up, or dealt with as if he had been either *Magician*, or *Self-murtherer*. Which boldness and pertinacity of the woman, though after the confession of the fact, did in some measure work upon the Council, and put them to a stand.

But while these things are in agitation, to the astonishment of the inhabitants of the place, there appears a *Spectrum* in the exact shape and habit of the deceased, and that not only in the night, but at mid-day. Those that were asleep it terrified with horrible visions; those that were waking it would strike, pull, or press, lying heavy upon them like an *Ephialtes* [from the Greek, meaning nightmare]: so that there were perpetual complaints every morning of their last night's rest through the whole Town. But the more freaks this *Spectrum* play'd, the more diligent were the friends of the deceased to suppress the rumours of them, or at least to hinder the effects of those rumours; and therefore made their addresses to the President, complaining how unjust a thing it was, that so much credit should be given to idle reports and blind suspicions, and therefore beseech'd him that he would hinder the Council from digging up the corpse of the deceased, and from all ignominious usage of him: adding also, that they intended to appeal to the Emperour's Court, that their Wisdoms might decide the Controversy, than that the cause should be determined from the light conjectures of malicious men.

But while by this means the business was still protracted, there were such stirs and tumults all over the Town, that they are hardly to be described. For no sooner did the Sun hide his head, but this *Spectrum* would be sure to appear, so that every body was fain to look about him, and stand upon his guard, which was a sore trouble to those whom the Labours of the Day made more sensible of the want of rest in the night. For this terrible *Apparrition* would sometimes stand by their bed-sides, sometimes cast itself upon the midst of their beds, would lie close to them, would miserably suffocate them, and would so strike them and pinch them, that not only blue marks, but plain impressions of his fingers would be upon sundry parts of their bodies in the morning. Nay, such was the violence and impetuousness of this Ghost, that when men forsook their beds, and kept their dining-rooms, with Candles lighted, and many of them in company together, the better to secure themselves from fear and disturbance; yet he would then appear to them, and have a bout with some of them, notwithstanding all this provision against it. In brief, he was so troublesome, that the people were ready to forsake their houses, and seek other dwellings, and the Magistrates so awakened at the perpetual complaints of them, that at last they resolved, the President agreeing thereto, to dig up the Body.

He had lain in the ground near eight months, *viz.* from *Sept. 22, 1591*, to *April 18, 1592*. When he was digged up, which was in the presence of the Magistracy of the Town, his body was found entire, not at all putrid, no ill smell about him, saving the mustiness of the Grave-cloaths, his joints limber and flexible, as in those that are alive, his skin only flaccid, but a more flesh grown in the room of it, the wound of his throat gaping, but no gear nor corruption in it; there was also observed a Magical mark in the great toe of his right foot, *viz.* an Excrescency in the form of a Rose. His body was kept out of the earth from *April 18*, to the *24th*, at what time many both of the same time and others came daily to view him. These unquiet stirs did not cease for all this, which they after attempted to appease, by burying the corpse under the Gallows, but in vain; for they were as much as ever, if not more, he now not sparing his own Family: insomuch that his Widow at last went her self to the Magistrate, and told him, that she should by no longer against it, if they thought fit to fall upon some course of more strict proceedings touching her Husband.

Wherefore the seventh of *May* he was again digged up, and it was observable, that he was grown more sensibly fleshy since his last interment. To be short, they cut off the Head, Arms, and Legs of the Corps, and opening his Back, took out his Heart, which was as fresh and intire as in a Calf new kill'd. These together with his Body, they put on a pile of wood, and burnt them to Ashes, which they carefully sweeping together, and putting into a Sack (that none might get them for wicked uses) poured them into the River, after which the Spectrum was never seen more.

As it also happen'd in his Maid that dy'd after him, who appeared within eight days after her death, to her fellow servant and lay so heavy upon her, that she brought upon her a great swelling of the eyes. She so grievously handled a Child in the cradle, that if the Nurse had not come to his help, he had been quite spoil'd; but she crossing her self, and calling upon the Name of *Jesus*, the Spectre vanished. The next night she appeared in the shape of an *Hen*, which, when one of the Maids of the house took to be so indeed, and followed her, the Hen grew into an immense bigness, and presently caught the Maid by the throat, and made it swell, so that she could neither eat nor drink of a good while after.

She continued these stirs for a whole month, slapping some so smartly, that the stroke were heard of them that stood by, pulling the bed also from under others, and appearing sometime in one shape, sometimes in another, as of a Woman, of a Dog, of a Cat, and of a Goat. But at last her body being digged up and burnt, the Apparition was never seen more.

These things being done at *Breslaw* in *Silesia*, where this *Weinrichius* then lived, which makes the Narration more considerable. This concealing the name of the parties, I conceive, was in way of civility to his deceased Towns-man, his Towns-man's Widow, and their Family.

The other story he sets down he is not the first Pen-man of (though the things were done in his time, and, as I conceive, some while after what was above related, as a passage in the Narration seems to intimate) but he transcrib'd it from one that not only dwelt in the place, but was often infested with the noisom occursions of that troublesome *Ghost*, that did so much mischief to the place where he dwelt. The Relation is somewhat large. I shall bring it into as narrow compass as I can.

Johannes Cuntius, a Citizen of *Pentsch* in *Silesia*, near sixty years of age, and one of the *Aldermen* of the town, very fair in his carriage, and unblameable, to men's thinking, in the whole course of his life, having been sent to the *Mayor's* house (as being a very understanding man, and dexterous at the dispatch of businesses) to end some controversies concerning certain Waggoners, and a Merchant of *Pannonia* having made an end of those affairs, is invited by the *Mayor* to Supper: he gets leave first to go home to order some businesses, leaving this sentence behind him, *It's good to be merry while we may, for mischiefs grow up fast enough daily.*

This *Cuntius* kept five lusty geldings in his Stable, one whereof he commanded to be brought out, and his shoe being loose, had him ty'd to the next post: his Master with a Servant busied themselves to take up his leg to look on his hoof, the Horse being mad and mettlesome, struck them both down; but *Cuntius* received the greatest share of the blow: one that stood next by help'd them both up again. *Cuntius* no sooner was up and came to him self, but cry'd out, *Wo is me, how do I burn and am all on a fire!* which he often repeated. But the parts he complain'd of most, the Women being put out of the room, when they were searched, no appearance of any stroke or hurt was found upon them. To be short, he fell downright sick, and grievously afflicted in Mind, loudly complaining that his Sins were such, that they were utterly unpardonable, and that the least part of them were bigger than all the Sins of the World besides; but would have no Divine come to him, nor did particularly confess them to any. Several rumours indeed there were that once he had sold one of his Sons, but when, and to whom, it was uncertain; and that he had made a Contract with the Devil, and the like. But it was observed, and known for certain, that he had grown beyond all expectation rich, and that four days before this mischance, he being witness to a Child, said, that that was the last he should be ever witness to.

The night he dy'd, his eldest Son watched with him. He gave up the Ghost about the third hour of the night, at what time a black Cat, opening the Casement with her nails, (for it was shut) ran to his bed, and did so violently scratch his face and the bolster, as if she endeavoured by force to remove him out of the place where he lay. But the Cat afterwards suddenly was gone, and she was no sooner gone, but he breathed his last. A fair Tale was made to the Pastor of the Parish, and the Magistracy of the Town allowing it, he was buried on the right side of the Altar, his Friends paying well for it. No sooner *Cuntius* was dead but a great Tempest arose, which raged most at his very Funeral, there being such impetuous Storms of Wind with Snow, that it made men's bodies quake, and their teeth chatter in their heads. But so soon as he was interred, of a sudden all was calm.

He had not been dead a day or two, but several rumours were spread in the town of a *Spiritus incubus*, or *Ephialtes*, in the shape of *Cuntius*, that would have forced a Woman. This happen'd before he was buried. After his burial, the same *Spectre* awaken'd one that was sleeping in his dining room, saying, *I can scarce withhold my self from beating thee to death.* The voice was the voice of *Cuntius*. The watchmen of the town also affirmed, that they heard every night great stirs in *Cuntius* his House, the fallings and throwings of things about, and that they did see the gates stand wide open betimes in the mornings, though they were ever so diligently shut o'er night; that his Horses were very unquiet in the Stable, as if they'd kick'd, and bit one another; besides unusual barkings and howlings of the Dogs all over the Town. But these were but preludious suspicions to further evidence, which I will run over as briefly as I may.

A Maid-servant of one of the Citizens of *Pentsch* (while these Tragedies and Stirs were so frequent in the Town) heard, together with some others lying in their beds, the noise and tramplings of one riding about the House, who at last ran against the Walls with that violence, that the whole House shaked again, as if it would fall, and the windows were all fill'd with flashings of light. The Master of the House being informed of it, went out of doors in the morning to see what the matter was; and he beheld in the Snow the impressions of strange feet, such as were like neither Horses, nor Cows, nor any Creature that he knew.

Another time, about eleven of the clock in the night, *Cuntius* appears to one of his Friends that was a witness to a Child of his, speaks unto him, and bids him be of good courage, for he came only to communicate unto him a matter of great importance. *I have left behind me,* said he, *my youngest Son* James, *to whom you are God-father, Now there is at my eldest Son Steven's, a Citizen of Jegerdorf, a certain Chest, wherein I have put four hundred and fifteen Florens: This I tell you, that your God-son may not be defrauded of any of them, and it is your duty to look after it; which if you neglect, wo be to you.* Having said this, the *Spectre* departed, and went up into the upper rooms of the House, where he walked so stoutly that all rattled again, and the roof swagged with his heavy stampings. This *Cuntius* his friend told to the Parson of the Parish a day or two after for a certain truth.

But there are also several other notorious passages of this *Cuntius*. As his often speaking to the Maid that lay with her Mistress, his Widow, to give him place, for it was his right; and if she would not give it to him, he would writh his neck behind her.

His galloping up and down like a wanton horse in the Court of his House. He being divers times seen to ride, not only in the streets, but along the vallies of the fields, and on the Mountains, with so strong a trot, that he made the very ground flash with fire under him.

His bruising of the body of a Child of a certain Smiths, and making his very bones so soft, that you might wrap the corpse on heaps like a glove.

His miserable tugging all night with a *Jew* that had taken up his Inn in the Town, and tossing him up and down in the lodging where he lay.

His dreadful accosting of a Waggoner, an old acquaintance of his, while he was busie in the stable, vomiting out fire against him to terrify him, and biting of him so cruelly by the foot, that he made him lame.

What follows, as I have above intimated, concerns the Relator himself, who was the Parson of the Parish, whom his Fury so squeez'd and press'd when he was asleep, that wakening he found himself utterly spent, and his strength quite gone, but could not imagine the reason. But while he lay musing with himself what the matter might be, this *Spectre* returns again to him, and holding him all over so fast, that he could not wag a finger, rowled him in his bed backwards and forwards a good many times together. This same happen'd also to his Wife another time, whom *Cuntius*, coming thro' the casement in the shape of a little Dwarf, and running to her bed-side, so wrung and pulled as if he would have torn her throat out, had not her two Daughters come in to help her.

He pressed the lips together of one of this *Theologer's* Sons so, that they could scarcely get them asunder.

His House was so generally disturbed with this unruly Ghost, that the Servants were fain to keep together anights in one room, lying upon straw, and watching the approaches of this troublesome Fiend. But a Maid of the House, being more courageous than the rest, would needs one night go to bed, and forsake her company. Whereupon *Cuntius* finding her alone, presently assaults her, pulls away the bedding, and would have carried her away with him; but she hardly escaping fled to the rest of the Family, where she espied him standing by the candle, and straightaway after, vanishing.

Another time he came into her Master's Chamber, making a noise like a Hog that eats grain, smacking and grunting very sonorously. They could not chase him away, by speaking to him, but ever as they lighted a Candle, he would vanish.

On another Time about Evening, when this *Theologer* was sitting with his Wife and Children about him, exercising himself in Musick, according to his usual manner, a most grievous stink arose suddenly, which by degrees spread itself to every corner of the room. Here upon he commends himself and his family to God by Prayer. The smell nevertheless encreased, and became above all measure pestilently noisom, insomuch that he was forced to go up to his chamber. He and his Wife had not been in bed a quarter of an hour, but they find the same stink in the bed-chamber; of which, while they are complaining one to another, out steps the Spectre from the Wall, and creeping to his bed-side, breathes upon him an exceeding cold breath, of so intolerable stinking and malignant a scent, as is beyond all imagination and expression. Here upon the *Theologer*, good soul, grew very ill, and was fain to keep his bed, his face, belly, and guts swelling as if he had been poysoned; whence he also was troubled with a difficulty of breathing, and with a putrid inflammation of his eyes, so that he could not well use them of a long time after.

But taking leave of the sick Divine, if we should go back, and recount what we have omitted, it would exceed the number of what we have already recounted. As for example, the trembling and sweating of *Cuntius* his Gelding, from which he was not free night nor day: the burning blue of the Candles at the approaches of *Cuntius* his Ghost: His drinking up the milk in the milk-bowls, his flinging dung into them, or turning the milk into blood: His pulling up posts deep set in the ground, and so heavy, that two lusty Porters could not deal with them: his discoursing with several men he met concerning the affairs of the Waggoners: His strangling of old men: His holding fast the Cradles of Children, or taking them out of them: His frequent endeavouring to force women: His defiling the water in the Font, and fouling the Cloth

on the Altar on that side that did hang toward his grave with
dirty bloody spots: His catching up Dogs in the streets and
knocking their brains against the ground: His sucking dry the
Cows, and tying their tails like the tail of an Horse: His devouring of Poultry, and his flinging of Goats bound into the Racks:
His tying of an Horse to an empty oat-tub in the Stable, to clatter up and down with it, and the hinder foot of another to his
own head-stall: His looking out the window of a low Tower, and
then suddenly changing himself into the form of a long staff:
His chiding of a Matron for suffering her servant to wash dishes
on a Thursday, at what time he laid his hand upon her, and she
said, it felt more cold than ice: His pelting one of the Women
that washed his corps, so forcibly, that the print of the Clods he
flung, were to be seen upon the wall: His attempting to ravish
another, who excusing herself and saying, *My* Cuntius, *thou seest
how old, wrinkled and deformed I am, and how unfit for those
kind of sports*, he suddenly set up a loud laughter and vanished.

But we must insist upon these things; only we will add one
passage more that is not a little remarkable. His gravestone was
turned on one side, shelving, and there were several holes in the
earth, about the bigness of mouse-holes, that went down to his
very Coffin, which, however they were filled up with earth over
night, yet they would be sure to be laid open the next morning.

It would be a tedious business to recite all these things at large,
and prosecute the Story in all its particular Circumstances. To
conclude therefore, their calamity was such, from their frequent
occursions of his restless fury, that there was none but either pitied them, or despis'd them; none would lodge in their Town,
Trading was decay'd, and the Citizens impoverished by the con-
tinual stirs and tumults of this unquiet Ghost.

And though the *Atheist* may perhaps laugh at them, as men
undone by their own Melancholy and vain imaginations, or by
the waggery of some ill neighbours: yet if he seriously consider
what has already been related, there are many passages that are
by no means to be resolved into any such Principles: but what I
shall now declare, will make it altogether unlikely that any of
them are.

To be short therefore, finding no rest, nor being able to excogitate any better remedy, they dig up *Cuntius* his body with several others buried both before and after him. But those both after and before were so putrify'd and rotten, their Sculls broken, and the Sutures of them gaping, that they were not to be known by their shape at all, having become in a manner but a rude mass of earth and dirt; but it was quite otherwise in Cuntius: His Skin was tender and florid, his Joynts not at all stiff, but limber and moveable, and a staff being put into his hand, he grasped it with his fingers very fast; his Eyes also of themselves would be one time open, and another time shut; they opened a vein in his Leg, and the blood sprang out as fresh as in the living; his Nose was entire and full, not sharp, as in those that are ghastly sick, or quite dead: and yet *Cuntius* his body had lien in the grave from *Feb 8* to *July 20* which is almost half a year.

It was easily discernable where the fault lay. However, nothing was done rashly, but Judges were constituted, Sentence was pronounced upon *Cuntius* his Carcase, which (being animated thereto from success in the like case, some years before in this very Province of *Silesia*, I suppose he means at *Breslaw*, where the Shoemakers body was burnt) they adjudged to the fire.

Wherefore there were Masons provided to make a hole in the wall near the Altar to get his body through, which being pulled at with a rope, it was so exceeding heavy, that the rope brake, and they could scarce stir him. But when they had pull'd him through, and gotten him on a Cart without, which *Cuntius* his Horse that had struck him (which was a lusty bodied Jade) was to draw; yet it put him to it so, that he was ready to fall down ever and anon, and was quite out of breath with striving to draw so intolerable a load, who not withstanding could run away with two men in the same Cart presently after, their weight was so inconsiderable to his strength.

His body when it was brought to the fire, proved as unwilling to be burnt, as before to be drawn; so that the Executioner was fain with hooks to pull him out, and cut him into pieces to make him burn. Which, while he did, the blood was found so pure and spirituous, that it spurted into his face as he cut him; but at last, not without the expense of two hundred and fifteen great billets, all was turned into ashes. Which they carefully sweeping up to-

246

gether and casting them into the River, the Spectre never more
appeared.

I must confess, I am so slow witted myself that I cannot so
much as imagine, what the *Atheist* will excogitate for a subter-
fuge or hiding place, from so plain and evident Convictions.

« » « » « »

What makes the foregoing especially intriguing is that the revenants described seem to possess characteristics that relate to not
only vampires but ghosts, poltergeists, and classical demons as
well.

On the subject of demons, it can be said that though the European variety may have lacked many of the exotic physical attrib-
utes of the non-Western variety, they were certainly not absent
from the scene. There were the maras of Scandinavia, the moras
of Bohemia, the alps of old Germany, and others, all of which
had similarities, including the tendency to weigh heavily on the
chests of their victims at night, causing terrifying dreams, suffo-
cation, and general discomfort. Indeed, the word *nightmare* itself
has its roots in the concept of these nocturnal demons.

A number of them share vampirish qualities, such as the Portuguese bruxsa, who is described by Richard Andrée, who says,
"At night she leaves her resting-place and flies far from home in
the form of some gigantic night-bird. The bruxsas keep tryst with
their diabolical lovers and seduce, terrify and torment lonely
wanderers. On returning from their nocturnal journey of pleasure
they suck the blood of their own children." Then there is the
Rumanian nosferat. Quoting from an earlier source, the late Ernest Jones writes:

> The nosferat not only sucks the blood of sleeping people, but also
> does mischief as an incubus or succubus. The nosferat is the still-
> born, illegitimate child of two people who are similarly illegitimate.

It is hardly put under the earth before it awakes to life and leaves its grave never to return. It visits people by night in the form of a black cat, a black dog, a beetle, a butterfly or even a simple straw. When its sex is male, it visits women; when female, men. With young people it indulges in sexual orgies until they get ill and die of exhaustion. In this case it also appears in the form of a handsome youth or a pretty girl, while the victim lies half awake and submits unresistingly. It often happens that women are impregnated by the creature and bear children who can be recognized by their ugliness and by their having hair over the whole body. They then become witches, usually moroiu. The nosferat appears to bridegrooms and brides and makes them impotent and sterile.

Such depraved evil spirits, though on the surface nothing but trouble, were a convenience to society that is completely lacking in the atomic age. Not only were they ideal bogies with which to frighten and control recalcitrant children; imagine what handy alibis they provided for embarrassing pregnancies resulting from otherwise devastating sexual indiscretions.

Regardless of what they were called from place to place, such lewd spirits were directly descended from the incubi and succubi mentioned earlier. Occupying a unique position in European tradition, incubi and succubi kept many a Church Father awake nights pondering their true nature. To explain them away as figments of the imagination would have been too simple; besides, there was the matter of those bothersome pregnancies that had to have been caused by something more substantial than spirits of the air.

As far as anyone could determine, they were nonhuman entities capable of assuming either male or female form. Their chief if not sole occupation was coming in the night to the beds of their victims and forcing them into sexual submission. When appearing in masculine form they were known as incubi, and when in the female as succubi or succubae. To complicate matters they generally appeared in the likenesses of individuals familiar to their victims, thereby causing no end of embarrassment to those they impersonated. This was especially true when they appeared as bishops, priests, public officials, physicians, or in-laws.

The controversy as to what exactly incubi and succubi were was sparked by Saint Augustine who stated unequivocally that demons had "corporeal immortality and passions like human beings." He elaborated by declaring that, though incapable of producing semen themselves, they collected it from the bodies of men and injected it into those of women, thereby impregnating them. Chaucer, though uninvolved personally in any ecclesiastical contentions, was certainly not above making wry comments on the subject of what incubi might actually be. Associating them with wandering limiters, or mendicant friars, he wrote in "The Wife of Bath's Tale":

> For there as wont to walken was an elf,
> There walketh now the limitour himself,
> Women may now go safely up and down;
> In every bush, and under every tree,
> There is no other Incubus than hee,
> And he ne will dou them no dishonor.

A fifteenth-century theologian named De Spina advanced the original idea that incubi and succubi were "formed from the odor and sperm of men and women in intercourse." And one of his contemporaries, a French priest, William of Paris, had this to say of them, "That there exist such beings as are commonly called incubi and succubi, and that they indulge in their burning lusts, and that children, as it is freely acknowledged, can be born from them, is attested by the unimpeachable and unshakable witness of many men and women who have been filled with foul imaginings by them, and endured their lecherous assaults and lewdness."

Apparently no one placed any significance on the fact that young and pretty women were more likely to suffer from the nocturnal assaults of incubi than old and ugly ones. Husbands who caught demons in bed with their wives rarely thought it odd that the culprits resisted attack but invariably vanished in the darkness. Nor did anyone seem concerned over the fact that more women were disturbed by incubi than men by succubi.

Of all the books written on the subject, the most complete was a seventeenth-century work called *Demoniality* by Ludovico Maria Sinistrari, a member of the Franciscan Order, and professor of philosophy at Pavia. In addition to his theological background, Sinistrari was well versed in the Greek and Roman classics. He was a fair poet, and a writer of clear, concise prose. As an expert in canon law he served as a consultant to the Supreme Tribunal of the Holy Inquisition, so when he made a statement, churchmen high and low listened.

He disagreed with Saint Augustine and other Church Fathers as to the basic nature of incubi. He asserted that they were not demons, and that they generated their own semen. He based his arguments against their demonic nature on the fact that prayers, holy relics, holy names, etc., had no effect on them at all (noxious fumes and herbs seemed the best remedies, he said). Their sexual assaults and lustful behavior, he declared, were due strictly to their basic nature, and their visitations were not carried out for the purpose of luring humans from grace. He even went so far as to state that they were of a more noble nature than humans, which meant that men and women having sexual relations with them did not degrade themselves. All sin (in connection with them) he felt lay in the belief that they were connected with the Devil. In other words, the sin resided in the intention of the human partner.

Although Sinistrari's *Demoniality* abounds with case histories, the majority of them deal with women who had succumbed to incubi. An incredible account of a succubus was recorded by a Venetian priest named Brognoli, who said that the events in question occurred in the town of Bergamo in the year 1650. The victim was a twenty-two-year-old man. He had just retired one night when he heard the sound of footsteps approaching his bed. Lighting a candle, he was amazed to see his fiancée, Teresa. Appearing highly distraught, she explained that her parents had driven her out of their house for no reason, and since she had nowhere else to go she had come here for shelter. Although he said later that he had been suspicious at the time, the youth said that he had allowed her to get into bed with him. Her lust was so boundless, however, that by dawn the poor fellow was exhausted. When the sun came up she confessed that she was not his fiancée at all, but a succubus. For reasons that Father Brognoli did not elaborate on, she forced the young man to submit again the next night and she kept it up until he could take it no longer. Staggering finally to the confessional, he begged the priest for deliverance. Brognoli wrote: "This monstrous commerce lasted for several months; but God finally delivered him through my entreaty and he did suitable penitence for his sins."

When we shake our heads today and ask ourselves, "How could intelligent men and women believe such things?" let us remember, there were other factors besides pure credulity involved. The strong Italian sense of honor, for example, played a big part in this particular phase of the human comedy. A sixteenth- or seventeenth-century Italian would have found it impossible to endure the disgrace that would have resulted had another man dishonored his marital bed. His whole world would have come crashing down about him with the same impact as, say, that of a contemporary banker caught with his hand in the till. On the other hand, if that same Italian gentleman were to discover that his wife had been violated by a lascivious demon, it would be regrettable, to be sure, but something a man could live with— even if the demon looked exactly like the parish priest. It was just one of those things.

There were cases, however, where the incubi, or folletti, as they were known in the Italian vernacular, did not succeed when confronted by unshakable virtue, as the following case from the files of Sinistrari illustrates.

The lady in question was named Hieronyma, and she lived in Sinistrari's own city of Pavia. Her incubus did not appear suddenly in her bedroom one night; he apparently decided to soften her up in advance by sending her a gift in the form of a Venetian pastry. After being persuaded by the baker who delivered it to her house that the dough had come from her kitchen, she accepted it and ate it, sharing it with her husband, her three-year-old daughter, and her maid.

The following night, while in bed with her husband, Hieronyma was suddenly awakened from a sound sleep by a tiny voice that sounded like a shrill hissing in her ear, which said, "Did you like the cake?"

Thoroughly frightened at this, she fervently crossed herself and repeatedly called upon Jesus and Mary.

"Don't be afraid," insisted the voice. "I mean you no harm; quite the opposite, I am prepared to do anything to please you. Your beauty captivates me. I desire nothing more than to enjoy the sweetness of your embraces."

Hieronyma became aware of what felt like someone kissing her cheeks softly. It was as though she were being stroked by the finest of downy feathers. Throughout the entire episode her husband snored soundly as the voice kept whispering sweet words into her ears. She continued to resist, however, repeatedly crossing herself and calling upon holy names. Finally, seeing that he was getting nowhere, the tempter left the room.

The next day Hieronyma sought out her confessor as soon as she could. She related the entire incident to him, and he recommended that she continue to resist with all her strength and provide herself with some additional armor in the form of holy relics. Night after night the incubus came to her and tempted her with soft words and tender kisses, but she continued to rebuff him.

After several weeks of such wearying nocturnal struggles, it was decided by her confessor and several other learned men that Hieronyma should have herself exorcised. The rites were performed, but it was determined that she was not possessed by any demon. The priests then blessed her house, her bedroom, her bed, and sternly ordered the incubus to get out and leave the poor woman alone. But they might just as well have been talking to the walls. His nightly visits continued and lasted until the small hours of the morning. He wept, he moaned, he cried out with lovesick wails, pleading with Hieronyma in order to melt her heart and persuade her to bestow her embraces upon him. But she remained steadfast and continued to resist his exhortations.

Next he tried a new approach. He appeared to her in the form of a handsome young man with golden hair, sea-green eyes, and rich Spanish attire. He even began appearing to her during the day, when she was in the company of others. Of course, she was the only one who saw or heard him; for the rest of the group, he always remained invisible.

She continued to spurn him, until after many months of wooing the incubus became angry and started a new form of persecution. He stole all of her holy relics, things which she had always carried on her person; in addition he made off with all her rings, jewelry, and other baubles, which were locked securely in a solid chest. The latter feat he accomplished without tampering with the locks.

He began to beat her. He would snatch her child away while the girl was on her lap. He began to act like a poltergeist, knocking over furniture, smashing dishes and other utensils, which, when he felt so inclined, he would put back together again. One night while Hieronyma was in bed with her husband, the incubus came and made his usual demands. This time, upon being refused, he flew into a rage, disappeared, and returned with a load of heavy flagstones. He then proceeded to build a solid wall around the bed so that the couple were unable to get out in the morning without the aid of a ladder. Fortunately the wall was not cemented, so it was relatively easy to take it down. The stones were piled in a corner, where they remained for two days. Many friends came to the house and saw them, but after the two days, the stones mysteriously vanished.

Not long afterward, when Hieronyma and her husband were having a dinner party, the dining table, which was freshly laid for the meal and laden with utensils and food, disappeared from sight. Everyone in the house began searching frantically for the table, but it was nowhere to be seen. Embarrassed and upset, the husband offered to take his friends out for their meal, when suddenly a mighty crash was heard from the dining room. Rushing in to see what had happened, the company found that a different table had been returned to the former one's location, but now, instead of having upon it the same things which had been there before, it was, in Sinistrari's words, "laid with napery, napkins, salt cellars, silver cruets, castors, trenchers and trays that did not belong to the house, and groaning with rich meats, tasties, pullets and puddings, which certainly had not been cooked there." In addition, on the sideboard there were strange and beautiful flagons of silver and crystal, golden cups, decanters and bottles, all filled with exotic wines from the far corners of the world.

At first Hieronyma and her husband feared to let their guests touch anything, lest they be tainted with diabolical influence, but caution gave way to hunger, and they finally sat down and ate heartily. Everything proved to be magnificent. Then, after dinner, as they were sitting about the fire and discussing the amazing things that had taken place, the strange table with all its wonderful utensils vanished from sight, and in its place reappeared the table which had been there in the first place, laid with the identical foods and dishes placed there by the servants.

In desperation, the unhappy Hieronyma went to a nearby church, where the body of a saint lay to be venerated by parishioners. She vowed that, should he intercede on her behalf, she would dress in a "sad colored frock, girt about her waist with a cord," for an entire year. This extreme measure, she felt, would certainly rid her of the incubus.

The following day, while attending mass in her own church, she had barely crossed the threshold when all her clothes and jewels fell to the ground and disappeared in a blast of wind, leaving her as naked as the day she had been born. Blushing with embarrassment, she let out a heartrending scream. Fortunately, two gentlemen who were standing by, seeing what had happened, immediately took off their cloaks and covered her nudity. They hurriedly took her from the church, put her in a coach, and escorted her home. Six months passed before the incubus returned the clothing and jewelry he had taken that day.

The irksome spirit continued to plague Hieronyma for many years before he eventually grew tired and came to realize that, no matter what he did, she would never succumb to his amorous demands. When he came to this conclusion he left her alone, and she spent the rest of her life in peace.

« »   « »   « »

Although virtually all the best-known writings on incubi, succubi, and other demons on the European scene indicate a deep involvement with Christianity, a second look reveals that there were instances of outsiders as well. The Jews, so often regarded by Christian neighbors with hostility, faced their other-worldly enemies without sectarian distinction. There were hosts of demons with which medieval Jews had to contend, affecting all aspects of their daily life. The best-known and most greatly feared was Death itself, not exactly a demon, but a destroying angel, whom all men somehow secretly hoped to outwit but never did. Then there were the dybbuks, spirits who possessed the bodies of innocent victims and could be driven away only by means of powerful exorcisms. There were also demons of uncleanliness who caused diseases, and others that made men impotent and women barren.

Demons, according to medieval Jews, established preferred territories, and when humans trespassed, serious repercussions could result. There is a story about a group of Hungarian Jews who settled in a particular district, after which their death rate rose sharply. Neither their fasting nor their prayers seemed to do them any good. Then one day the elder of the community encountered a large band of strangers led by a man mounted on a lion that had a snake for a bridle. The strangers, it developed, were demons, and the Jews had unwittingly settled in their meeting place. On being ordered by the leader of the demons to vacate the premises, the Jews obeyed and once more resumed a reasonably tranquil existence.

One of the most curious cases involving the uneasy relations between men and demons is said to have reached its climax in the city of Posen in the year 1681 or thereabouts.

On one of the city's main streets there stood an old house of stone, the cellar of which was always kept locked. One day an intruder succeeded in breaking the lock and forcing his way into the cellar. Instead of finding anything to steal, he met death. Shortly after his body was found on the threshold, strange things began happening in the house. Furniture was thrown about, ashes were hurled into pots of food, candlesticks were smashed, and any loose objects were liable at any time to go flying through the air. All this was accompanied by appropriate tumult and clamor.

Naturally, the people living in the house were terrified, and though nothing ever happened to harm any of them physically, the strain was so great that they finally abandoned the place. News of these disturbances spread throughout the city, and, despite the efforts of all the learned men from the Jesuits on, no one was able to rid the house of the troublesome demons that were haunting it.

Finally an appeal was made to a certain Rabbi Joel of Zamosz, who had the reputation of being the most accomplished miracle-worker of the time. He came to the house and proceeded to perform a series of potent incantations. He didn't get rid of the demons, but at least he forced them to reveal who they were. They claimed that they had every legal right to the property and that they would not abandon it without a fight. So sure of themselves were they that they even offered to defend their position before a court of law.

Rabbi Joel listened to them and agreed to convene such a court in the house itself. The judges were human, but the demons were permitted to choose a demon attorney to be their advocate. During the course of the trial, we are told, he could be heard, but not seen.

The contention of the demons was simple. A former owner of the house had engaged in an illicit affair with a beautiful succubus, who over a period of time bore children. When the man's wife learned of her husband's infidelity she consulted a rabbi, who confronted the guilty man and forced him to confess. When this was accomplished, the rabbi forced him to break off the affair and bound him by means of a powerful amulet to keep his word. This he did, but shortly before he died, the succubus came to her former lover, and begged him to leave her and her demon offspring the cellar of the house as an inheritance. He agreed to this and died. Now, said the demon advocate, all the human descendants of the man had died as well, leaving only the demon descendants as the lawful heirs.

The new owners of the house disputed this, saying that they had bought the place in good faith, paying full price, and thereby rightfully obtaining full title to the property. They furthermore contended that the mother of the demons, being a succubus, had forced herself on their father against his will. Finally, they said, demons were not entitled to the same rights as humans insofar as human affairs were concerned.

As both sides rested their cases, the judges deliberated and finally decided against the demons, declaring that their legitimate abode was not among humans, but in deserts and wastelands. To enforce the court's decision, Rabbi Joel then performed a terrible and potent exorcism, which rid the house not only of the demons, but of the cellar as well, thereby permanently settling the matter.

« »   « »   « »

One variety of supernatural entity about which Jews and Christians shared some beliefs was the werewolf. In general, perhaps to some extent because of horror movies, most people today think of werewolves in conjunction with vampires. In some instances certain confusions may arise in connection with them. The chief difference between the werewolf and the vampire—and this can be said of just about any country in which beliefs concerning the two prevail—is that there are innumerable accounts of individuals becoming werewolves voluntarily, but *never* do they voluntarily become vampires.

In the many variations, we encounter werewolves who behave very much like vampires, and werewolves who after death become vampires. But the roads to becoming a werewolf are numerous and range from such things as casting spells and performing incantations to donning wolfskin girdles or consulting witches who do the job for a fee. Such methods, mentioned in numerous writings on the subject, of course cover only those situations in which individuals chose to become werewolves of their own free will.

It is fascinating to see that during the period of history when witch trials were the order of the day, there was also a significant number of werewolf trials. France especially witnessed many such trials, and what is sometimes surprising to modern readers is how many of the defendants freely confessed. But when we read the details of the indictments along with the statements of the accused, then compare them to accounts of certain contemporary crimes of violence, credulity diminishes somewhat. In times when learned men believed that witches could anoint their bodies with unguents and fly through the air to attend sabbats, it was not difficult for them to believe that persons making pacts with the Devil were granted the ability to assume the shape of wolves in order to prey upon human victims. Furthermore, when we examine the actual content of certain witches' concoctions in light of contemporary knowledge of drugs, it is even easier to understand why they were able to swear under oath that they did indeed fly through the air.

Involuntary werewolves were the ones who were to be pitied. Some were doomed to this fate, it is said, by inadvertently performing such innocent acts as drinking water from streams that had become lycanthropous by virtue of wolves drinking from it. Drinking water that had gathered in the depressions left by wolves' footsteps was also a risky proposition, and then there was the matter of being victims of curses. Many such unhappy werewolves, we are told, fell into that sad estate merely by antagonizing witches or sorcerers. Others, though, became lycanthropes through their own misdeeds, having had the state thrust upon them as a form of punishment. In a twelfth-century chronicle, *Topographica Hibernica*, its author, Giraldus Cambrensis, gives a detailed account of lycanthropy in Ireland that falls into this latter category. We are told that the inhabitants of the ancient Irish kingdom of Ossory were cursed for their wicked behavior by the abbot, (later Saint) Natalis in the sixth century. According to the terms of this terrible malediction, two persons of the region were doomed to assume the shape of wolves every seven years. If they survived, they would be permitted to resume their lives as humans at the end of this period, when two others had to carry on the tradition.

The most significant aspect of the chronicler's narrative is the thought contained in his final paragraph, where he writes:

> We hold then with S. Augustine that neither demons nor sorcerers can either create or essentially change their natures; but those, whom God has created are able by His permission to metamorphize themselves so far as mere outward appearance is concerned, so that they appear to be what truly they are not, and the senses of men beholding them are fascinated and deceived by glamour, so

that things are not seen as they really exist, but by some phantom power or magic spell the human vision is deluded and mocked inasmuch as its rests upon unreal and fictitious forms.

Ironically enough, though Giraldus refers to "some phantom power or magic spell" that fascinates, deludes, and captures the imaginations of men in a totally negative sense, he has nonetheless unwittingly provided us with the key to supernatural fiction. After all, aren't the best ghost stories the ones that enable us to suspend belief and totally immerse ourselves in the dark worlds of the storytellers?

Which brings us to our dessert, as it were.

Although we have poked about in a fairly substantial number of offbeat supernatural corners, we have for the most part skirted around the relatively modern supernatural horror story. That is as it should be, however, for this has been intended essentially as an armchair journey through the more esoteric regions of the unknown. Still, it would be less than fair to ignore completely the rich vein of story material rooted strictly in the Western tradition. Certainly no aficionado could possibly deny Western fiction a place in the highest ranks of the supernatural-horror genre. But for that very reason it is a difficult proposition to select examples of that tradition which are at the same time high in quality and relatively obscure.

There is no real need to offer a prologue of any sort to the stories that comprise our journey's end, because each speaks for itself. Although none of them are new, neither have they become stale from overexposure. That they span Continental Europe, England, America, and Australia is all the introduction they need.

The Horrible Legacy of the Cannibal Chef

Although the truth is often more incredible than fiction, the two at times become so intertwined that it is frequently impossible to distinguish between them. When the truth is a horrible one, one which people would prefer not to believe, it becomes seasoned in time with fantasy. The terrible history of Gaston Donnet (if indeed that was his name) is just such a tale.

According to newspaper accounts of the time, beginning in the year 1849, a New Orleans store on Common Street not far from Saint-Charles was said to be haunted by a horrible collection of ghosts. They were apparently so evident that crowds of frightened neighbors occasionally gathered in front of the place to protest or voice their fears. About twenty-five years later a man, anxious to find out the cause of the alleged hauntings, took it upon himself to do some investigating on his own. He began to poke around in the third floor of the building, for it was from there that many claimed to have heard the strange sounds after dark. Behind a loose brick near the fireplace he found a small hollow containing an old red morocco diary and a pair of small high-heeled yellow-gold slippers. Between the ghastly revelations of the diary and longstanding rumors concerning the haunted building, a legend was born.

About 1828 a young cook named Gaston Donnet had learned his trade so well that he was engaged as an assistant chef by the Palais Sauvinet, one of the best restaurants in Paris. It was at this time that he began to keep a diary.

Having grown up during the Napoleonic era, Gaston was deeply impressed by the grandeur of royalty and nobility. Whenever possible he exerted his most strenuous efforts to ingratiate himself with the restaurant's more distinguished guests. Consequently, by 1830 he had risen to the position of head chef. Not long after his elevation to *maître de cuisine*, the establishment was visited unexpectedly by a certain count with a party of prominent companions. Gaston was overjoyed. Working like a demon, he prepared a feast that would have drawn the praises of an emperor, let alone a mere count. Consequently, when the pantry boy, Pierre, whispered much later that Monsieur le Comte had criticized one of his dishes, poor Gaston was devastated. This affront to his artistic talents whipped him up to a frenzy of rage. He swore that if that nobleman ever dared set foot in the place again he would be fed on the entrails of dogs. Gaston's curses, however, did not assuage his temper.

That night he fought with everyone who crossed his path, but especially with Pierre. They had a terrible row. The shouts and oaths echoed through the dimly lighted kitchen and finally culminated in a piercing scream as Pierre slumped to the floor with a huge knife protruding from his chest.

The rage drained from Gaston in a flash. He had to get rid of the body. Suddenly he was struck with a brilliant, though diabolical idea. After dragging the boy's limp body into his private *petite cuisine*, Gaston locked the door and set to work feverishly. As long as he remained enclosed in this tiny chamber he knew that he was safe, for it was the chef's personal retreat, off limits to everyone, even the owners of the Palais Sauvinet.

First he got rid of Pierre's clothes and burned them in the little fireplace which was used to incinerate discarded scraps of bone, skin, feathers, and other debris. Next he dismembered the body with the skilled hand of an experienced butcher. Using sharp knives designed exactly for that purpose, he deftly removed every bit of flesh from the skeleton. After charring the bones beyond recognition in the fireplace, he prepared the flesh in a number of ways—some he pickled; portions were stuffed, marinated, chopped; and a little was even made into small sausages. As for the blackened bones, Gaston broke them up, placed them in a sack, and dumped them into the Seine just before dawn.

A little later, as Paris began to awaken, Gaston put on a convincing act. He began to search for the missing Pierre. He ranted, he cursed, he screamed and shouted epithets at the absent scullery boy. He carried on so that before the day was over a replacement had been hired. That evening a familiar guest appeared. It was the count who had dared to speak disparagingly of Gaston's culinary ability. Delighted at the opportunity thus presented him, the cunning chef laid out a sumptuous feast. The count and his friends agreed to a man that what they had eaten was superb and made a special point of sending their compliments to Gaston. What they did not know, of course, was that they had consumed the mortal remains of the late Pierre.

Unfortunately, Gaston outdid himself. Monsieur le Comte had been so favorably impressed with the banquet that he returned in less than a week in hopes of attending a repeat performance of the amazing chef's gastronomic symphony. Gaston succeeded in convincing his distinguished admirer to return on the following night, explaining that such a repast could not be whipped up on a moment's notice. The excuse seemed satisfactory, and the count agreed to come back the next evening. Although he did not like the idea, Gaston knew that there was only one thing for him to do, and in that moment the fate of the new pantry boy was sealed.

That night Gaston repeated his bloody preparations, only this time with far greater efficiency than he had on the previous occasion. For now he had a certain degree of experience to guide his hands.

The count's dinner party was a huge success, of course. If anything, it was even more so than it had been the first time.

On the following day, fortunately for Gaston, there were two developments which forced him to make a fast decision. The mothers of the two missing pantry boys had, in the course of their frantic searching, turned up a pair of clues connecting the two disappearances—a shoe belonging to one, a lucky piece that had been carried by the other. Shortly after hearing about these disturbing discoveries, Gaston received a royal summons from King Louis Philippe to appear at the palace. Obviously it was not going to be so easy to obtain the necessary ingredients to provide banquets similar to those which had enchanted the count and his friends. Thus it was that the talented head chef of the Palais Sauvinet disappeared from Paris forever.

Several weeks later there arrived in New Orleans an emigrant calling himself Lucien Feraud. He said that he was a shoemaker, and within a few weeks he proved to be a very good one. In time he married and rented a three-story building on Common Street.

Living comfortably with his wife on the top floor, the shoemaker maintained his thriving shop on the street level. Between the two, on the second floor, was a small but elegant private dining salon known as La Petite Coquille. It was run by a gastronomical genius from Paris named Valentin Dumestre. His prices were stratospheric, his clientele was limited to the extremely wealthy, and his reputation as a superb chef was widespread.

What nobody knew was that the silver-haired, taciturn shoemaker and the mustachioed, raven-haired Monsieur Valentin were one and the same man. Similarly, not a single aristocratic patron of La Petite Coquille had an inkling that he might be an unwitting cannibal—yet such was the case. For the truth was that Valentin—or Feraud, if you will—had been serving the flesh of carefully selected slaves whom he had bought cheaply, fattened for a pittance, and slaughtered secretly for the table. Being a thrifty man, he did not let the skins of his Negro victims go to waste. By carefully curing and tanning them he was able to create the most exquisite slippers that ever graced the feet of a wealthy Creole belle.

One night in 1848 the shoemaker's wife, who by now had grown weary of being left alone every night, decided to take a little peek into the exclusive *salle á manger* downstairs. Imagine her shock, then, when she recognized the proprietor, Valentin Dumestre, as none other than her husband, Lucien. Her initial reaction was one of furious outrage. Determined to prevent an embarrassing scene that might reveal his true identity, he ushered her into the kitchen on a pretext of some sort and coldly bashed her skull in with a heavy mallet. He could take no chances. This man of many names liked being rich, and he thoroughly intended to become richer. Laughing sardonically to himself as he returned to his paying guests, he determined to prepare a very special dish on the following night.

Now it so happened that Feraud the shoemaker shared a number of customers with Valentin the restaurateur. One in particular had recently ordered a special pair of dancing slippers for his daughter, one of the prettiest girls in New Orleans. It suddenly occurred to the shoemaker, just as he was about to retire, that he could now fashion the most beautiful slippers of his career, for he now had available a fine white skin of which to make them. He fell asleep dreaming of every detail—how he would cure it, finish it, and rub it with real gold dust until it gleamed like the settings of royal jewels.

It is at this point that fact and fantasy become so inextricably enmeshed that it is difficult to say for certain what actually happened. Did the crushing burden of Gaston Donnet's guilt finally overwhelm him and cause him to crack, or did the events recorded in his fantastic diary actually take place? Whatever may be the case, the only thing that can be done here is to retell what he wrote there.

When the shoemaker finished the golden dancing slippers, even he had to admit that they were the crowning achievement of his career—at least, this particular career. He was convinced, therefore, that the young lady who was to wear them would be equally entranced by his handiwork. But she was not. Several days after they had been delivered, the girl's father stormed angrily into Feraud's shop and hurled the slippers into their startled maker's face.

"Take these cursed things back, you scoundrel!" he roared. "They are the spawn of Satan! They whine, they moan, they dance by themselves. They cry aloud that they were worn by another for an entire lifetime!"

Pausing briefly at the door before leaving, he crossed himself and said, "I'll never set foot in this damned place again!"

With that he turned and disappeared into the street, slamming the door behind him so hard that the walls rattled.

By now Feraud was trembling all over. Chills coursed up and down his spine. He looked at the slippers incredulously as they jumped unassisted from the table and began moving towards him, moaning in a voice strangely reminiscent of his murdered wife's. He stumbled backward and fell to the floor, as the shoes kept coming nearer, then climbed upon him and dug their heels into his throat. Tearing them away, he flung them across the room with all his might and sprang to his feet. When he saw them come after him again, he turned and bolted up the stairs, taking refuge in the dimly lighted parlor of his living quarters on the third floor. He tried to keep the shoes out, but it was no use. No matter what he tried, it was impossible to imprison or destroy them.

Just then his mounting fear was interrupted by a loud knocking on the door of the shop below. Composing himself as best he could, he ran downstairs again to see who it was. He opened the door and found two strangers. One was looking for Gaston Donnet, and the other for Valentin Dumestre.

"Good God!" he thought to himself. "They've finally caught up with me."

Fighting to maintain an outwardly calm appearance, he told the men that he would go upstairs and summon the gentlemen they sought.

Locking himself once more in his apartment, he opened the door to the secret back room and selected a long, sharp knife. While he was contemplating it he heard a hideous concert of wails, moans, shrieks, and cries that filled the gloom as if they had suddenly risen from the depths of Hell. Whirling around in terror, he brandished the knife. There before him were dozens of raw, slimy, stinking shapes that dripped blood as they closed in on him. They pointed accusing fingers at him as their dangling eyeballs glistened horribly, like peeled, bloodshot clams. He dashed back to the secret room and seized another knife—why, he did not know. Certainly one was all he needed to cut his throat. It was better that way than to succumb to the slimy terrors that now closed in around him. But there was no escaping them. They snatched the gleaming knives from him and flung them aside. Howling now like all the fiends of the underworld turned loose, they fell upon him and began tearing him to pieces, drowning out his agonized screams with their gurgling, squishing, snarling, and gasping. And there, slicing at his burning flesh, were the slippers, giggling demoniacally as they slid down his back.

Next, says the diary, the hideous forms receded. A strangely transformed figure—that of the young Gaston Donnet— glided silently toward the fireplace, took away a loose brick, and removed a little red morocco-bound book from the cavity. After reading it over he sat down, reached for his pen, and added two final pages of writing. Then, closing the book for the last time, he put it back into the secret niche, but just before he could replace the brick which concealed it, the golden shoes danced into the hole and perched atop the diary. Suddenly the place became a screaming madhouse again. As the slimy red shapes of things that were once humans pressed in again on their victim, he disappeared.

For several weeks Lucien Feraud the shoemaker was seen by no one. When the authorities finally broke into the rooms on the third floor of the building on Common Street, the stench of death assailed their nostrils. After they had overcome their shock, they discovered that the corpse—completely skinned—had once been Lucien Feraud. They concluded that he had gone mad and flayed himself alive. Of course, they had not read his diary, for it told a far different story.

An ironic footnote must be added at this point. The two men who came looking for Gaston Donnet and Valentin Dumestre were not policemen. One came bearing an offer to buy La Petite Coquille for an outrageously high sum. The other had come to New Orleans all the way from Paris after searching for months. It seems that a certain wealthy count had died and left a large quantity of money to a certain Gaston Donnet, a wonderful chef he had once known years before. . . .

The Screaming Skull

BY F. MARION CRAWFORD

I have often heard it scream. No, I am not nervous, I am not imaginative, and I have never believed in ghosts, unless that thing is one. Whatever it is, it hates me almost as much as it hated Luke Pratt, and it screams at me.

If I were you, I would never tell ugly stories about ingenious ways of killing people, for you never can tell but that someone at the table may be tired of his or her nearest and dearest. I have always blamed myself for Mrs. Pratt's death, and I suppose I was responsible for it in a way, though heaven knows I never wished her anything but long life and happiness. If I had not told the story she might be alive yet. That is why she screams at me, I fancy.

She was a good little woman, with a sweet temper, all things considered, and a nice gentle voice; but I remember hearing her shriek once when she thought her little boy was killed by a pistol that went off, though everyone was sure that it was not loaded. It was the same scream; exactly the same, with a sort of rising quaver at the end; do you know what I mean? Unmistakable.

The truth is, I had not realized that the doctor and his wife were not on good terms. They used to bicker a bit now and then when I was not here, and I often noticed that little Mrs. Pratt got very red and bit her lip hard to keep her temper, while Luke grew pale and said the most offensive things. He was that sort when he was in the nursery, I remember, and afterward at school. He was my cousin, you know; that is how I came by his house; after he died, and his boy Charley was killed in South Africa, there were no relations left. Yes, it's a pretty little property, just the sort of thing for an old sailor like me who has taken to gardening.

One always remembers one's mistakes much more vividly than one's cleverest things, doesn't one? I've often noticed it. I was dining with the Pratts one night, when I told them the story that afterwards made so much difference. It was a wet night in November, and the sea was moaning. Hush!—if you don't speak you will hear it now. . . .

Do you hear the tide? Gloomy sound, isn't it? Sometimes, about this time of the year—hallo!—there it is! Don't be frightened, man—it won't eat you—it's only a noise, after all! But I'm glad you've heard it, because there are always people who think it's the wind, or my imagination, or something. You won't hear it again tonight, I fancy, for it doesn't often come more than once. Yes—that's right. Put another stick on the fire, and a little more stuff into that weak mixture you're so fond of. Do you remember old Blauklot the carpenter, on that German ship that picked us up when the *Clontarf* went to the bottom. We were hove to in a howling gale one night, as snug as you please, with no land within five hundred miles, and the ship coming up and falling off as regularly as clockwork—"Biddy to boor beebles ashore tis night, poys!" old Blauklot sang out, as he went off to his quarters with the sailmaker. I often think of that, now that I'm ashore for good and all.

Yes, it was on a night like this, when I was at home for a spell, waiting to take the *Olympia* out on her first trip—it was on the next voyage that she broke the record, you remember—but that dates it. Ninety-two was the year, early in November.

The weather was dirty, Pratt was out of temper, and the dinner was bad, very bad indeed, which didn't improve matters, and cold, which made it worse. The poor little lady was very unhappy about it, and insisted on making a Welsh rarebit on the table to counteract the raw turnips and half-boiled mutton. Pratt must have had a hard day. Perhaps he had lost a patient. At all events, he was in a nasty temper.

"My wife is trying to poison me, you see!" he said. "She'll succeed some day." I saw that she was hurt and I made believe to laugh, and said that Mrs. Pratt was much too clever to get rid of her husband in such a simple way; and then I began to tell them about Japanese tricks with spun glass and chopped horsehair and the like.

Pratt was a doctor, and knew a lot more than I did about such things, but that only put me on my mettle, and I told a story about a woman in Ireland who did for three husbands before anyone suspected foul play.

Did you ever hear the tale? The fourth husband managed to keep awake and caught her, and she was hanged. How did she do it? She drugged them, and poured melted lead into their ears through a little horn funnel when they were asleep. . . . No—that's the wind whistling. It's backing up to the southward again. I can tell by the sound. Besides, the other thing doesn't often come more than once in an evening even at this time of year—when it happened. Yes, it was in November. Poor Mrs. Pratt died suddenly in her bed not long after I dined there. I can fix the date, because I got the news in New York by the steamer that followed the *Olympia* when I took her out on her first trip. You had the *Leofric* the same year? Yes, I remember. What a pair of old buffers we are coming to be, you and I. Nearly fifty years since we were apprentices together on the *Clontarf*. Shall you ever forget old Blauklot? "Biddy to boor beebles ashore, poys!" Ha, ha! Take a little more, with all that water. It's the old Hulstkamp I found in the cellar when this house came to me, the same I brought Luke from Amsterdam five-and-twenty years ago. He had never touched a drop of it. Perhaps he's sorry now, poor fellow.

Where did I leave off? I told you that Mrs. Pratt died suddenly—yes. Luke must have been lonely here after she was dead, I should think; I came to see him now and then, and he looked worn and nervous, and told me that his practice was growing too heavy for him, though he wouldn't take an assistant on any account. Years went on, and his son was killed in South Africa, and after that he began to be queer. There was something about him not like other people. I believe he kept his senses in his profession to the end; there was no complaint of his having made bad mistakes in cases, or anything of that sort, but he had a look about him—

Luke was a red-headed man with a pale face when he was young, and he was never stout; in middle age he turned a sandy gray, and after his son died he grew thinner, till his head looked like a skull with parchment stretched over it very tight, and his eyes had a sort of glare in them that was very disagreeable to look at.

He had an old dog that poor Mrs. Pratt had been fond of, and that used to follow her everywhere. He was a bulldog, and the sweetest-tempered beast you ever saw, though he had a way of hitching his upper lip behind one of his fangs that frightened strangers a good deal. Sometimes, of an evening, Pratt and Bumble—that was the dog's name—used to sit and look at each other a long time, thinking about old times, I suppose, when Luke's wife used to sit in that chair you've got. That was always her place, and this was the doctor's, where I'm sitting. Bumble used to climb up by the footstool—he was old and fat by that time, and could not jump much, and his teeth were getting shaky. He would look steadily at Luke, and Luke looked steadily at the dog, his face growing more and more like a skull with two little coals for eyes; and after about five minutes or so, though it may have been less, old Bumble would suddenly begin to shake all over, and all on a sudden he would set up an awful howl, as if he had been shot, and tumble out of the easy chair and trot away, and hide himself under the sideboard, and lie there making odd noises.

Considering Pratt's looks in those last months, the thing is not surprising, you know. I'm not nervous or imaginative, but I can quite believe he might have sent a sensitive woman into hysterics—his head looked so much like a skull in parchment.

At last I came down one day before Christmas, when my ship was in dock, and I had three weeks off. Bumble was not about, and I said casually that I supposed the old dog was dead.

"Yes," Pratt answered, and I thought there was something odd in his tone even before he went on after a little pause. "I killed him," he said presently. "I could not stand it any longer."

I asked what it was that Luke could not stand, though I guessed well enough.

"He had a way of sitting in her chair and glaring at me, and then howling." Luke shivered a little. "He didn't suffer at all, poor old Bumble," he went on in a hurry, as if he thought I might imagine he had been cruel. "I put dionine into his drink to make him sleep soundly, and then I chloroformed him gradually, so that he could not have felt suffocated even if he was dreaming. It's been quieter since then."

I wondered what he meant, for the words slipped out as if he could not help saying them. I've understood since. He meant that he did not hear that noise so often after the dog was out of the way. Perhaps he thought at first that it was old Bumble in the yard howling at the moon, though it's not that kind of noise, is it? Besides, I know what it is, if Luke didn't. It's only a noise, after all, and a noise never hurt anybody yet. But he was much more imaginative than I am. No doubt there really is something about this place that I don't understand; but when I don't understand a thing, I call it a phenomenon, and I don't take it for granted that it's going to kill me, as he did. I don't understand everything, by long odds, nor do you, nor does any man, who has been to sea. We used to talk of tidal waves, for instance, and we could not account for them; now we account for them by calling them submarine earthquakes, and we branch off into fifty theories, any one of which might make earthquakes quite comprehensible if we only knew what they are. I fell in with one of them once, and the inkstand flew straight up from the table against the ceiling of my cabin. The same thing happened to Captain Lecky—I dare say you've read about it in his "Wrinkles." Very good. If that sort of thing took place ashore, in this room for instance, a nervous person would talk about spirits and levitation and fifty things that mean nothing, instead of just quietly setting it down as a "phenomenon" that has not been explained yet. My view of that voice, you see.

Besides, what is there to prove that Luke killed his wife? I would not even suggest such a thing to anyone but you. After all, there was nothing but the coincidence that poor little Mrs. Pratt died suddenly in her bed a few days after I told that story at dinner. She was not the only woman who ever died like that. Luke got the doctor over from the next parish, and they agreed that she had died of something the matter with her heart. Why not? It's common enough.

Of course, there was the ladle. I never told anybody about that and it made me start when I found it in the cupboard in the bedroom. It was new, too—a little tinned ladle that had not been in the fire more than once or twice, and there was some lead in it that had been melted, and stuck to the bottom of the bowl, all gray, with hardened dross on it. But that proves nothing. A country doctor is generally a handy man, who does everything for himself, and Luke may have had a dozen reasons for melting a little lead in a ladle. He was fond of sea-fishing, for instance, and he may have cast a sinker for a night-line; perhaps it was a weight for the hall clock, or something like that. All the same, when I found it I had a rather queer sensation, because it looked so much like the thing I had described when I told them the story. Do you understand? It affected me unpleasantly, and I threw it away; it's at the bottom of the sea a mile from the Spit, and it will be jolly well rusted beyond recognizing if it's ever washed up by the tide.

You see, Luke must have bought it in the village, years ago, for the man sells just such ladles still. I suppose they are used in cooking. In any case, there was no reason why an inquisitive housemaid should find such a thing lying about, with lead in it, and wonder what it was, and perhaps talk to the maid who heard me tell the story at dinner—for that girl married the plumber's son in the village, and may remember the whole thing.

You understand me, don't you? Now that Luke Pratt is dead and gone, and lies buried beside his wife with an honest man's tombstone at his head, I should not care to stir up anything that could hurt his memory. They are both dead, and their son, too. There was trouble enough about Luke's death, as it was.

How? He was found dead on the beach one morning, and there was a coroner's inquest. There were marks on his throat, but he had not been robbed. The verdict was that he had come to his end "by the hands or teeth of some person or animal unknown," for half the jury thought it might have been a big dog that had thrown him down and gripped his windpipe, though the skin of his throat was not broken. No one knew at what time he had gone out, nor where he had been. He was found lying on his back above high-water mark, and an old cardboard bandbox that had belonged to his wife lay under his hand, open. The lid had fallen off. He seemed to have been carrying home a skull in the box—doctors are fond of collecting such things. It had rolled out and lay near his head, and it was a remarkably fine skull, rather small, beautifully shaped, and very white, with perfect teeth. That is to say, the upper jaw was perfect, but there was no lower one at all, when I first saw it.

Yes, I found it here when I came. You see, it was kept very white and polished, like a thing meant to be kept under a glass case, and the people did not know where it came from, nor what to do with it; so they put it back into the bandbox and set it on the shelf of the cupboard in the best bedroom, and of course, they showed it to me when I took possession. I was taken down to the beach, too, to be shown the place where Luke was found, and the old fisherman explained just how he was lying, and the skull beside him. The only point he could not explain was why the skull had rolled up the sloping sand toward Luke's head instead of rolling downhill to his feet. It did not seem odd to me at the time, but I have often thought of it since, for the place is rather steep. I'll take you there tomorrow if you like—I made a sort of cairn of stones there afterward.

When he fell down, or was thrown down—whichever happened—the bandbox struck the sand, and the lid came off, and the thing came out and ought to have rolled down. But it didn't. It was close to his head, almost touching it, and turned with the face toward it. I say it didn't strike me as odd when the man told me; but I could not help thinking about it afterward, again and again, till I saw a picture of it all when I closed my eyes; and then I began to ask myself why the plaguey thing had rolled up instead of down, and why it stopped near Luke's head instead of anywhere else, a yard away, for instance.

You naturally want to know what conclusion I reached, don't you? None that at all explained the rolling, at all events. But I got something else into my head, after a time, that made me feel downright uncomfortable. Oh, I don't mean as to anything supernatural! There may be ghosts, or there may not be. If there are, I'm not inclined to believe that they can hurt living people except by frightening them, and for my part, I would rather face any shape of ghost than a fog in the Channel when it's crowded. No. What bothered me was just a foolish idea, that's all, and I cannot tell how it began, nor what made it grow until it turned into a certainty.

I was thinking about Luke and his poor wife one evening over my pipe and a dull book, when it occurred to me that the skull might possibly be hers, and I have never got rid of the thought since. You'll tell me there's no sense in it, no doubt; that Mrs. Pratt was buried like a Christian and is lying in the churchyard where they put her, and that it's perfectly preposterous to suppose her husband kept her skull in her old bandbox in his bedroom. All the same, in the face of reason, and common sense, and probability, I'm convinced that he did. Doctors do all sorts of queer things that would make men like you and me feel creepy, and those are just the things that don't seem probable, nor logical, nor sensible to us.

Then, don't you see?—if it really was her skull, poor woman, the only way of accounting for his having it is that he really killed her, and did it in that way, as the woman killed her husbands in the story, and that he was afraid there might be an examination some day which would betray him. You see, I told that too, and I believe it had really happened some fifty or sixty years ago. They dug up the three skulls, you know, and there was a small lump of lead rattling about in each one. That was what hanged the woman. Luke remembered that, I'm sure. I don't want to know what he did when he thought of it; my taste never ran in the direction of horrors, and I don't fancy you care for them either, do you? No. If you did, you might supply what is wanting to the story.

It must have been rather grim, eh? I wish I did not see the whole thing so distinctly, just as everything must have happened. He took it the night before she was buried, I'm sure, after the coffin had been shut, and when the servant girl was asleep. I would bet anything, that when he'd got it, he put something under the sheet in its place to fill it up and look like it. What do you suppose he put there, under the sheet?

I don't wonder you take me up on what I'm saying! First I tell you that I don't want to know what happened, and that I hate to think about horrors, and then I describe the whole thing to you as if I had seen it. I'm quite sure that it was her work bag that he put there. I remember the bag very well, for she always used it of an evening; it was made of brown plush, and when it was stuffed full it was about the size of—you understand. Yes, there I am, at it again! You may laugh at me, but you don't live here alone, where it was done, and you didn't tell Luke the story about the melted lead. I'm not nervous, I tell you, but sometimes I begin to feel that I understand why some people are. I dwell on all this when I'm alone, and I dream of it, and when that thing screams —well, frankly, I don't like the noise any more than you do, though I should be used to it by this time.

I ought not to be nervous. I've sailed in a haunted ship. There was a Man in the Top, and two-thirds of the crew died of the West Coast fever inside of ten days after we anchored; but I was all right, then and afterward. I have seen some ugly sights, too, just as you have, and all the rest of us. But nothing ever stuck in my head in the way this does.

You see, I've tried to get rid of the thing, but it doesn't like that. It wants to be there in its place, in Mrs. Pratt's bandbox in the cupboard in the best bedroom. It's not happy anywhere else. How do I know that? Because I've tried it. You don't suppose that I've not tried, do you? As long as it's there it only screams now and then, generally at this time of the year, but if I put it out of the house it goes on all night, and no servant will stay here twenty-four hours. As it is, I've often been left alone and have been obliged to shift for myself for a fortnight at a time. No one from the village would ever pass a night under the roof now, and as for selling the place, or even letting it, that's out of the question. The old women say that if I stay here I shall come to a bad end myself before long.

I'm not afraid of that. You smile at the mere idea that anyone could take such nonsense seriously. Quite right. It's utterly blatant nonsense, I agree with you. Didn't I tell you that it's a noise, after all, when you started and looked around as if you expected to see a ghost behind your chair?

I may be all wrong about that skull, and I like to think that I am—when I can. It may be just a fine specimen which Luke got somewhere long ago, and what rattles about inside when you shake it may be nothing but a pebble, or a bit of hard clay, or anything. Skulls that have lain long in the ground generally have something inside them that rattles, don't they? No, I've never tried to get it out, whatever it is; I'm afraid it might be lead, don't you see? And if it is, I don't want to know the fact, for I'd much rather not be sure. If it really is lead, I killed her quite as much as if I had done the deed myself. Anybody must see that, I should think. As long as I don't know for certain, I have the consolation of saying that it's all utterly ridiculous nonsense, that Mrs. Pratt died a natural death and that the beautiful skull belonged to Luke when he was a student in London. But if I were quite sure, I believe I should certainly have to leave the house; give up trying to sleep in the best bedroom where the cupboard is.

You ask me why I don't throw it into the pond—yes, but please don't call it a "confounded bugbear"—it doesn't like being called names.

There! Lord, what a shriek! I told you so! You're quite pale, man. Fill up your pipe, and take some more drink. Old Hollands never hurt anybody yet. I've seen a Dutchman in Java drink half a jug of Hulstkamp in a morning without turning a hair. I don't take much rum myself, because it doesn't agree with my rheumatism, but you are not rheumatic and it won't damage you. Besides, it's a very damp night outside. The wind is howling again, and it will soon be in the southwest; do you hear how the windows rattle? The tide must have turned too, by the moaning.

We should not have heard that thing again if you had not said that. I'm pretty sure we should not. Oh yes, if you choose to describe it as a coincidence, you are quite welcome, but I would rather that you should not call the thing names again, if you don't mind. It may be that the poor little woman hears, and perhaps it hurts her, don't you know? Ghost? No! You don't call anything a ghost that you can take in your hands and look at in broad daylight, and that rattles when you shake it. Do you, now? But it's something that hears and understands; there's no doubt about that.

I tried sleeping in the best bedroom when I first came to the house, just because it was the best and the most comfortable, but I had to give it up. It was their room, and there's the big bed she died in, and the cupboard is in the thickness of the wall, near the head on the left. That's where it likes to be kept, in its bandbox. I only used the room for a fortnight after I came, and then I turned out and took the little room downstairs next to the surgery, where Luke used to sleep when he expected to be called to a patient during the night.

I was always a good sleeper ashore; eight hours is my dose, eleven to seven when I'm alone, twelve to eight when I have a friend with me. But I could not sleep after three o'clock in the morning in that room—a quarter past, to be accurate—as a matter of fact, I timed it with my old pocket chronometer, which still keeps very good time, and it was always at exactly seventeen minutes past three. I wonder whether that was the hour when she died?

It was not what you heard. If it had been that I could not have stood it two nights. It was just a start and a moan and hard breathing for a few seconds in the cupboard, and it could never have waked me under ordinary circumstances, I'm sure. I suppose you are like me in that, and we are just like other people who have been to sea. No natural sounds disturb us at all, not all the racket of a square-rigger hove to in a heavy gale, or rolling on her beam ends before the wind. But if a lead pencil gets adrift and rattles in the drawer of your cabin table, you are awake in a moment. Just so—you always understand. Very well, the noise in the cupboard was no louder than that, but it waked me instantly.

I said it was like a "start." I know what I mean, but it's hard to explain without seeming to talk nonsense. Of course you cannot exactly "hear" a person "start"; at the most, you might hear the quick drawing of the breath between the parted lips and closed teeth, and the almost imperceptible sound of clothing that moved suddenly though very slightly. It was like that.

You know how one feels what a sailing vessel is going to do, two or three seconds before she does it, when one has the wheel. Riders say the same thing of a horse, but that's less strange, because the horse is a live animal with feelings of its own, and only poets and landsmen talk about a ship being alive, and all that. But I have always felt somehow that besides being a steaming machine or a sailing machine for carrying weights, a vessel at sea is a sensitive instrument, and a means of communication between nature and man, and most particularly the man at the wheel, if she is steered by hand. She takes her impressions directly from wind and sea, tide and stream, and transmits them to the man's hand, just as the wireless telegraph picks up the interrupted currents aloft and turns them out below in the form of a message.

You see what I am driving at; I felt that something started in the cupboard, and I felt it so vividly that I heard it, though there may have been nothing to hear, and the sound inside my head waked me suddenly. But I really heard the other noise. It was as if it were muffled inside a box, as far away as if it came through a long distance telephone; and yet I knew that it was inside the cupboard near the head of my bed. My hair did not bristle and my blood did not run cold that time. I simply resented being waked up by something that had no business to make a noise, any more than a pencil should rattle in the drawer of my cabin on board ship. For I did not understand; I just supposed that the cupboard had some communication with the outside air, and that the wind had got in and was moaning through it with a sort of very faint screech. I struck a light and looked at my watch, and it was seventeen minutes past three. Then I turned over and went to sleep on my right ear. That's my good one; I'm pretty deaf with the other, for I struck the water with it when I was a lad in diving from the foretopsail yard. Silly thing to do, it was, but the result is very convenient when I want to sleep when there's a noise.

That was the first night, and the same thing happened again and several times afterward, but not regularly, though it was always at the same time to a second; perhaps I was sometimes sleeping on my good ear, and sometimes not. I overhauled the cupboard and there was no way by which the wind could get in, or anything else, for the door makes a good fit, having been meant to keep out moths, I suppose; Mrs. Pratt must have kept her winter things in it, for it still smells of camphor and turpentine.

After about a fortnight I had had enough of the noises. So far I had said to myself that it would be silly to yield to it and take the skull out of the room. Things always look differently by daylight, don't they? But the voice grew louder—I suppose one may call it a voice—and it got inside my deaf ear, too, one night. I realized that when I was wide awake, for my good ear was jammed down on the pillow, and I ought not to have heard a foghorn in that position. But I heard that, and it made me lose my temper, unless it scared me, for sometimes the two are not far apart. I struck a light and got up, and I opened the cupboard, grabbed the bandbox and threw it out of the window, as far as I could.

Then my hair stood on end. The thing screamed in the air, like a shell from a twelve-inch gun. It fell on the other side of the road. The night was very dark, and I could not see it fall, but I know it fell beyond the road. The window is just over the front door, it's fifteen yards to the fence, more or less, and the road is ten yards wide. There's a quickset hedge beyond, along the glebe that belongs to the vicarage.

I did not sleep much more that night. It was not more than half an hour after I had thrown the bandbox out when I heard a shriek outside—like what we've had tonight, but worse, more despairing, I should call it; and may have been my imagination, but I could have sworn that the screams came nearer and nearer each time. I lit a pipe, and walked up and down for a bit, and then took a book and sat up reading, but I'll be hanged if I can remember what I read nor even what the book was, for every now and then a shriek came up that would have made a dead man turn in his coffin.

A little before dawn someone knocked at the front door. There was no mistaking that for anything else, and I opened my window and looked down, for I guessed that someone wanted the doctor, supposing that the new man had taken Luke's house. It was rather a mild relief to hear a human knock after that awful noise.

You cannot see the door from above, owing to the little porch. The knocking came again, and I called out, asking who was there, but nobody answered, though the knock was repeated. I sang out again, and said that the doctor did not live here any longer. There was no answer, but it occurred to me that it might be some old countryman who was stone deaf. So I took my candle and went down to open the door. Upon my word, I was not thinking of the thing yet, and I had almost forgotten the other noises. I went down convinced that I should find somebody outside, on the doorstep, with a message. I set the candle on the hall table, so that the wind should not blow it out when I opened. While I was drawing the old-fashioned bolt I heard the knocking again. It was not loud, and it had a queer, hollow sound, now that I was close to it, I remember, but I certainly thought it was made by some person who wanted to get in.

It wasn't. There was nobody there, but as I opened the door inward, standing a little on one side, so as to see out at once, something rolled across the threshold and stopped against my foot.

I drew back as I felt it, for I knew what it was before I looked down. I cannot tell you how I knew, and it seemed unreasonable, for I am still quite sure that I had thrown it across the road. It's a

French window that opens wide, and I got a good swing when I flung it out. Besides, when I went out early in the morning, I found the bandbox beyond the thickset hedge.

You may think it opened when I threw it, and that the skull dropped out; but that's impossible, for nobody could throw an empty cardboard box so far. It's out of the question; you might as well try to fling a ball of paper twenty-five yards, or a blown bird's egg.

To go back, I shut and bolted the hall door, picked the thing up carefully, and put it on the table beside the candle. I did that mechanically, as one instinctively does the right thing in danger without thinking at all—unless one does the opposite. It may seem odd, but I believe that my first thought had been that somebody might come and find me there on the threshold while it was resting against my foot, lying a little on its side, and turning one hollow eye up at my face, as if it meant to accuse me. And the light and shadow from the candle played in the hollows of the eyes as it stood on the table, so that they seemed to open and shut at me. Then the candle went out quite unexpectedly, though the door was fastened and there was not the least draft; and I used up at least half a dozen matches before it would burn again.

I sat down rather suddenly, without quite knowing why. Probably I had been badly frightened, and perhaps you will admit there was no great shame in being scared. The thing had come home, and it wanted to go upstairs, back to its cupboard. I sat still and stared at it for a bit, till I began to feel very cold; then I took it and carried it up and set it in its place, and I remember that I spoke to it, and promised that it should have its bandbox again in the morning.

You want to know whether I stayed in the room till daybreak? Yes, but I kept a light burning, and sat up smoking and reading, most likely out of fright; plain, undeniable fear, and you need not call it cowardice either, for that's not the same thing. I could not have stayed alone with that thing in the cupboard; I should have been scared to death, though I'm not more timid than other people. Confound it all man, it had crossed the road alone, and had got up the doorstep and had knocked to be let in.

When the dawn came, I put on my boots and went out to find

the bandbox. I had to go a good way round, by the gate near the highroad, and I found the box open and hanging on the other side of the hedge. It had caught on the twigs by the string, and the lid had fallen off and was lying on the ground below it. That shows that it did not open till it was well over; and if it had not opened as soon as it left my hand, what was inside it must have gone beyond the road too.

That's all. I took the box upstairs to the cupboard, and put the skull back and locked it up. When the girl brought me my breakfast she said she was very sorry, but that she must go, and she did not care if she lost her month's wages. I looked at her, and her face was a sort of greenish, yellowish white. I pretended to be surprised, and asked what was the matter; but that was of no use, for she just turned on me and wanted to know whether I meant to stay in a haunted house, and how long I expected to live if I did, for though she noticed I was sometimes a little hard of hearing, she did not believe that even I could sleep through those screams again—and if I could, why had I been moving about the house and opening and shutting the front door, between three and four in the morning? There was no answering that, since she had heard me, so off she went, and I was left to myself. I went down to the village during the morning and found a woman who was willing to come and do the little work there is and cook my dinner, on condition that she might go home every night. As for me, I moved upstairs that day, and I have never tried to sleep in the best bedroom since. After a while I got a brace of middle-aged Scotch servants from London, and things were quiet enough for a long time. I began by telling them that the house was in a very exposed position, and that the wind whistled round it a good deal in the autumn and winter, which had given it a bad name in the village, the Cornish people being inclined to superstition and telling ghost stories. The two hard-faced, sandy-haired sisters almost smiled, and they answered with great contempt that they had no great opinion of any Southern bogy whatever, having been in service in two English haunted houses, where they had never seen so much as the Boy in Gray, whom they reckoned no very particular rarity in Forfashire.

They stayed with me several months, and while they were in

the house we had peace and quiet. One of them is here again now, but she went away with her sister within the year. This one—she was the cook—married the sexton, who works in my garden. That's the way of it. It's a small village and he has not much to do, and he knows enough about flowers to help me nicely, besides doing most of the hard work; for though I'm fond of exercise, I'm getting a little stiff in the hinges. He's a sober, silent sort of fellow, who minds his own business, and he was a widower when I came here—Trehearn is his name, James Trehearn. The Scotch sisters would not admit that there was anything wrong with the house, but when November came they gave me warning that they were going, on the ground that the chapel was such a long walk from here, being in the next parish, and that they could not possibly go to our church. But the younger one came back in the spring, and as soon as the banns could be published, she was married to James Trehearn by the vicar, and she seems to have no scruples about hearing him preach since then. I'm quite satisfied, if she is! The couple live in a small cottage that looks over the churchyard.

I suppose you are wondering what all this has to do with what I was talking about. I'm alone so much that when an old friend comes to see me, I sometimes go on talking just for the sake of hearing my own voice. But in this case there really is a connection of ideas. It was James Trehearn who buried poor Mrs. Pratt, and her husband after her in the same grave, and it's not far from the back of his cottage. That's the connection in my mind, you see. It's plain enough. He knows something; I'm quite sure that he does, by his manner, though he's such a reticent beggar.

Yes, I'm alone in the house at night now, for Mrs. Trehearn does everything herself, and when I have a friend the sexton's niece comes in to wait on the table. He takes his wife home every evening in the winter, but in summer, when there's light, she goes by herself. She's not a nervous woman, but she's less sure than she used to be that there are no bogies in England worth a Scotchwoman's notice. Isn't it amusing, the idea that Scotland has a monopoly of the supernatural? Odd sort of national pride, I call that, don't you?

That's a good fire, isn't it? When driftwood gets started at last there's nothing like it, I think. Yes, we get lots of it, for I'm sorry to say there are still a great many wrecks about here. It's a lonely coast, and you may have all the wood you want for the trouble of bringing it in. Trehearn and I borrow a cart now and then, and load between here and the Spit. I hate a coal fire when I can get wood of any sort. A log is company, even if it's only a piece of deck beam or timber sawn off, and the salt in it makes pretty sparks. See how they fly, like Japanese hand-fireworks! Upon my word, with an old friend and a good fire and a pipe, one forgets all about that thing upstairs, especially now that the wind has moderated. It's only a lull, though, and it will blow a gale before morning.

You think you would like to see the skull? I've no objection. There's no reason why you shouldn't have a look at it, and you never saw a more perfect one in your life, except that there are two front teeth missing in the lower jaw.

Oh yes—I had not told you about the jaw yet. Trehearn found it in the garden last spring when he was digging a pit for a new asparagus bed. You know we make asparagus beds six or eight feet deep here. Yes, yes—I had forgotten to tell you that. He was digging straight down, just as he digs a grave; if you want a good asparagus bed made, I advise you to get a sexton to make it for you. Those fellows have a wonderful knack at that sort of digging.

Trehearn had got down about three feet when he cut into a mass of white lime in the side of the trench. He had noticed that the earth was a little looser there, though he says it had not been disturbed for a number of years. I suppose he thought that even old lime might not be good for asparagus, so he broke it out and threw it up. It was pretty hard, he says, in biggish lumps, and out of sheer force of habit he cracked the lumps with his spade as they lay outside the pit beside him; the jawbone of a skull dropped out of one of the pieces. He thinks he must have knocked out the two front teeth in breaking up the lime, but he did not see them anywhere. He's a very experienced man in such things, as you may imagine, and he said at once that the jaw had probably belonged to a young woman, and that the teeth had been complete when she died. He brought it to me, and asked me if I wanted to keep it; if I did not, he said he would drop it into the next grave he made in the churchyard, as he supposed it was a Christian jaw, and ought to have decent burial, wherever the rest of the body might be. I told him that doctors often put bones into quicklime to whiten them nicely, and that I supposed Dr. Pratt had once had a little lime pit in the garden for that purpose, and had forgotten the jaw. Trehearn looked at me quietly.

"Maybe it fitted that skull that used to be in the cupboard upstairs, sir," he said. "Maybe Dr. Pratt had put the skull into the lime to clean it, or something, and when he took it out he left the lower jaw behind. There's some human hair sticking in the lime, sir."

I saw that there was, and that was what Trehearn said. If he did not suspect something, why in the world would he have suggested that the jaw might fit the skull? Besides, it did. That's proof that he knows more than he cares to tell. Do you suppose he looked before she was buried? Or perhaps—when he buried Luke in the same grave—

Well, well, it's of no use to go over that, is it? I said I would keep the jaw with the skull, and I took it upstairs and fitted it into its place. There's not the slightest doubt about the two belonging together, and together they are.

Trehearn knows several things. We were talking about plastering the kitchen a while ago, and he happened to remember that it had not been done since the very week when Mrs. Pratt died. He did not say that the mason must have left some lime on the place, but he thought it, and that it was the very same lime he had found in the asparagus pit. He knows a lot. Trehearn is one of your silent beggars who can put two and two together. That grave is very near the back of his cottage, too, and he's one of the quickest men with a spade I ever saw. If he wanted to know the truth, he could, and no one else would ever be the wiser unless he chose to tell. In a quiet village like ours, people don't go and spend the night in the churchyard to see whether the sexton potters about by himself between ten o'clock and daylight.

What is awful to think of, is Luke's deliberation, if he did it; his cool certainty that no one would find him out; above all, his nerve, for that must have been extraordinary. I sometimes think it's bad enough to live in the place where it was done, if it really was done. I always put in the condition, you see, for the sake of his memory, and a little bit for my own sake, too.

I'll go upstairs and fetch the box in a minute. Let me light my pipe; there's no hurry! We had supper early, and it's only half-past nine o'clock. I never let a friend go to bed before twelve, or with less than three glasses—you may have as many as you like, but you shan't have less, for the sake of old times.

It's breezing up again, do you hear? That was only a lull just now, and we are going to have a bad night.

A thing happened that made me start a little when I found that the jaw fitted exactly. I'm not very easily startled in that way myself, but I have seen people make a quick movement, drawing their breath sharply, when they thought they were alone and suddenly turned and saw someone very near them. Nobody can call that fear. You wouldn't, would you? No. Well, just when I had set the jaw in its place under the skull, the teeth closed sharply on my finger. It felt exactly as if it were biting me hard, and I confess that I jumped before I realized that I had been pressing the jaw and the skull together with my other hand. I assure you that I was not at all nervous. It was broad daylight, too, and a fine day, and the sun was streaming into the best bedroom. It would have been absurd to be nervous, and it was only a quick mistaken impression, but it really made me feel queer. Somehow, it made me think of the funny verdict of the coroner's jury on Luke's death, "by the hand or teeth of some person or animal unknown." Ever since that I've wished I had seen those marks on his throat, though the lower jaw was missing then.

I have often seen a man do insane things with his hands that he does not realize at all. I once saw a man hanging on by an old awning top with one hand, leaning backward, outboard, with all his weight on it, and he was just cutting the stop with the knife in his other hand when I got my arms around him. We were in mid-ocean, going twenty knots. He had not the smallest idea what he was doing; neither had I when I managed to pinch my finger between the teeth of that thing, I can feel it now. It was exactly as if it were alive and were trying to bite me. It would if it could, for I know it hates me, poor thing! Do you suppose that what rattles about inside is really a bit of lead? Well, I'll get the box down presently, and if whatever it is happens to drop out into your hands that's your affair. If it's only a clod of earth or a pebble, the whole matter would be off my mind, and I don't believe I should ever think of the skull again; but somehow I cannot bring myself to shake out the bit of hard stuff myself. The mere idea that it may be lead makes me confoundedly uncomfortable, yet I've got the conviction that I shall know before long. I shall certainly know, I'm sure Trehearn knows, but he's such a silent beggar.

I'll go upstairs now and get it. What? You had better go with me? Ha, ha! do you think I'm afraid of a bandbox and a noise? Nonsense!

Bother the candle, it won't light! As if the ridiculous thing understood what it's wanted for! Look at that—the third match. They light fast enough for my pipe. There, do you see? It's a fresh box, just out of the tin safe where I keep the supply on account of the dampness. Oh, you think the wick of the candle may be damp, do you? All right, I'll light the beastly thing in the fire. That won't go out, at all events. Yes, it sputters a bit, but it will keep lighted now. It burns just like any other candle, doesn't it? The fact is, candles are not very good about here. I don't know where they come from, but they have a way of burning low occasionally, with a greenish flame that spits tiny sparks, and I'm often annoyed by their going out by themselves. It cannot be helped, for it will be long before we have electricity in our village. It really is rather a poor light, isn't it?

You think I had better leave you the candle and take the lamp, do you? I don't like to carry lamps about, that's the truth. I never dropped one in my life, but I have always thought I might, and it's so confoundedly dangerous if you do. Besides, I am pretty well used to these rotten candles by this time.

You may as well finish that glass while I'm getting it, for I don't mean to let you off with less than three before you go to bed. You won't have to go upstairs, either, for I've put you in the old study next to the surgery—that's where I used to live myself. The fact is, I never ask a friend to sleep upstairs now. The last man who did was Crackenthorpe, and he said he was kept awake all night. You remember old Crack, don't you? He stuck to the Service, and they've just made him an admiral. Yes, I'm off now—unless the candle goes out. I couldn't help asking if you remembered Crackenthorpe. If anyone had told us that the skinny little idiot he used to be was to turn out the most successful of the lot of us, we should have laughed at the idea, shouldn't we? You and I did not do badly, it's true—but I'm really going now. I don't mean to let you think that I've been putting it off by talking! As if there were anything to be afraid of! If I were scared, I should tell you so quite frankly, and get you to go upstairs with me.

Here's the box. I brought it down very carefully, so as not to disturb it, poor thing. You see, if it were shaken, the jaw might get separated from it again, and I'm sure it wouldn't like that. Yes, the candle went out as I was coming downstairs, but that was the draft from the leaky window on the landing. Did you hear anything? Yes, there was another scream. Am I pale, do you say? That's nothing. My heart is a little queer sometimes, and I went upstairs too fast. In fact, that's one reason why I prefer to live altogether on the ground floor.

Wherever that shriek came from, it was not from the skull, for I had the box in my hand when I heard the noise, and here it is now; so we have proved definitely that the screams are produced by something else. I've no doubt I shall find out some day what makes them. Some crevice in the wall, of course, or a crack in a chimney, or a chink in the frame of a window. That's the way all ghost stories end in real life. Do you know, I'm jolly glad I thought of going up and bringing it down for you to see, for that last shriek settles the question. To think that I should have been so weak as to fancy that the poor skull could really cry out like a living thing!

Now I'll open the box, and we'll take it out and look at it under the bright light. It's rather awful to think that the poor lady used to sit there, in your chair, evening after evening, in just the same light, isn't it? But then—I've made up my mind that it's all rubbish from beginning to end, and that it's just an old skull that Luke had when he was a student; and perhaps he put it into the lime merely to whiten it, and could not find the jaw.

I made a seal on the string, you see, after I had put the jaw in its place, and I wrote on the cover. There's the old white label on it still, from the milliner's addressed to Mrs. Pratt when the hat was sent to her, and as there was room I wrote on the edge: "A skull, once the property of the late Luke Pratt, M.D." I don't quite know why I wrote that, unless it was with the idea of explaining how the thing happened to be in my possession. I cannot help wondering sometimes what sort of hat it was that came in the bandbox. What color was it, do you think? Was it a gay spring hat with a bobbing feather and pretty ribands? Strange that the very same box should hold the head that wore the finery—perhaps. No—we made up our minds that it just came from the hospital in London where Luke did his time. It's far better to look at it in that light, isn't it? There's no more connection between that skull and poor Mrs. Pratt than there was between my story about the lead and—

Good Lord! Take the lamp—don't let it go out, if you can help it—I'll have the window fastened in a second—I say, what a gale! There, it's out! I told you so! Never mind, there's the firelight—I've got the window shut—the bolt was only half down. Was the box blown off the table? Where the deuce is it? There! That won't open again, for I've put up the bar. Good dodge, an old fashioned bar—there's nothing like it. Now, you find the bandbox while I light the lamp. Confound those wretched matches! Yes, a pipe spill is better—it must light in the fire—I hadn't thought of it—thank you—there we are again. Now, where's the box? Yes, put it back on the table, and we'll open it.

That's the first time I've known the wind to burst that window open; but it was partly carelessness on my part when I last shut it. Yes, of course I heard the scream. It seemed to go all around the house before it broke in at the window. That proves that it's always been the wind and nothing else, doesn't it? When it was not the wind, it was my imagination. I've always been a very imaginative man: I must have been, though I did not know it. As we grow older we understand ourselves better, don't you know?

I'll have a drop of Hulstkamp neat, by way of an exception,

since you are filling up your glass. That damp gust chilled me, and with my rheumatic tendency I'm very much afraid of a chill, for the cold sometimes seems to stick in my joints all winter when it once gets in.

By George, that's good stuff! I'll just light a fresh pipe, now that everything is snug again, and then we'll open the box. I'm so glad we heard that last scream together, with the skull here on the table between us, for a thing cannot possibly be in two places at the same time, and the noise most certainly came from outside, as any noise the wind makes must. You thought you heard it scream through the room after the window burst open? Oh yes, so did I but that was natural enough when everything was open. Of course we heard the wind, What could one expect?

Look here please. I want you to see that the seal is intact before we open the box together. Will you take my glasses? No, you have your own. All right. The seal is sound, you see, and you can read the words of the motto easily, "Sweet and low"— that's it—because the poem goes on "Wind of the Western sea," and says, "Blow him again to me," and all that. Here is the seal of my watch chain, where it's hung for more than forty years. My poor little wife gave it to me when I was courting, and I never had any other. It was just like her to think of those words—she was always fond of Tennyson.

It's of no use to cut the string, for it's fastened to the box, so I'll break the wax and untie the knot, and afterward we'll seal it up again. You see, I like to feel that the thing is safe in its place, and that nobody can take it out. Not that I should suspect Trehearn of meddling with it, but I always feel that he knows a lot more than he tells.

You see, I've managed it without breaking the string, though when I fastened it I never expected to open the bandbox again. The lid comes off easily enough. There! Now look!

What? Nothing in it? Empty? It's gone, man, the skull is gone!

No, there's nothing the matter with me. I'm only trying to collect my thoughts. It's so strange. I'm positively certain that it was inside when I put on the seal last spring. I can't have imagined that: it's utterly impossible. If I ever took a stiff glass with a friend now and then, I would admit that I might have made some idiotic mistake when I had taken too much. But I don't, and I never did. A pint of ale at supper and half a go of rum at bedtime was the most I ever took in my good days. I believe it's always we sober fellows who get rheumatism and gout! Yet there was my seal, and there is the empty bandbox. That's plain enough.

I say, I don't half like this. It's not right. There's something wrong about it, in my opinion. You needn't talk to me about supernatural manifestations, for I don't believe in them, not a little bit! Somebody must have tampered with the seal and stolen the skull. Sometimes when I go out to work in the garden in summer, I leave my watch and chain on the table. Trehearn must have taken the seal then, and used it, for he would be quite sure that I should not come in for at least an hour.

If it was not Trehearn—oh, don't talk to me about the possibility that the thing has got out by itself! If it has, it must be somewhere about the house, in some out of the way corner, waiting. We may come upon it anywhere, waiting for us, don't you know?—just waiting in the dark. Then it will scream at me; it will shriek at me in the dark, for it hates me, I tell you!

The bandbox is quite empty. We are not dreaming, either of us. There, turn it upside down.

What's that? Something fell out as I turned it over. It's on the floor, it's near your feet, I know it is, and we must find it. Help me to find it, man. Have you got it? For God's sake, give it to me, quickly!

Lead! I knew it when I heard it fall. I knew it couldn't be anything else by the little thud it made on the hearth-rug. So it was lead after all, and Luke did it.

I feel a little bit shaken up—not exactly nervous, you know, but badly shaken up, that's the fact. Anybody would, I should think. After all, you cannot say that it's fear of the thing, for I went up and brought it down—at least, I believed I was bringing it down, and that's the same thing, and by George, rather than give in to such silly nonsense, I'll take the box upstairs again and put it back in its place. It's not that. It's the certainty that the poor little woman came to her end in that way, by my fault, because I told the story. That's what's so dreadful. Somehow, I had always hoped that I should never be quite sure of it, but there is no doubting it now. Look at that!

Look at it! That little lump of lead with no particular shape. Think of what it did, man! Doesn't it make you shiver? He gave her something to make her sleep, of course, but there must have been one moment of awful agony. Think of having boiling lead poured into your brain. Think of it. She was dead before she could scream, but only think of—oh! there it is again—it's just outside—I know it's just outside—I can't keep it out of my head!—oh!—oh!

You thought I had fainted? No, I wish I had, for it would have stopped sooner. It's all very well to say that it's only a noise, and that a noise never hurt anybody—you're as white as a shroud yourself. There's only one thing to be done, if we hope to close any eye tonight. We must find it and put it back into its bandbox and shut it up in the cupboard where it likes to be. I don't know how it got out, but it wants to get in again. That's why it screams so awfully tonight—it was never so bad as this— never since I first—

Bury it? Yes, if we can find it, we'll bury it, if it takes us all night. We'll bury it six feet deep and ram down the earth over it so that it shall never get out again, and if it screams, we shall hardly hear it so deep down. Quick, we'll get the lantern and look for it. It cannot be far away; I'm sure it's just outside—it was coming in when I shut the window, I know it.

Yes, you're quite right. I'm losing my senses, and I must get hold of myself. Don't speak to me for a minute or two; I'll sit quite still and keep my eyes shut and repeat something I know. That's the best way.

"Add together the altitude, the latitude, and the polar distance, divide by two and subtract the altitude from the half-sum; then add the logarithm of the secant of the latitude, the cosecant of the polar distance, the cosine of the half-sum and the sine of the half-sum minus the altitude"—there! Don't say that I'm out of my senses, for my memory is all right, isn't it?

Of course, you may say that it's mechanical, and that we never forget the things we learned when we were boys and have used almost every day for a lifetime. But that's the very point. When a man is going crazy, it's the mechanical part of his mind that gets out of order and won't work right; he remembers things that never happened, or he sees things that aren't real, or he hears noises when there is perfect silence. That's not what is the matter with either of us, is it?

Come, we'll get the lantern and go round the house. It's not raining—only blowing like old boots, as we used to say. The lantern is in the cupboard under the stairs in the hall, and I always keep it trimmed in case of a wreck.

No use to look for the thing? I don't see how you can say that. It was nonsense to talk of burying it, of course, for it doesn't want to be buried; it wants to go back into its bandbox and be taken upstairs, poor thing! Trehearn took it out, I know, and made the seal over again. Perhaps he took it to the churchyard and he may have meant well. I daresay he thought that it would not scream any more if it were quietly laid in consecrated ground, near where it belongs. But it has come home. Yes, that's it. He's not half a bad fellow, Trehearn, and rather religiously inclined, I think. Doesn't that sound natural, and reasonable, and well meant? He supposed it screamed because it was not decently buried—with the rest. But he was wrong. How should he know it screams at me because it hates me, and because it's my fault that there was that little lump of lead in it?

No use to look for it anyhow? Nonsense! I tell you it wants to be found— Hark! what's that knocking? Do you hear it? Knock—knock—knock—three times, then a pause, and then again. It has a hollow sound, hasn't it?

It has come home. I've heard that knock before. It wants to come in and be taken upstairs, in its box. It's at the front door.

Will you come with me? We'll take it in. Yes, I own that I don't like to go alone and open the door. The thing will roll in and stop against my foot, just as it did before, and the light will go out. I'm a good deal shaken by finding that bit of lead, and besides, my heart isn't quite right—too much strong tobacco, perhaps. Besides, I'm quite willing to own that I'm a bit nervous tonight, if I never was before in my life.

That's right, come along! I'll take the box with me, so as not to come back. Do you hear the knocking? It's not like any other knocking I ever heard. If you will hold the door open, I can find the lantern under the stairs by the light from this room without bringing the lamp into the hall—it would only go out.

The thing knows we are coming—hark! It's impatient to get in. Don't shut the door till the lantern is ready, whatever you do. There will be the usual trouble with the matches, I suppose— no, the first one, by Jove! I tell you it wants to get in, so there's no trouble. All right with that door now; shut it, please. Now come and hold the lantern, for it's blowing so hard outside that I shall have to use both hands. That's it, hold the light low. Do you hear the knocking still? Here goes—I'll just open enough with my foot against the bottom of the door—now!

Catch it! It's only the wind that blows it across the floor, that's all—there's half a hurricane outside, I tell you! Have you got it? The bandbox is on the table. One minute, and I'll have the bar up. There!

Why did you throw it into the box so roughly? It doesn't like that, you know.

What do you say? Bitten your hand? Nonsense, man! You did just what I did. You pressed the jaws together with your other hand and pinched yourself. Let me see. You don't mean to say you have drawn blood? You must have squeezed hard, by Jove, for the skin is certainly torn. I'll give you some carbolic solution for it before we go to bed, for they say a scratch from the skull's tooth may go bad and give trouble.

Come inside and let me see it by the lamp. I'll bring the bandbox—never mind the lantern, it may just as well burn in the hall, for I shall need it presently when I go up the stairs. Yes, shut the door if you will; it makes it more cheerful and bright. Is your finger still bleeding? I'll get you the carbolic in an instant; just let me see the thing.

Ugh! There's a drop of blood on the upper jaw. It's on the eye-tooth. Ghastly, isn't it? When I saw it running along the floor of the hall, the strength almost went out of my hands, and I felt my knees bending; then I understood that it was the gale, driving it over the smooth boards. You don't blame me? No, I should think not! We were boys together, and we've seen a thing or two, and we may just as well own to each other that we were both in a beastly funk when it slid across the floor at you. No wonder you pinched your finger picking it up, after that, if I did the same thing out of sheer nervousness, in broad daylight, with the sun streaming in on me.

Strange that the jaw should stick to it so closely, isn't it? I suppose it's the dampness, for it shuts like a vise—I have wiped off the drop of blood, for it was not nice to look at. I'm not going to try to open the jaws, don't be afraid! I shall not play any tricks with the poor thing, but I'll just seal the box again, and we'll take it upstairs and put it away where it wants to be. The wax is on the writing table by the window. Thank you. It will be long before I leave my seal lying about again, for Trehearn to use, I can tell you. Explain? I don't explain natural phenomena, but if you choose to think that Trehearn had hidden it somewhere in the bushes, and that the gale blew it into the house against the door, and made it knock, as if it wanted to be let in, you're not thinking the impossible, and I'm quite ready to agree with you.

Do you see that? You can swear that you've actually seen me seal it this time, in case anything of the kind should occur again. The wax fastens the strings to the lid, which cannot possibly be lifted, even enough to get in one finger. You're quite satisfied, aren't you? Yes. Besides, I shall lock the cupboard and keep the key in my pocket hereafter.

Now we can take the lantern and go upstairs. Do you know? I'm very much inclined to agree with your theory that the wind blew it against the house. I'll go ahead, for I know the stairs; just hold the lantern near my feet as we go up. How the wind howls and whistles! Did you feel the sand on the floor under your shoes as we crossed the hall?

Yes—this is the door of the best bedroom. Hold up the lantern, please. This side, by the head of the bed. I left the cupboard open when I got the box. Isn't it queer how the faint odor of women's dresses will hang about an old closet for years? This is the shelf. You've seen me set the box there, and now you see me turn the key and put it into my pocket. So that's done!

Good night. Are you sure you're quite comfortable? It's not much of a room, but I daresay you would as soon sleep here as upstairs tonight. If you want anything, sing out; there's only a lath and plaster partition between us. There's not so much wind on this side by half. There's the Hollands on the table, if you'll have one more nightcap. No? Well, do as you please. Good night again, and don't dream about that thing, if you can.

The following paragraph appeared in the *Penraddon News,* 23rd November, 1906:

MYSTERIOUS DEATH OF A RETIRED SEA CAPTAIN

The village of Tredcombe is much disturbed by the strange death of Captain Charles Braddock, and all sorts of impossible stories are circulating with regard to the circumstances, which certainly seem difficult of explanation. The retired captain, who had successfully commanded in his time the largest and fastest liners belonging to one of the principal transatlantic steamship companies, was found dead in his bed on Tuesday morning in his own cottage, a quarter of a mile from the village. An examination was made at once by the local practitioner, which revealed the horrible fact that the deceased had been bitten in the throat by a human assailant, with such amazing force as to crush the windpipe and cause death. The marks of the teeth of both jaws were so plainly visible on the skin that they could be counted, but the perpetrator of the deed had evidently lost two lower middle incisors. It is hoped that this peculiarity may help identify the murderer, who can only be a dangerous escaped maniac. The deceased, though over sixty-five years of age, is said to have been a hale man of considerable physical strength, and it is remarkable that no signs of any struggle were visible in the room, nor could it be ascertained how the murderer had entered the house. Warning has been sent to all the insane asylums in the United Kingdom, but as yet no information has been received regarding the escape of any dangerous patient.

The coroner's jury returned a somewhat singular verdict that Captain Braddock came to his death "by the hands or teeth of some person unknown." The local surgeon is said to have expressed privately the opinion that the maniac is a woman, a view he deduces for the small size of the jaws, as shown by the marks of the teeth. The whole affair is shrouded in mystery. Captain Braddock was a widower, and lived alone. He leaves no children.

[Note: *Students of ghost lore and haunted houses will find the foundation of the foregoing story in the legends about a skull which is still preserved in the farm house called Bettiscombe Manor, situated, I believe, on the Dorsetshire coast.*]

The Haunted Station

BY HUME NISBET

It looked as if a curse rested upon it, even under that glorious southern morn which transformed all that it touched into old oak and silver-bronze.

I use the term silver-bronze, because I can think of no other combination to express that peculiar bronzy tarnish, like silver that has lain covered for a time, which the moonlight in the tropics gives to the near objects upon which it falls—tarnished silver surfaces and deep sepia-tinted shadows.

I felt the weird influence of that curse even as I crawled into the gully that led to it; a shiver ran over me as one feels when they say some stranger is passing over your future grave; a chill gripped at my vitals as I glanced about me apprehensively, expectant of something ghoulish and unnatural to come upon me from the sepulchral gloom and mystery of the overhanging boulders under which I was dragging my wearied limbs. A deathly silence brooded within this rutlike and treeless gully that formed the only passage from the arid desert over which I had struggled, famishing and desperate; where it led to I neither knew nor cared, so that it did not end in a cul-de-sac.

At last I came to what I least expected to see in that part, a house of two stories, with the double gables facing me as it stood on a mound in front of a water hole, the mellow full moon behind the shingly roof, and glittering whitely as it repeated itself in the still water against the inky blackness of the reflections cast by the denser masses of the house and vegetation about it.

It seemed to be a wooden erection, such as squatters first raise for their homesteads after they have decided to stay; the intermediate kind of station, which takes the place of the temporary shanty while the proprietor's bank account is rapidly swelling, and his children are being educated in the city boarding schools to know their own social importance. By and by, when he is out of the mortgagee's hands, he may discard this comfortable house, as he has done his shanty, and go in for stateliness and stone work, but to the tramp or the bushranger, the present house is the most welcome sight, for it promises to the one shelter, and to the other a prospect of loot.

There was a veranda round the basement that stood clear above the earth on piles, with a broad ladder stair leading down to the garden walk which terminated at the edge of the pool or water hole; under the iron roofing of the veranda I could make out the vague indications of french doors that led to the reception rooms, etc., while above them were bedroom windows, all dark with the exception of one of the upper windows, the second one from the end gable, through which a pale greenish light streamed faintly.

Behind the house, or rather from the center of it, as I afterwards found out, projected a gigantic and lifeless gum tree, which spread its fantastic limbs and branches wildly over the roof, and behind that again a mass of chaotic and planted greenery, all softened and generalized in the thin silvery mist which emanated from the pool and hovered over the ground.

At the first glance it appeared to be the abode of a romantic owner, who had fixed upon a picturesque site, and afterwards devoted himself to making it comfortable as well as beautiful. He had planted creepers and trained them over the walls, passion fruit and vines clung closely to the posts and trellis work and broke the square outlines of windows and angles, a wild tangle of shrubs and flowers covered the mound in front and trailed into the water without much order, so that it looked like the abode of an imaginative poet rather than the station of a practical, money-grubbing squatter.

As I quitted the desolate and rockbound gully and entered upon this romantic domain, I could not help admiring the artful manner in which the owner had left Nature alone where he could do so; the gum trees which he had found there were still left as they must have been for ages, great trees shooting up hundreds of feet into the air, some of them gaunt and bald with time, others with their leafage still in a flourishing condition, while the more youthful trees were springing out of the fertile soil in all directions, giving the approach the appearance of an English park, particularly with the heavy night dew that glistened over them.

But the chill was still upon me that had gripped me at the entrance of the gully, and the same lifeless silence brooded over the house, garden, pool and forest which had awed me amongst the boulders, so that as I paused at the edge of the water and regarded the house, I again shuddered as if specters were round me, and murmured to myself, "Yes, it looks like a place upon which has fallen a curse."

Two years before this night, I had been tried and condemned to death for murder, the murder of the one I loved best on earth, but, through the energy of the press and the intercession of a number of influential friends, my sentence had been mercifully commuted to transportation for life in Western Australia.

The victim, whom I was proved by circumstantial evidence to have murdered, was my young wife, to whom I had been married only six months before; ours was a love match, and until I saw her lying stark before me, those six months had been an uninterrupted honeymoon, without a cloud to cross it, a brief term of heaven, which accentuated the after misery.

I was a medical practitioner in a small country village which I need not name, as my supposed crime rang through England. My practice was new but growing, so that, although not too well off, we were fairly comfortable as to position, and, as my wife was modest in her desires, we were more than contented with our lot.

I suppose the evidence was strong enough to place my guilt beyond a doubt to those who could not read my heart and the heart of the woman I loved more than life. She had not been very well of late, yet, as it was nothing serious, I attended her myself; then the end came with appalling suddenness, a post mortem examination proved that she had been poisoned, and that the drug had been taken from my surgery, by whom or for what reason is still a mystery to me, for I do not think that I had an enemy in the world, nor do I think my poor darling had one either.

At the time of my sentence, I had only one wish, and that was to join the victim of this mysterious crime, so that I saw the judge put on the fatal black cap with a feeling of pleasure, but when afterwards I heard it was to be transportation instead, then I flung myself down in my cell and hurled imprecations on those officious friends who had given me slavery and misery instead of release. Where was the mercy in letting me have life, since all had been taken from it which made it worth holding?—the woman who had lain in my arms while together we built up glowing pictures of an impossible future, my good name lost, my place amongst men destroyed; henceforward I would be only recognized by a number, my companions the vilest, my days dragged out in chains, until the degradation of my lot encrusted over that previous memory of tenderness and fidelity, and I grew to be like the other numbered felons, a mindless and emotional animal.

Fortunately, at this point of my sufferings, oblivion came in the form of delirum, so that the weeks passed in a dream, during which my lost wife lived once more with me as we had been in the past, and by the time the ship's doctor pronounced me recovered we were within a few days of our dreary destination. Then my wife went from me to her own place, and I woke up to find that I had made some friends amongst my fellow convicts, who had taken care of me during my insanity.

We landed at Fremantle, and began our life, road-making; that is, each morning we were driven out of the prison like cattle, chained together in groups, and kept in the open until sundown, when we were once more driven back to sleep.

For fourteen months this dull monotony of eating, working and sleeping went on without variation, and then the chance came that I had been hungering for all along; not that liberty was likely to do me much good, only that the hope of accomplishing it kept me alive.

Three of us made a run for it one afternoon, just before the gun sounded for our recall, while the rest of the gang, being in our confidence, covered our escape until we had got beyond gunshot distance. We had managed to file through the chain which linked us together, and we ran towards the bush with the broken pieces in our hands as weapons of defense.

My two comrades were desperate criminals, who, like myself,

had been sentenced for life, and, as they confessed themselves, were ready to commit any atrocity rather than be caught and taken back.

That night and the next day we walked in a straight line about forty miles through the bush, and then, being hungry and tired, and considering ourselves fairly safe, we lay down to sleep without any thought of keeping watch.

But we had reckoned too confidently upon our escape, for about daybreak the next morning we were roused up by the sound of galloping horses, and, springing to our feet and climbing a gum tree, we saw a dozen of mounted police, led by two black trackers, coming straight in our direction. Under the circumstances there were but two things left for us to do, either to wait until they came and caught us, or run for it until we were beaten or shot down.

One of my companions decided to wait and be taken back, in spite of his bravado the night before; an empty stomach demoralizes most men; the other one made up his mind, as I did, to run as long as we could. We started in different directions, leaving our mate sitting under the gum tree, he promising to keep them off the track as long as possible.

The fact of him being there when the police arrived gave us a good start. I put all my speed out, and dashed along until I had covered, I daresay, about a couple of miles, when all at once the scrub came to an end, and before me I saw an open space, with another stretch of bush about half a mile distant, and no shelter between me and it.

As I stood for a few minutes to recover my breath, I heard two or three shots fired to the right, the direction my companion had taken, and on looking that way I saw that he also had gained the open, and was followed by one of the trackers and a couple of the police. He was still running, but I could see that he was wounded from the way he went.

Another shot was sent after him, that went straight to its mark, for all at once he threw up his arms and fell prone upon his face, then, hearing the sounds of pursuit in my direction, I waited no longer, but bounded full into the morning sunlight, hoping as I ran, that I might be as lucky as he had been, and get a bullet between my shoulders and so end my troubles.

I knew that they had seen me, and were after me almost as soon as I had left the cover, for I could hear them shouting for me to stop, as well as the clatter of their horses' hoofs on the hard soil, but still I kept to my course, waiting upon the shots to sound which would terminate my wretched existence, my back nerves quivering in anticipation and my teeth meeting in my underlip.

One!

Two!

Two reports sounded in my ears; a second after the bullets had whistled past my head; and then, before the third and fourth reports came, something like hot iron touched me above my left elbow, while the other bullet whirred past me with a singing wail, cooling my cheek with the wind it raised, and then I saw it ricochet in front of me on the hillside, for I was going up a slight rise at the time.

I had no pain in my arm, although I knew that my humerus was splintered by that third shot, but I put on a final spurt in order to tempt them to fire again.

What were they doing? I glanced over my shoulder as I rushed, and saw that they were spreading out, fanlike, and riding like fury, while they hurriedly reloaded. Once more they were taking aim at me, and then I looked again in front.

Before me yawned a gulf, the depth of which I could not estimate, yet in width it was over a hundred feet. My pursuers had seen this impediment also, for they were reining up their horses, while they shouted to me, more frantically than ever, to stop.

Why should I stop? flashed the thought across my mind as I neared the edge. Since their bullets had denied me the death I courted, why should I pause at the death spread out for me so opportunely?

As the question flashed through me, I answered it by making the leap, and as I went down I could hear the reports of the rifles above me.

Down into shadow from the sun glare I dropped, the outer branches of a tree breaking with me as I fell through them. Another obstacle caught me a little lower, and gave way under my weight, and then with an awful wrench, that nearly stunned me, I felt myself hanging by the remnant of the chain which was still riveted to my waist band, about ten feet from the surface, and with a hundred and fifty feet of a drop below me before I could reach the bottom. The chain had somehow got entangled in a fork of the last tree through which I had broken.

Although that sudden wrench was excruciating, the exigency of my position compelled me to collect my faculties without loss of time. Perhaps my months of serfdom and intercourse with felons had blunted my sensibility, and rendered me more callous to danger and bodily pain than I had been in my former and happier days, or the excitement of that terrible chase was still surging within me, for without more than a second's pause, and an almost indifferent glance downwards to those distant boulders, I made a wild clutch with my unwounded arm at the branch which had caught me, and with an effort drew myself up to it, so that the next instant I was astride it, or rather crouching, where my loose chain had caught. Then, once more secure, I looked upwards to where I expected my hunters to appear.

When I think upon it now, it was a marvel how I ever got to be placed where I was, for I was under the shelving ledge from which I had leapt, that is, it spread over me like a roof, therefore, I must conclude that the first tier of branches must have bent inwards, and so landed me on to the second tree at a slant. At least, this is the only way in which I can account for my position.

The tree on which I sat grew from a crevice on the side of the precipice, and from the top could not be seen by those above, neither could I see them, although they looked down after me, but I could hear them plainly enough and what they said.

"That fellow has gone right enough, Jack, although I don't see his remains below; shall we try to get down and make sure?" I heard one say, while another replied:

"What's the good of wasting time, he's as dead as the other chap, after that drop, and they will both be picked clean enough, so let us get back to Fremantle with the living one, and report the other two as wiped out; we have a long enough journey before us, Sergeant."

"Yes, I suppose so," answered the sergeant. "Well, boys, we may say that there are two promising bushrangers the less for this colony to support, so right about, home's the word."

I heard their horses wheel round and go off at a canter after this final speech, and then I was left alone on my airy perch, to plan out how best I was to get down with my broken arm, for it was impossible to get up, and also what I was likely to do with my liberty in that desolate region.

Desperate men are not very particular about the risks they run, and I ran not a few before I finally reached the bottom of that gulch, risky drops from one ledge to another, frantic clutchings at branches and tree roots; sufficient that I did reach the level ground at last more nearly dead than alive, so that I was fain to lie under the shadow of a boulder for hours without making an effort to rise and continue my journey.

Then, as night was approaching, I dragged myself along until I came to some water, where, after drinking and bracing up my broken arm with a few gum-trunk shards, and binding them round with some native grasses, while I made my supper of the young leaves of the eucalyptus bushes, I went on.

On, on, on for weeks, until I had lost all count of time, I wandered, carrying my broken fetters with me, and my broken arm gradually mending of its own accord. Sometimes I killed a snake or an iguana during the day with the branch I used for a stick, or a 'possum or wild cat at night, which I devoured raw. Often I existed for days on grass roots or the leaves of the gum tree, for anything was good enough to fill up the gap.

My convict garb was in tatters and my feet bootless by this time, and my hair and beard hung over my shoulders and chest, while often I went for days in a semi-conscious state, for the fierce sun seemed to wither up my blood and set fire to my brain.

Where I was going I could not tell, and still, with all the privation and misery, the love of life was once again stronger in me than it had been since I had lost my place amongst civilized men, for I was at liberty and alone to indulge in fancy.

And yet it did not seem altogether fancy that my lost wife was with me on that journey. At first she came only when I lay down to sleep, but after a time she walked with me hand in hand during the day as well as in my dreams.

Dora was her name, and soon I forgot that she had been dead, for she was living and beautiful as ever as we went along together, day after day, speaking to each other like lovers as we used to speak, and she did not seem to mind my ragged, degraded costume, or my dirty, tangled beard, but caressed me with the same tenderness as of yore.

Through the bush, down lonely gullies, over bitter deserts and salt marshes, we passed as happy and affectionate as fond lovers could be who are newly married, and whom the world cannot part, my broken chain rattling as I staggered onwards while she smiled as if pleased with the music, because it was the chain which I was wearing for her dear sake.

Let me think for a moment—was she with me through that last desert before I came to that gloomy gully? I cannot be quite sure of that, but this I do know, that she was not with me after the chill shadows of the boulders drew me into them, and I was quite alone when I stood by the water hole looking upon that strange and silent house.

It was singular that the house should be here at all in this far off and as yet unnamed portion of Western Australia, for I naturally supposed that I had walked hundreds of miles since leaving the convict settlement, and as I had encountered no one, not even a single tribe of wandering blacks, it seemed impossible to believe that I was not the first white man who had penetrated so far, and yet there it loomed before me, substantial-looking in its masses, with painted weather-boards, shingles, iron sheeting, carved posts and trellis work, french windows, and the signs of cultivation about it, although bearing the traces of late neglect.

Was it inhabited? I next asked myself as I looked steadily at that dimly illumined window; seemingly it was, for as I mentally asked the question, a darkness blotted out the light for a few moments and then moved slowly aside, while the faint pallor once more shone out; it appeared to be from the distance a window with a pale green blind drawn down, behind which a lamp turned low was burning, possibly for some invalid who was restlessly walking about, while the rest of the household slept.

Would it be well to rouse them up at this hour of the night? I next queried as I paused, watching the chimney tops from which no wreath of smoke came, for although it did not seem late, judging from the height of the moon, yet it was only natural to suppose that in this isolated place the people would retire early. Perhaps it would be better to wait where I was till morning and see what they were like before I ventured to ask hospitality from them, in my ragged yet unmistakably convict dress. I would rather go on as I was than run the risk of being dragged back to prison.

How chilly the night vapors were which rose from this large pool, for it was more like the moat from some ancient ruin than an ordinary Australian water hole. How ominous the shadows that gathered over this dwelling, and which even the great and lustrous moon, now clear of the gable end, seemed unable to dissipate, and what a dismal effect that dimly burning lamp behind the pale green blind gave to it.

I turned my eyes from the window to the pond from which the ghostly vapors were steaming upwards in such strange shapes; they crossed the reflections like gray shadows and floated over the white glitter which the moon cast down, like specters following each other in a stately procession, curling upwards interlaced, while the gaunt trees behind them altered their shapes and looked demoniac in their fantastic outlines, shadows passing along and sending back doleful sighs, which I tried with all my might to think was the night breeze but without succeeding.

Hush! was that a laugh that wafted from the house, a low, but blood curdling cachinnation such as an exultant devil might utter who had witnessed his fell mischief accomplished, followed by the wail of a woman, intermixed with the cry of a child!

Ah! what a fool I was to forget the cry of the Australian kingfisher; of course that was it, of course, of course, but—

The shapes are thickening over that mirror-like pool, and as I look I see a woman with a chalk-white face and eyes distended in horror, with a child in her hands—a little girl—and beside them the form of a man whose face changes into two different men, one the face of death, and the other like that of a demon with glaring eyeballs, while he points from the woman and child to the sleeping pool.

What is the devil-specter pointing at, as he laughs once more while the woman and child shrink with fright?

The face that he himself wore a moment ago, the face of the dead man whom I can see floating amongst that silver luster.

I must have fainted at the weird visions of the night before, or else I may have fallen asleep and dreamt them, for when I opened my eyes again, the morning sun was pouring over the landscape and all appeared changed.

The pool was still there but it looked like a natural Australian water hole which had been deepened and lengthened, and artificially arranged by a tasteful proprietor to beautify his estate; water lilies grew round the edges and spread themselves in graceful patches about; it was only in the center portion, where the moonlight had glinted and the other reflections cast themselves, that the water was clear of weeds, and there it still lay inky and dangerous-like in its depth.

Over the building itself clustered a perfect tangle of vegetable parasites, star-of-Bethlehem, maiden-blush roses, and gloire-de-Dijon, passion flowers and convolvulus, intermingling with a large grape-laden vine going to waste, and hanging about in half-wild, neglected festoons; a woman's hand had planted these tendrils, as well as the garden in front, for I could see that flowers predominated.

As for the house itself, it still stood silent and deserted-looking, the weather-boards had shrunk a good deal with the heat of many suns beating upon them, while the paint, once tasteful in its varied tints, was bleached into dry powder; the trellis work also on the veranda had in many places been torn away by the weight of the clinging vines, and between the window frames and the windows yawned wide fissures where they had shrunk from each other.

I looked round at the landscape, but could see no trace of sheep, cattle, nor humanity; it spread out a sunlit solitude where Nature, for a little while trained to order, had once more asserted her independent lavishness.

A little of my former awe came upon me as I stood for a few moments hesitating to advance, but at the sight of those luscious-looking bunches of grapes, which seemed to promise some fare more substantial inside, the dormant cravings for food which I had so long subdued came upon me with tenfold force, and, without more than a slight tremor of superstitious dread, I hurriedly crushed my way through the tangle of vegetation, and made for the veranda and open door of the hall.

Delicious grapes they were, as I found when, after tearing off a huge bunch, and eating them greedily, I entered the silent hall and began my exploration.

The dust and fine sand of many "brick-fielders," i.e., sand-storms, lay thickly on every object inside, so that as I walked I left my footprints behind me as plainly as if I had been walking over snow. In the hall I found a handsome stand and carved table with chairs, a hat and riding-whip lay on the table, while on the rack I saw two or three coats and hats hanging, with sticks and umbrellas beneath, all white with dust.

The dining-room door stood ajar, and as I entered I could see that it also had been undisturbed for months, if not for years. It had been handsomely furnished, with artistic hangings and stuffed leather chairs and couches, while on the elaborately carved chiffonier was a plentiful supply of spirit and wine decanters, with cut glasses standing ready for use. On the table stood a bottle of Three Star brandy, half emptied, and by its side a water-filter and glass as they had been left by the last user.

I smelt the bottle, and found that the contents were mellow and good, and when, after dusting the top, I put it to my mouth, I discovered that the bouquet was delicious; then, invigorated by that sip, I continued my voyage of discovery.

The chiffonier was not locked, and inside I discovered rows of sealed bottles, which satisfied me that I was not likely to run short of refreshments in the liquid form at any rate, so, content with this pleasant prospect, I ventured into the other apartments.

The drawing-room was like the room I had left, a picture of comfort and elegance, when once the accumulation of dust and sand had been removed.

The library or study came next, which I found in perfect order, although I left the details for a more leisurely examination.

I next penetrated the kitchen, which I saw was comfortable, roomy and well-provided, although in more disorder than the other rooms; pans stood rusting in the fireplace, dishes lay dirty and in an accumulated pile on the table, as if the servants had left in a hurry and the owners had been forced to make what shifts they could during their absence.

Yet there was no lack of such provisions as an up-country sta-

tion would be sure to lay in; the pantry I found stored like a provision shop, with flitches of bacon, hams sewn in canvas, tinned
meats and soups of all kinds, with barrels and bags and boxes of
flour, sugar, tea and other sundries, enough to keep me going for
years if I was lucky enough to be in possession.

I next went upstairs to the bedrooms, up a thickly carpeted
staircase, with the white linen overcloth still upon it. In the first
room I found the bed with the bedclothes tumbled about as if the
sleeper had lately left it; the master of the house, I supposed, as I
examined the wardrobe and found it well stocked with male apparel. At last I could cast aside my degrading rags, and fit myself
out like a free man, after I had visited the workshop and filed my
fetters from me.

Another door attracted me on the opposite side of the lobby,
and this I opened with some considerable trepidation, because it
led into the room which I had seen lighted up the night before.

It seemed untenanted, as I looked in cautiously, and like the
other bedroom was in a tumble of confusion, a woman's room,
for the dresses and underclothing were lying about, a bedroom
which had been occupied by a woman and a child, for a crib
stood in one corner, and on a chair lay the frock and other articles belonging to a little girl of about five or six years of age.

I looked at the window, it had venetian blinds upon it, and
they were drawn up, so that my surmise had been wrong about
the pale green blind, but on the end side of the room was another
window with the blinds also drawn up, and thus satisfied I
walked in boldly; what I had thought to be a light, had only
been the moonlight streaming from the one window to the other,
while the momentary blackening of the light had been caused,
doubtless, by the branches of the trees outside, moved forward by
the night breeze. Yes, that must have been the cause, so that I
had nothing to fear, the house was deserted, and my own property, for the time at least.

There was a strange and musty odor in this bedroom, which
blended with the perfume that the owner had used, and made me
for a moment almost giddy, so the first thing I did was to open
both windows and let in the morning air, after which I looked
over to the unmade bed, and then I staggered back with a cry of
horror.

There amongst the tumble of bedclothes lay the skeletons of what had been two human beings, clad in embroidered nightdresses. One glance was enough to convince me, with my medical knowledge, that the gleaming bones were those of a woman and a child, the original wearers of those dresses which lay scattered about.

What awful tragedy had taken place in this richly furnished but accursed house? Recovering myself, I examined the remains more particularly, but could find no clue, they were lying reposefully enough, with arms interlacing as if they had died or been done to death in their sleep, while those tiny anatomists, the ants, had found their way in, and cleaned the bones completely, as they very soon do in this country.

With a sick sensation at my heart, I continued my investigations throughout the other portions of the station. In the servants' quarters I learnt the cause of the unwashed dishes; three skeletons lay on the floor in different positions as they had fallen, while their shattered skulls proved the caused of their end, even if the empty revolver that I picked up from the floor had not been evidence enough. Someone must have entered their rooms and woke them rudely from their sleep in the night time, for they lay also in their bloodstained nightdresses, and beside them, on the boards, were dried up markings which were unmistakable.

The rest of the house was as it had been left by the murderer or murderers. Three domestics, with their mistress and child, had been slaughtered, and then the guilty wretches had fled without disturbing anything else.

It was once again night, and I was still in the house, which my first impulse had been to leave with all haste after the gruesome discoveries that I had made.

But several potent reasons restrained me from yielding to that impulse. I had been wandering for months, and living like a wild beast, while here I had everything to my hand which I needed to recruit my exhausted system. My curiosity was roused, so that I wanted to penetrate the strange mystery if I could, by hunting after and reading all the letters and papers that I might be able to find, and to do this required leisure; thirdly, as a medical practitioner who had passed through the anatomical schools, the presence of five skeletons did not have much effect upon me, and lastly, before sundown the weather had broken, and one of those fierce storms of rain, wind, thunder and lightning had come on, which utterly prevented anyone who had the chance of a roof to shelter him from turning out to the dangers of the night.

These were some of my reasons for staying where I was, at least the reasons that I explained to myself, but there was another and a more subtle motive which I could not logically explain, and which yet influenced me more than any of the others. I could not leave the house, now that I had taken possession of it, or rather, if I may say it, now that the house had taken possession of me.

I had lifted the bucket from the kitchen, and found my way to the draw-well in the back garden, with the uncomfortable feeling that some unseen force was compelling me to stay here. I discovered a large file and freed myself from my fetters, and then, throwing my rags from me with disgust, I clad myself in one of the suits that I found in the wardrobe upstairs, then I set to work dusting and sweeping out the dining room, after which I lit a fire, retrimmed the lamps, and cooked a substantial meal for myself, then the storm coming on decided me, so that I spent the remainder of the afternoon making the place comfortable, and when darkness did come, I had drawn the blinds down and secured the shutters, and with a lighted lamp, a bottle of good wine, and a box of first-class cigars which I also found in the chiffonier, with a few volumes that I had taken from the bookshelves at random, and an album of photographs that I picked up from the drawing-room table, I felt a different man from what I had been the night previous, particularly with that glowing log fire in the grate.

I left the half-emptied bottle of brandy where I had found it, on the table, with the used glass and water filter untouched, as I did also the chair that had been beside them. I had a repugnance to those articles which I could not overcome; the murderer had used them last, possibly as a reviver after his crimes, for by this time I had reasoned out that one hand only had been at the work, and that man's the owner of the suit which I was then wearing and which fitted me so exactly, otherwise why should the house have been left in the condition that it was?

As I sat at the end of the table and smoked the cigar, I rebuilt the whole tragedy, although as yet the motive was not so clear, and as I thought the matter out, I turned over the leaves of the album and looked at the photographs.

Before me, on the walls, hung three oil portraits, enlargements they were, and as works of art vile things, yet doubtless they were faithful enough likenesses. In the album, I found three cabinet portraits from which the paintings had been enlarged.

They were the portraits of a woman of about twenty-six, a girl of five years, and a man of about thirty-two.

The woman was good-looking, with fresh color, blue eyes and golden-brown hair. The girl—evidently her daughter—for the likeness was marked between the two, had one of those seraphic expressions which some delicate children have who are marked out for early death, that places them above the plane of grosser humanity. She looked, as she hung between the two portraits, with her glory of golden hair, like the guardian angel of the woman who was smiling so contentedly and consciously from her gilded frame.

The man was pallid-faced and dark, clean-shaven, all except the small black mustache, with lips which, except the artist had grossly exaggerated the color, were excessively and disagreeably vivid. His eyes were deep set, and glowing as if with the glitter of a fever.

"These would be the likenesses of the woman and child whose skeletons lay unburied upstairs, and the pallid-faced feverish-eyed ghoul, the fiend who had murdered them, his wife and child," I murmured to myself as I watched the last portrait with morbid interest.

"Right and wrong, Doctor, as you medical men mostly are," answered a deep voice from the other end of the table.

I started with amazement, and looked from the painting to the vacant chair beside the brandy bottle, which was now occupied by what appeared to be the original of the picture I had been looking at, face, hair, vivid scarlet lips were identical, and the same deep-set fiery eyes, which were fixed upon me intently and mockingly.

How had he entered without my observing him? By the window? No, for that I had firmly closed and secured myself, and as I glanced at it I saw that it still remained the same. By the door? Perhaps so, although he must have closed it again after he had entered without my hearing him, as he might easily have done during one of the claps of thunder which were now almost incessant, as were the vivid flashes of wildfire or lightning that darted about, while the rain lashed against the shutters outside.

He was dripping wet, as I could see, so that he must have come from that deluge, bareheaded and dripping, with his hair and mustache draggling over his glistening, ashy cheeks and bluish chin, as if he had been submerged in water while weeds and slime hung about his saturated garments; a gruesome sight for a man who fancied himself alone to see start up all of a sudden, and no wonder that it paralyzed me and prevented me from finding the words I wanted at the moment. Had he lain hidden somewhere watching me take possession of his premises, and being, as solitary men sometimes are, fond of dramatic effect, slipped in while my back was turned from the door to give me a surprise? If so he had succeeded, for I never before felt so craven-spirited or horror-stricken, my flesh was creeping and my hair bristling, while my blood grew to ice within me. The very lamp seemed to turn dim, and the fire smoldered down on the hearth, while the air was chill as a charnel vault, as I sat with shivering limbs and chattering teeth before this evil visitor.

Outside, the warring elements raged and fought, shaking the wooden walls, while the forked flames darted between us, lighting up his face with a ghastly effect. He must have seen my horror, for he once more laughed that low malicious chuckle that I had heard the night before, as he again spoke.

"Make yourself at home, Doctor, and try some of this cognac instead of that washy stuff you are drinking. I am only sorry that I cannot join you in it, but I cannot just yet."

I found words at last and asked him questions, which seemed impertinent in the extreme, considering where I was.

"Who are you? Where do you come from? What do you want?"

Again that hateful chuckle, as he fixed his burning eyes upon me with a regard which fascinated me in spite of myself.

"Who am I, do you ask? Well, before you took possession of this place I was its owner. Where do I come from? From out of there last."

He pointed backwards towards the window, which burst open as he uttered the words, while through the driving rain a flash of lightning seemed to dart from his outstretched finger and disappear into the center of the lake, then after that hurried glimpse, the shutters clashed together again and we were as before.

"What do I want? You, for lack of a better."

"What do you want with me?" I gasped.

"To make you myself."

"I do not understand you, what are you?"

"At present nothing, yet with your help I shall be a man once more, while you shall be free and rich, for you shall have more gold than you ever could dream of."

"What can I do for you?"

"Listen to my story and you will see. Ten years ago I was a successful gold finder, the trusting husband of that woman, and fond father of that girl. I had likewise a friend whom I trusted, and took to live with me as a partner. We lived here together, my friend, myself, my wife and my daughter, for I was romantic and had raised this house to be close to the mine which I had discovered, and which I will show you if you consent to my terms.

"One night my friend murdered me and pitched my body into that water-hole, where the bones still lie. He did this because he coveted my wife and my share of the money."

I was calm now, but watchful, for it appeared that I had to deal with a madman.

"In my lifetime I had been a trusting and guileless simpleton, but no sooner was my spirit set free than vengeance transformed its nature. I hovered about the place where all my affections had been centered, watching him beguile the woman who had been mine until he won her. She waited three years for me to return, and then she believed his story that I had been killed by the natives, and married him. They traveled to where you came from, to be married, and I followed them closely, for that was the chance I waited upon. The union of those two once accomplished, he was in my power forever, for this had established the link that was needed for me to take forcible possession of him."

"And where was his spirit meantime?" I asked to humor the maniac.

"In my grasp also, a spirit rendered impotent by murder and ingratitude; a spirit which I could do with as I pleased, so long as the wish I had was evil. I took possession of his body, the mirage of which you see now, and from that moment until the hour that our daughter rescued her from his clutches, he made the life of my former wife a hell on earth. I prompted his murder-embued spirit to madness, leaving him only long enough to himself after I had braced him up to do the deed of vengeance."

"How did the daughter save the mother?"

"By dying with her, and by her own purity tearing the freed spirit from my clutches. I did not intend the animal to do all that he did, for I wanted the mother only, but once the murder lust was on him, I found that he was beyond my influence. He slew the two by poison, as he had done me, then, frenzied, he murdered the servants, and finally exterminated himself by flinging himself into the pool. That was why I said that I came last from out of there, where both my own remains and his lie together."

"Yes, and what is my share in this business?"

"To look on me passively for a few moments, as you are at present doing, that is all I require."

I did not believe his story about his being only a mirage or specter, for he appeared at this moment corporal enough to do me a considerable amount of bodily harm, and therefore to humor him, until I could plan a way to overpower him, I fixed my eyes upon his steadfastly, as he desired.

Was I falling asleep, or being mesmerized by this homicidal lunatic? As he glared at me with those fiery orbs and an evil contortion curling the blood-red lips, while the forked lightning played around him, I became helpless. He was creeping slowly toward me as a cat might steal upon a mouse, and I was unable to move, or take my eyes from his eyes, which seemed to be charming my life-blood from me, when suddenly, I heard the distant sound of music, through the lull of the tempest, the rippling of a piano from the drawing-room with the mingling of a child's silvery voice as it sang its evening hymn, and at the sound his eyes shifted while he fell back a step or two, with an agonized spasm crossing his ghastly and dripping wet face.

Then the hurricane broke loose once more, with a resistless fury, while the door and window burst open, and the shutters were dashed into the room.

I leapt to my feet in a paroxysm of horror, and sprang towards the open door with that demon, or maniac, behind me.

Merciful heavens! the drawing-room was brilliantly lighted up, and there, seated at the open piano, was the woman whose bones I had seen bleaching upstairs, with the seraphic-faced child singing her hymn.

Out to the tempest I rushed madly, and heedless of where I went, so that I escaped from that accursed and haunted house, on, past the water-hole and into the glade, where I turned my head back instinctively, as I heard a wilder roar of thunder and the crash as if a tree had been struck.

What a flash that was which lighted up the scene and showed me the house collapsing as an erection of cards. It went down like an avalanche before the zigzag flame, which seemed to lick round it for a moment, and then disappear into the earth.

Next instant I was thrown off my feet by the earthquake that shook the ground under me, while, as I still looked on where the house had been, I saw that the ruin had caught fire, and was blazing up in spite of the torrents that still poured down, and as it burned, I saw the mound sink slowly out of sight, while the reddened smoke eddied about in the same strange shapes which the vapors had assumed the night before, scarlet ghosts of the demon and his victims.

Two months after this, I woke up to find myself in a Queensland back-country station. They had found me wandering in a delirious condition over one of their distant runs six weeks before my return to consciousness, and as they could not believe that a pedestrian, without provisions, could get over that unknown stretch of country from Fremantle, they paid no attention to my ravings about being an escaped convict, particularly as the rags I had on could never have been prison-made. Learning, however, that I had medical knowledge, by the simple method of putting it to the test, my good rescuers set me up in my old profession, where I still remain—a Queensland back-country doctor.

Selected Bibliography

Alpers, Antony. *Legends of the South Seas*, New York, 1970

Andersen, Johannes C. *The Maori Tohunga and his Spirit World*, New Plymouth, New Zealand, 1948

Bell, Sir Hesketh. *Witches and Fishes*, London, 1948

Birkhead, Edith. *The Tale of Terror; a Study of the Gothic Romance*, New York, 1920

Burton, Sir Richard (trans.). *Vikram and the Vampire*, London, 1870

Calmet, Dom Augustin. *Dissertations sur les apparitions des esprits, et sur les vampires*, Paris, 1746. (English translation by Henry Christmas, published as *The Phantom World*, London, 1850)

Collison-Morley, Lacy. *Greek and Roman Ghost Stories* (limited ed.), London, 1912

Conway, Moncure Daniel. *Demonology and Devil Lore*, New York, 1879

Crowe, Catherine. *The Night Side of Nature*, London, 1850

Eisler, Robert. *Man into Wolf, an Anthropological Interpretation of Sadism, Masochism, and Lycanthropy* (a lecture delivered at a meeting of the Royal Society of Medicine), London, 1951

Erman, Adolf. *The Literature of the Ancient Egyptians*. (English translation by A. B. Blackman, London, 1927)

Frazer, Sir James G. *Fear of the Dead in Primitive Religion*, London, 1933

Giles, Herbert A. *Strange Stories from a Chinese Studio*, New York, 1925

Gray, Louis Herbert, ed. *Mythology of All Races*, Boston, 1920 (Vol. IV, Vol. VII, Vol. XI)

Hamel, Frank. *Human Animals*, London, 1915

Hearn, Lafcadio. *Kwaidan*, New York and Boston, 1904

———. *Some Chinese Ghosts*, New York, 1887

———. *Kotto*, New York, 1902

———. *In Ghostly Japan*, Boston, 1899

———. *A Japanese Miscellany*, Boston, 1906

Herskovits, Melville J. and Frances S. *Dahomean Narrative*, Evanston, Ill., 1958

Howells, William W. *The Heathens, Primitive Man and His Religions*, New York, 1948

Hungarian Quarterly, New York, 1941, Vol. 7, pp. 327–332

Hurwood, Bernhardt J. *Terror by Night*, New York, 1963

———. *Monsters Galore*, New York, 1965

———. *Monsters and Nightmares*, New York, 1967

———. *Vampires, Werewolves and Ghouls*, New York, 1968

Jones, Ernest. *On the Nightmare*, London, 1949

Journal of American Folklore, 1923, Vol. 34, pp. 223–253

Lovecraft, H. P. *Supernatural Horror in Literature*, New York, 1945

Michelet, Jules. *La Sorcière*. (English translation by L. J. Trotter, London, 1863)

Mitford, A. B. *Tales of Old Japan*, London, 1871

More, Henry. *An Antidote against Atheism*, London, 1655

Murray, Margaret Alice. *The Witch Cult in Western Europe*, London, 1921

———. *The God of the Witches*, New York, 1952

Nisbet, Hume. *The Haunted Station and Other Stories*, London, 1894

O'Donnell, Elliott. *Werewolves*, London, 1912

Quong, Rose. *Chinese Ghost and Love Stories*, New York, 1946

Radcliffe, John Netten. *Fiends, Ghosts and Sprites*, London, 1854

Robbins, Rossell Hope. *The Encyclopedia of Witchcraft and Demonology*, New York, 1963

Runeberg, Arne. *Witches, Demons, and Fertility Magic*, Helsinki, 1947

Sagges, H. W. F. *The Greatness That Was Babylon*, New York, 1962

Scarborough, Dorothy. *The Supernatural in Modern English Fiction*, New York, 1917

Scott, Sir Walter. *Letters on Demonology and Witchcraft*, London, 1830

Shedden-Ralston, William R. *Russian Folk Tales*, London, 1873

Skeat, W. W. *Malay Magic*, London, 1900

Sinistrari, Ludovico Maria. *Demoniality or Incubi and Succubi*, Paris, 1879 (Latin and English)

Soulie, George. *Strange Stories from the Lodge of Leisure*, New York and Boston, 1913

Spence, Lewis. *The Myths of Mexico and Peru*, New York, 1913

Sprenger, Jakob, and Kramer, Heinrich. *Malleus Maleficarum*, Cologne, 1486. (English translation ed. by Montague Summers, London, 1928)

Summers, Montague. *The History of Witchcraft and Demonology*, London, 1926

——. *The Vampire, His Kith and Kin*, London, 1928

——. *The Vampire in Europe*, London, 1929

——. *Supernatural Omnibus*, New York, 1932

——. *The Werewolf*, London, 1933

Talbot, P. Almaury. *In the Shadow of the Bush*, London, 1912

Thompson, R. C. *The Devils and Evil Spirits of Babylonia* (2 vols.), London, 1903

Thompson, Stith. *Motif-Index of Folk Literature* (6 vols.), 1932–1936, Bloomington, Indiana

Trachtenberg, Joshua. *Jewish Magic and Superstition*, New York, 1939

Willoughby-Meade, G. *Chinese Ghouls and Goblins*, New York, 1928